1994 IUCN Red List of
Threatened
Animals

D1516784

The World Conservation Union

SPECIES SURVIVAL COMMISSION

WORLD CONSERVATION
MONITORING CENTRE

WWF

NYZS
The WILDLIFE
CONSERVATION
SOCIETY

Sultanate of Oman

BirdLife
INTERNATIONAL

Naturskydds
föreningen

Chicago Zoological Society

PEOPLE'S TRUST
FOR ENDANGERED SPECIES

IUCN – The World Conservation Union

IUCN – The World Conservation Union brings together States, government agencies and a diverse range of non-governmental organisations in a unique world partnership: some 770 members in all, spread across 123 countries.

As a union, IUCN exists to serve its members – to represent their views on the world stage and to provide them with the concepts, strategies and technical support they need to achieve their goals. Through its six Commissions, IUCN draws together over 5000 expert volunteers in project teams and action groups. A central secretariat coordinates the IUCN Programme and leads initiatives on the conservation and sustainable use of the world's biological diversity and the management of habitats and natural resources, as well as providing a range of services. The Union has helped many countries to prepare National Conservation Strategies, and demonstrates the application of its knowledge through the field projects it supervises. Operations are increasingly decentralised and are carried forward by an expanding network of regional and country offices, located principally in developing countries.

IUCN – The World Conservation Union seeks above all to work with its members to achieve development that is sustainable and that provides a lasting improvement in the quality of life for people all over the world.

World Conservation Monitoring Centre

The World Conservation Monitoring Centre (WCMC) is a joint venture between the three partners who developed the *World Conservation Strategy* and its successor, *Caring for the Earth*: IUCN – The World Conservation Union, UNEP – United Nations Environment Programme, and WWF – World Wide Fund For Nature (formerly World Wildlife Fund). Its mission is to support conservation and sustainable development through the provision of information on the world's biological diversity.

WCMC has developed a global overview database that includes threatened plant and animal species, habitats of conservation concern, critical sites, protected areas of the world, and the utilisation and trade in wildlife species and products. Drawing on this database, WCMC provides an information service to the conservation and development communities, governments and the United Nations agencies, scientific institutions, the business and commercial sector, and the media. WCMC produces a wide variety of specialist outputs and reports based on analyses of its data. It is also actively involved in building the capabilities of other institutions, particularly in developing countries, for promoting and planning their own biological resources.

1994 IUCN Red List of
Threatened Animals

Compiled by the
**World Conservation Monitoring Centre
Cambridge, UK**

in association with the
IUCN Species Survival Commission
and
BirdLife International

Edited by
Brian Groombridge

Guest Essay by
Georgina Mace

and

Foreword by
George Rabb

**IUCN – The World Conservation Union
1993**

The designations of geographical entities in this book, and the presentation of the material, do not imply the expression of any opinion whatsoever on the part of IUCN or WCMC concerning the legal status of any country, territory, or area or of its authorities, or concerning the delimitation of its frontiers or boundaries.

1994 IUCN Red List of Threatened Animals was made possible by the generous support of:

BirdLife International

Chicago Zoological Society

DEJA, Inc.

National Wildlife Federation

Svenska Naturskyddsföreningen (Swedish Society for the Conservation of Nature)

NYZS The Wildlife Conservation Society

People's Trust for Endangered Species

Peter Scott IUCN/SSC Action Plan Fund (Sultanate of Oman)

World Conservation Monitoring Centre

World Wide Fund for Nature

Published by: IUCN, Gland, Switzerland, and Cambridge, UK

The World Conservation Union

WORLD CONSERVATION
MONITORING CENTRE

Copyright: (1993) International Union for Conservation of Nature and Natural Resources

Citation: Groombridge B. (Ed.)(1993). *1994 IUCN Red List of Threatened Animals*, IUCN Gland, Switzerland and Cambridge, UK. lvi + 286pp.

ISBN: 2-8317-0194-5

Cover photo: *Bufo periglenes* (Golden Toad): Michael and Patricia Fogden

Cover design by: IUCN Publications Services Unit

Printed by: Page Bros (Norwich) Ltd., UK

Available from: IUCN Publications Services Unit
219c Huntingdon Road, Cambridge CB3 0DL, UK or
IUCN Communications and Corporate Relations Division
Rue Mauverney 28, CH-1196 Gland, Switzerland

The text of this book is printed on Fineblade Cartridge 90gsm low-chlorine paper

VCS AT

CONTENTS

FOREWORD

Periodically, the Red List forces us to take stock of where we are in our knowledge of the conservation status of species. Our knowledge has changed in expression through the years, as IUCN's small book *The Road to Extinction*[1], published in 1987 testifies. For some while, members of IUCN's Species Survival Commission have been considering the redefinition of the categories of threatened status of species in order to make them more realistic measures. The essay by Georgina Mace that follows is an up-to-date report on this process. We anticipate that the next Red List will reflect the adoption of new and redefined categories by IUCN. In the meantime we look to cooperation from all parties as systematic re-examination of the status of taxonomic groups and surveys of regional and national biotas proceed. To inform conservation actions we will need ever better specification of the population and distributional status of species the world over from people in touch with the real situations of these species.

In closing her essay, Dr Mace calls attention to other dimensions, both biological and human, that should be taken into account as we determine the best responses to the threats of extinction. One need is to link a quantitative grid of population and distribution criteria such as outlined in her essay to an assessment of the relative importance of a species. The evolutionary and ecological values of a species should be factored into our prioritization of conservation action. Weighting and decision making systems such as that developed by Williams, Vane-Wright, and Humphries, lend themselves to this purpose.[2] The integration of such systems will, however, require cooperation by systematists and ecologists with conservation biologists to a degree not previously envisaged.

Given that we can foresee a three-dimensional assessment of conservation status from a biological standpoint, it remains to factor in the human dimensions. From simple human population impact relationships on a species or its ecosystem to complexities of consumptive and non-consumptive uses of species, we need conservationists to foster collaboration by demographers, economists, and sociologists. The human domain in which issues of extinction generally will be settled is political, at local, national, and international levels. There a balance has to be struck among ethical, financial, socioeconomic, and biological considerations. We need the most cogent information to bring to the decisions in this realm, and we need it organized to best effect. To these ends, the conservation community must encourage the rapid development of systems for not only better categorizing the conservation status of species, but also for determining logical priorities for conservation action more comprehensively than we have in the past.

In signing off this foreword, it is a pleasure to acknowledge and commend the diligence of WCMC staff, in particular Dr Brian Groombridge, in compiling this new Red List. They have made it a much more informative catalogue than previous editions, incorporating tabular formats developed for *Global Biodiversity* (WCMC, 1992)[3], and have extended themselves in trying to minimize nomenclatorial confusions and choose appropriate taxonomies. I commend it to all concerned with the status of faunas worldwide, for the List makes obvious that all of us should be concerned by its magnitude and meaning for the existence of our fellow creatures.

George B. Rabb
Chairman, Species Survival Commission
IUCN - The World Conservation Union

[1] Fitter, R., and Fitter, M. (Eds.). 1987. *The Road to Extinction*. IUCN, Gland.

[2] Williams, P.H., Vane-Wright, R.I., and Humphries, C.J. (in press). Measuring biodiversity for choosing conservation areas. In, J. LaSalle and I.D. Gauld, (Eds.). *Hymenoptera and Biodiversity*. CAB International, Wallingford, UK.

[3] World Conservation Monitoring Centre. 1992. *Global Biodiversity: Status of the Earth's Living Resources*. Chapman and Hall, London.

INTRODUCTION

PURPOSE

The *IUCN Red List of Threatened Animals* includes lists of those species and subspecies known or suspected to be threatened with extinction, and those known or believed to have become extinct in the wild. The Red List complements the IUCN and IUCN/ICBP Red Data Books and the IUCN-SSC Action Plans, which contain more detailed information; it is published periodically, usually at two-year intervals.

The Red List is compiled and maintained for IUCN by the World Conservation Monitoring Centre (WCMC) with the advice of the IUCN-SSC Specialist Groups and the assistance, with regard to birds, of BirdLife International (formerly ICBP).

The present edition differs greatly from its predecessors. The contents have been rearranged, the size and layout have been redesigned to make the book easier to use, and more distribution information is given, usually including a full list of range states. We have endeavoured to update or correct information on nomenclature and distribution, to change categories as appropriate, and to add species that have been recognised as globally threatened since the last edition (a few species previously listed but now not considered threatened have been removed). For the first time in the Red List a more complete list of species known or believed to have become extinct in the wild since around 1600 AD is provided.

STRUCTURE OF THE 1994 RED LIST

The lists are arranged taxonomically. For each threatened species, the scientific name, IUCN status category and countries of occurrence are given (for widespread and strictly marine species a general description of the range is provided instead of a list of countries). For many species common names are indicated, usually in English but sometimes in other languages.

Previous editions of the Red List contained a single list. In order to improve clarity in the present edition we have divided the material as follows:

List 1: THREATENED SPECIES, comprising the central catalogue of threatened species, including species suspected to be threatened (category K);

List 2: EXTINCT SPECIES, including those species categorised by IUCN as Ex or Ex? together with other species that have become extinct since around 1600 AD but have not previously been categorised in the Red List;

List 3: THREATENED GENERA (etc), comprising entries for genera and other higher taxa used in previous editions that were not resolved to species level;

List 4: THREATENED AND EXTINCT SUBSPECIES, including all threatened subspecies whatever their category and extinct subspecies;

List 5: COMMERCIALLY THREATENED species.

The reader is referred to the Explanatory Notes below for further discussion of the content of these lists, and of the tables derived from them.

Our intention in making this rearrangement has been to provide the most sound basis possible for the next edition of the Red List, in which use of the new IUCN system of categorisation is envisaged. At the time of writing (late 1993) this is nearing its final formulation (see the Guest Essay for further discussion).

SOURCES OF STATUS INFORMATION AND OPINION

The threatened species lists are based on information provided by numerous scientists and naturalists working in the field. The core of the present Red List consists of species known or suspected to be threatened, as identified over many years during production by IUCN, WCMC and BirdLife International of earlier Red Data Books and Red Lists. In this revised edition of the Red List we have incorporated information from two main sources:

• the IUCN-SSC taxonomic and regional Specialist Groups;

• national Red Data Books or equivalent listings.

The Specialist Groups were notified of this revision process in February 1993 and the majority of groups responded, either with recommendations for no change, or with extensive new listings and re-categorisations. Compilation was completed in early October 1993.

We have added many threatened species from national Red Data Books available to us whenever we were able to determine that the species in question is endemic to that country, or virtually endemic, and so by definition globally threatened at the species level. Most such additions have been among the reptiles, amphibians or fishes; few invertebrates have been added from these sources because it has rarely been possible in the time available to determine which are single country endemics. No subspecies have been entered from national sources.

BirdLife International have, as in previous editions, been responsible for the basic list of bird species considered threatened, and for their categorisation. We have in a few cases modified the nomenclature of genera and species to accord with Sibley and Monroe (1990, 1993). A new global assessment and listing of threatened birds is in an advanced stage of preparation by Birdlife International, and rather than attempt a partial and provisional revision of the bird section of this present Red List, which would soon be outdated by the new bird list, it has jointly been decided to retain substantially the same species treated in *Birds to Watch* (the 1988 ICBP world list of threatened birds). These species were subsequently given an IUCN category in the 1990 IUCN Red List. This 1990 publication, revised to take account of *Threatened Birds of the Americas* (Collar *et al.*, 1992), has provided the basis for the present list. We have therefore not added any threatened and endemic bird species from national sources, or changed any categories, even in the many instances where this would have been possible. There are a few minor differences between the present list and *Birds to Watch* in addition to those consequent upon publication of *Threatened Birds of the Americas* (see Explanatory Notes: List 1).

The national Red Data Books and other national sources from which species have been extracted are listed in the References below. We have reviewed a large number of such sources but not all; several that have been reviewed contain no species that we were able to identify as nationally endemic; these sources are not listed. Most national Red Data Books or similar works have used IUCN status categories and, where this is so, we have entered the same category. Where other systems have been used, we have used the equivalent IUCN category where the category given was defined unambiguously; otherwise, we have used the 'Insufficiently Known' (K) category, unless sufficient background documentation was provided to allow us to assign a category independently. We have not added species from national lists which provide no category or documentation unless supporting information was available from another source.

The use of multiple sources of information entails the risk of taxonomic inconsistency; we have tried to verify the nomenclature and distribution given in national sources, but it remains possible that a few species may have been listed twice under different names, or taxa may have been listed at an inappropriate rank.

Our task during this revision has been primarily to gather and collate information, and to produce the listings. We have not attempted a comprehensive review of the existing list beyond revisions suggested by

Specialist Groups, nor have we been responsible for critically reviewing proposals from the Specialist Groups, or the listings given in national Red Data Books (other than the general conditions noted above). This kind of thorough review will of necessity be undertaken when the new revised IUCN status categories come into use.

We have unilaterally added a few species which were not proposed by a Specialist Group or were not derived from a national Red Data Book. An example is the recently-described Vu Quang bovid *Pseudoryx nghetinhensis* (Vu Van Dung *et al.*, 1993), which, in view of its very small estimated population size and very restricted known range, we have listed as Endangered.

In a very few cases we have unilaterally changed existing or proposed category designations, or removed species previously listed, where the existing criteria for a particular category, or for listing at all, were beyond dispute not satisfied. This has usually been on the basis of new evidence or opinion. In the absence of such evidence, we have left categories unchanged even where they might not withstand challenge. In one or two marginal cases, rather than risk removing a species prematurely, we have revised the existing category to indicate a lesser degree of threat, or less certainty (to Insufficiently Known).

THE EXTENT OF STATUS ASSESSMENT

The Red List is a global catalogue of those species that have been assessed in some degree and which meet, or are suspected to meet, the current criteria for threatened status. It is not comprehensive, because not all species have been collected and described, and the conservation status of all described species has not been evaluated.

The proportion of each phylum or class that has received such assessment differs greatly between groups. Virtually all bird species have been subject to at least provisional assessment. Probably a little more than half of mammal species have been considered, although a large number of insectivores, rodents and micro-bats remain unassessed. Our best estimates suggest that around 20% of reptiles, 12% of amphibians, probably less than 10% of fishes, and an insignificant proportion of invertebrate animals have been assessed (although many species in certain invertebrate groups, such as dragonflies, butterflies and molluscs have been considered). Informal estimates of the proportion of species assessed, and the proportion threatened, in vertebrate higher taxa are shown graphically in Figure 1.

It has not consistently been past practice in compiling Red Data Books or Red Lists to attempt to include each and every species that could be assigned to the categories Insufficiently Known or Rare. Such species will require attention in future if the goal is to increase the number of higher taxa that have been thoroughly assessed. One very large subset of these species is comprised of those known only from their type locality (in many instances, the type material was collected many decades ago). For example, of the 4,014 nominal species of amphibian listed in Frost (1985), around 700 are reportedly known only from the type locality. Each one of these is at least Insufficiently Known or Rare, on present information, and should be categorised as Indeterminate (ie. possibly Endangered) if habitat change has been extensive in the vicinity of the type locality. There will be no exact equivalent of the current Rare category in the proposed new category system, and 'type locality only' species are likely to be classed as Insufficiently Known until better data are available (this does not denote threatened status in the new system).

SOURCES OF TAXONOMIC INFORMATION

The conflicting interests of promoting stability, following the latest or best systematic opinion, and the preferences of particular SSC Specialist Groups, have resulted in some compromises.

The following paragraphs note the main taxonomic sources used. We have whenever possible used recent global checklists of species for both nomenclature and sequence of taxa. There is a good deal of merit in following the practice of the world list of amphibians edited by Frost (1985), where orders, families, genera

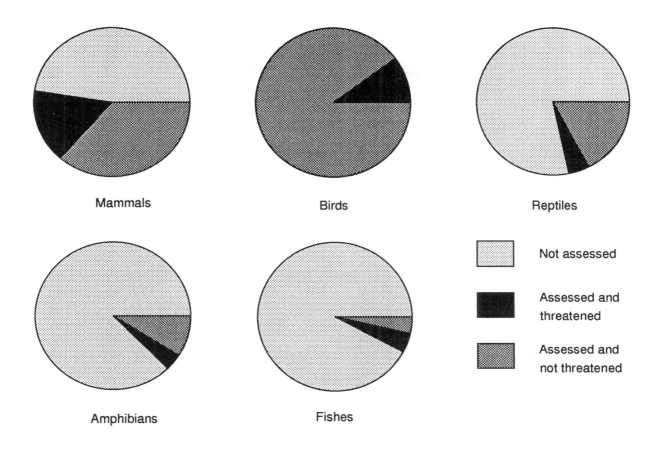

Figure 1. Pie charts to show the approximate percentage of species in major vertebrate groups that have been assessed for threatened status, together with the proportion of those assessed that are considered threatened or not threatened.

and species are all listed alphabetically. We did not adopt this for the present revision because many users are very familiar with the traditional and supposed evolutionary sequence in mammals and birds. Familiarity also caused us to adopt the conservative higher taxonomy of Morony, Bock and Farrand (1975) rather that the somewhat radical system of Sibley and Monroe (1990), although we have followed the latter source at the species level. Throughout the Red List, familiar synonyms (and sometimes other nomenclatural comments) are given in parentheses.

Mammals
The names and sequence of orders and families, and the species content of families follows Wilson and Reeder (1993). Genera and species are alphabetical within families. Species nomenclature generally also follows this source, except when a Specialist Group has expressed a very strong preference for another system, or has used nomenclature different from Wilson and Reeder and we have been unable to resolve consequent ambiguities about the population content of species and their distribution. Principal departures from Wilson and Reeder, relatively few in number, are found in the primates and bovids.

Birds
Nomenclature for genera and species follows Sibley and Monroe (1990, 1993). The names and sequence of orders and families, and the species content of families follows the more familiar system of Morony, Bock and Farrand (1975).

Reptiles
Turtles and tortoises generally follow Iverson (1992). The chief exception is *Chelonia agassizii*; recent work on mitochondrial DNA (K. Bjorndal, *in litt.*) has shown treatment at species rank separate from

Chelonia mydas, which many conservationists had adopted, to be inappropriate. Crocodilians follow King and Burke (1992). Names in common use, including by Specialist Groups or in national sources, have been employed for other groups of reptiles: there is as yet no standard world species checklist for lizards, amphisbaenians or snakes.

Amphibians
Nomenclature and sequence consistently follow Frost (1985).

Fishes
The names and sequence of orders and families, and the species content of families follows Eschmeyer (1990). Genera and species are alphabetical within families. Names in common use, including by Specialist Groups or in national sources, have been employed at the species level: there is as yet no published standard world species checklist for fishes. We have changed some family names given in contributions from the SSC Freshwater Fish Specialist Group in order to conform with the taxonomy of Eschmeyer. In particular, the Australasian Rainbowfish are given subfamily rank by Eschmeyer (Atherinidae: Melanotaeniinae) but family rank (Melanotaenidae) by local ichthyologists. Similarly, we have followed Eschmeyer in treating the Pseudomugilidae of Australasian sources, and the Austroglanidae used by Southern African sources, as subfamilies of Atherinidae and Bagridae, respectively.

Invertebrates
Parker (1982) has in general been followed for nomenclature at family level and above. Molluscs, which follow Vaughan (1989) for genera and above, are the primary exception. In one or two cases a contributor has recommended against use of a name in Parker (1982); for example, in view of current shifts in systematic opinion no family name is given for the terrestrial nemertean worms. A variety of sources, mostly listed in the references below, or cited therein, have been used for insects and other invertebrate groups.

TAXONOMY AND CONSERVATION

The interaction of taxonomy and conservation raises many issues, including the problem of identifying the units of conservation concern, and the divergence between the need for stability of nomenclature and the pursuit of systematic excellence.

In general, a threatened species tends to be given higher priority than a threatened subspecies, largely on the assumption (founded on the biological species concept) that a more distinct element of biodiversity is at risk. It is entirely legitimate, on both theoretical and pragmatic grounds, for the species to be the basic currency in global conservation action and biodiversity assessment. We have deliberately focused attention on threatened species in this Red List. Nevertheless, some difficulties must be recognised. Firstly, although the species is conceptually a real and fundamental unit in the biological hierarchy, there is no universal and operational definition of what constitutes 'a species'. The properties deemed sufficient to justify full species status vary among taxonomists working on the same group of animals. They also of necessity vary between groups (because they possess different features that can be identified as taxonomic characters), so that a species in a family of large mammals is not the precise equivalent of a species in a family of beetles. A second difficulty is that there is an opportunity for taxonomy to take on a strategic element, and for more populations to be recognised as species than might otherwise be the case.

These factors give rise to the basic truism that the delineation of species boundaries and the taxonomic rank of populations will have a fundamental impact on the conduct and efficiency of conservation actions. Similarly, they ensure that for the foreseeable future there will be a large margin of error associated with statistical treatment of biodiversity measures and listings of threatened and extinct species. This should be recalled when considering the various tabulations provided in this book.

Conservationists, particularly those involved in conservation legislation and control of illegal trade, require stability of nomenclature to help avoid misunderstandings, both unintentional and otherwise. This need underlies the widespread move toward use of 'standard taxonomy' by CITES (Convention on International Trade in Endangered Species of Wild Fauna and Flora). One risk of this approach is that it become difficult to take account quickly enough of new systematic evidence and opinion. Taxonomists generate nomenclature and classifications based on current systematic philosophy, hypotheses, and research tools, which ensures a degree of instability. Comparison of the first and second editions of the familiar *Mammal Species of the World* is of interest (the former volume was adopted by CITES as the standard taxonomy of mammals).

A total of 4,170 species were listed in the first edition of *Mammal Species of the World* (Honacki *et al.*, 1982) and 4,629 in the second (Wilson and Reeder, 1993); a net increase of 459 species. Only in the South American marsupial Orders Didelphimorphia (63 instead of 76), Paucituberculata (five instead of seven) and in Hyracoidea (six instead of seven) are there fewer species listed in 1993 than in 1982. The size of the net increase is somewhat surprising, given that mammals are a relatively well known group, but perhaps the most interesting point is that new species descriptions, of which 172 are recorded, comprise the lesser proportion of this total. The remaining 287 species of the

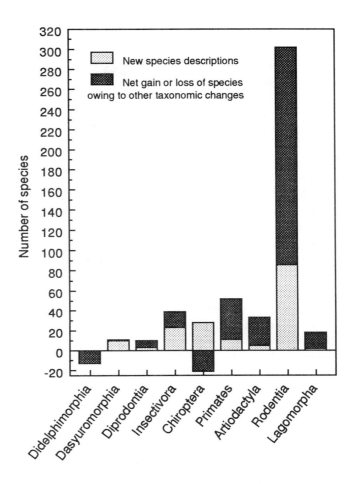

Figure 2. Changing concepts of species richness in mammals: 459 more species are recognised in the second (1993) edition of *Mammals of the World* than in the first (1982). Graph to show both (a) the number of new species descriptions and (b) net gain or loss of species largely or entirely because of changes in the taxonomic rank of populations. Note that taxonomic splitting has had greater effect on the overall increase in species number than new species descriptions. Based on data in Wilson and Reeder (1993); graph does not show Orders with trivial or no change.

total added in the second edition must be the result of taxonomic splitting (or largely so, if there is difference in the extent to which extinct species are listed, or some similar factor). Some of these changes are portrayed graphically in Figure 2. This very marked trend may be correlated with the fact that the second edition explicitly takes a far less consensual approach than the first, and so reflects closely the views of a relatively small number of mammalogists. The Orders Rodentia, Primates and Artiodactyla have increased most in species content, with in each case around 75% resulting from taxonomic splitting (and many of these primates appear in this Red List). Primates, with an additional 52 species, have undergone by far the largest percentage increase of any mammal Order (except for Notoryctemorphia, erected for *Notoryctes* which now has two species instead of one).

Clearly, changes in opinion on species boundaries such that populations formerly given subspecies rank (or perhaps not recognised as formal taxa) come to be treated as full species, have had a major impact on our world view of mammalian diversity and will in turn have repercussions for the users of this taxonomy, including the conservation community.

Some level of taxonomic change is both inevitable and desirable, if new methods and new studies are to be pursued, but taxonomists sometimes appear oblivious to the needs of users of taxonomies. As just one example, sources in Wilson and Reeder (1993) note that the dormouse genus *Glis* Brisson 1762 is invalid and the earliest valid replacement is *Myoxus* Gray 1821. Adoption of this name, not used for decades, requires changing the family name from Gliridae to Myoxidae, and denies mammalogists *Glis glis*, a name both familiar and euphonious. The pragmatic taxonomist would not have agonised over the validity or otherwise of eighteenth century names, but kept his own counsel, or petitioned the International Commission on Zoological Nomenclature to conserve the familiar name under Article 79 of the Code.

The case of the second *Sphenodon* (Tuatara), discussed by Daugherty *et al* (1990) exemplifies some practical consequences of changes in taxonomic rank of populations. This genus is of exceptional zoological interest as the only survivor of the Order Rhychocephalia, otherwise known by a wide diversity of fossil forms mainly of Triassic age. Since 1904 all extant Tuatara populations had been recognised as comprising the single species *Sphenodon punctatus*, restricted to offshore islands of New Zealand, although in neglected nineteenth century literature one additional extant species and one recently extinct were recognised. Recent analysis of allozymes and morphology reported by Daugherty *et al* demonstrated that the form originally described at species level but traditionally put in the synonymy of *S. punctatus* is indeed sufficiently distinct to require full species status as *Sphenodon guntheri*. The practical consequences are that while the Tuatara was perceived as monotypic, the 'species' appeared relatively abundant, although localised and at risk. Some 25% of island populations are known have become extinct during the past century, and *S. guntheri* could very easily have disappeared with little or no notice being taken. Now *guntheri* is recognised as the second Tuatara species it immediately takes on a very high priority for conservation, particularly because it is restricted to 1.7 ha of scrub on North Brother Island, its single world locality.

Given the general goal of maintaining biological diversity, it is in theory desirable to identify and promote the wise management of all genetically distinct populations; the existing scheme of biological taxonomy seems not in practice the best tool for identifying and cataloguing such populations, and was surely never intended to be. While a subspecific name can often serve as a useful label, and may reflect substantial genetic differences between geographically isolated populations on islands or mountain tops, where there is no correlated geographic isolation it may be a poor indicator of the magnitude of intraspecific genetic differentiation. Subspecific taxa seem too often based on small samples, arbitrary division of clinal variation, and superficial characters of pelage colour, squamation and suchlike (discussed for reptiles by Thorpe, 1980, 1984), to be universally a useful surrogate for assessment of the extent of geographic isolation and use of more direct markers of genetic differentiation.

THREATENED ANIMALS: COMMENTARY

Statistical data derived from the 1994 Red List are presented in Tables 1-6. Some preliminary remarks on these are provided below; the intention is to note some features of interest while further analysis of these and related data is pending.

The tables include threatened full species only, together with the extinct full species treated in Table 6. Subspecies and commercially threatened (CT) species are excluded. The species assigned to genera in List 3 have usually also been taken into account, but this has not been possible in all cases.

It is vital to keep in mind that these data are shaped by many factors. Some groups of species have been assessed more completely than others; some countries have carried out national assessments and produced national Red Data Books. These species and these countries will be represented in the lists more fully or more accurately than others. Further, there is significant variation in the way status categories have been interpreted and applied, and uncertainty over species boundaries and the taxonomic level of populations. However, although these data are not globally comprehensive, and have some margin of error arising from misclassification of entities into taxa or status categories, they are the best and most complete set of data available.

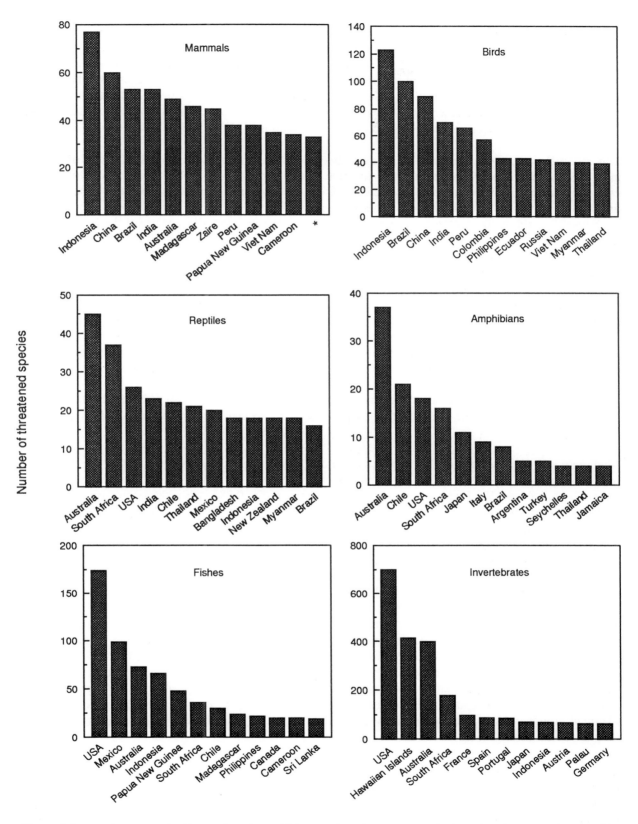

Figure 3. Bar graphs to show the 12 countries with the highest number of threatened species in each major taxonomic group. Note that this includes species suspected to be threatened (K) as well as those known to be threatened (E, V, R and I). The asterisk * in the mammal graph denotes three countries with an equal score (Argentina, Laos, Thailand).

Table 1 summarises the number of species in each threat category for each Order of animals in the Red List.

Virtually all animals are invertebrates, and most threatened animals are invertebrates, but the total number of invertebrates listed as threatened (2,754) is a scarcely perceptible proportion of the estimated global species richness of invertebrates. This last has been estimated conservatively at around ten million species, of which perhaps one-tenth have been described (Hammond, in WCMC, 1992).

This relatively very low representation of invertebrates seems probably to be more a reflection of the low level of information on the range and status of such animals, than an indication of a generally low risk of extinction, but this must be properly assessed on a group by group basis. Almost all the invertebrate species listed are molluscs or insects, in about equal proportion. Around half the insects are beetles, nearly half are butterflies and moths, most of the remainder are damsel- and dragonflies. Many of these animals can be monitored in the field without insuperable difficulty; molluscs because of the hard shells of most species, and the insects because many are relatively conspicuous diurnal winged forms.

Among the vertebrates, fishes and birds have similar numbers of species listed as threatened (977 and 971 respectively); these totals comprise about 4% of fish species but 10% of birds. This disparity is certainly due to a difference in the extent to which these two groups have been assessed. Many more fishes appear in this edition of the Red List than previously because more ichthyofaunas have been evaluated. One clear lesson to have emerged from this compilation is that wherever surveys are made, more fishes are found to be threatened, usually by introduced non-native fish species or habitat modification.

A total of 741 mammal species are considered threatened; this represents almost 16% of the 4,629 species now recognised. This is the highest proportion of the total species content for any of the higher taxa considered.

Mammals and birds have a similar number of Endangered category species, 177 and 188 respectively, representing 3.8% and 1.9% of all the species in each group. Reptiles, amphibians, fishes and invertebrates have 47, 32, 158 and 582 Endangered species, representing 0.7%, 0.7%, 0.6% and at the very most 0.05% of species in each group.

Two very small mammal Orders have all extant species listed as threatened: the two elephants and four sirenians. Most Perissodactyla, 12 of 18 species, are threatened. In terms of number alone, seven Orders have more than 50 threatened species listed. These are, in descending sequence: Rodentia 118, Primates 113, Carnivora 99, Artiodactyla 81, Cetacea 77, Insectivora 73 and Chiroptera 72. If Insufficiently Known taxa are excluded, there are five Orders with more than 50 species listed: Primates 105, Rodentia 87, Artiodactyla 75, Chiroptera 64 and Carnivora 63. It is interesting to note that the top three Orders are also those that have undergone most taxonomic splitting (Figure 2). If the five values are calculated as a percentage of described species in each Order, the sequence is: Primates 45%, Artiodactyla 34%, Carnivora 23%, Chiroptera 6.9% and Rodentia 4.3%. Primates, with 43, have by far the highest number of Endangered species among mammal Orders; Artiodactyla are second with 31, about twice as many as any of the remaining Orders. It remains to be seen whether continuing conservation assessment of other mammal groups, which generate less popular concern, will shift the balance of these figures, or whether they are an accurate measure of relative extinction risk.

Tables 2 and 3 give country-based data on threatened animals. Figure 3 shows countries with the highest number of threatened (E, V, R, I) and possibly-threatened (K) species combined in each higher taxonomic group. It is difficult objectively to disentangle the factors that contribute to these rankings. Certainly the extent to which countries have carried out national faunal surveys and conservation assessments is a major determinant, as is the extent to which IUCN-SSC Specialist Groups have been active. Species richness, land area and the magnitude of faunal depletion are other key factors.

Indonesia, Brazil, China and India are among the five countries with the most threatened mammals and birds. They are all also large, ecologically diverse and species-rich countries, and hold a large number of species in the better-assessed groups. Australia, USA and South Africa also figure prominently in Figure 3; these are similarly large and species-rich, and their faunas have been subject to detailed study and assessment. However, while the relationships involved are complex, there is no reason to suspect that the ranking of countries in this compilation is not a reasonable working indication of the overall geopolitical location of species at risk of extinction.

Table 5 summarises the number of species in each major taxonomic group listed as threatened in the 1990 and 1994 Red Lists. All groups except birds have many more species listed in 1994 than in 1990: approximately 1500 more species overall are listed in the present edition. This can not be interpreted directly as an overall increase in the risk of extinction. Among reptiles, amphibians, fishes and invertebrates, virtually all the increase can be attributed either to recent assessment of groups not or incompletely evaluated before, or to the inclusion in this edition of species from national Red Data Books and lists. Much the same appears true for mammals. For example, many more cetaceans and bats are listed following publication, respectively, of a Red Data Book and an Action Plan for these groups (Klinowska, 1991; Mickleburgh *et al.*, 1992). In several instances, and virtually only among mammals, species previously evaluated and not considered threatened have been moved to one of the threatened status categories; this may reflect the collection of new data, a deterioration in status, or inconsistency in the application of categories. Only the total for birds is lower in 1994 than in 1990. This reduction is mainly because a number of birds are no longer considered threatened *sensu* IUCN following reassessment during preparation of the *Threatened Birds of the Americas* Red Data Book (Collar *et al.*, 1992); changes to the taxonomic rank of a few populations have reduced the total of those listed at species level.

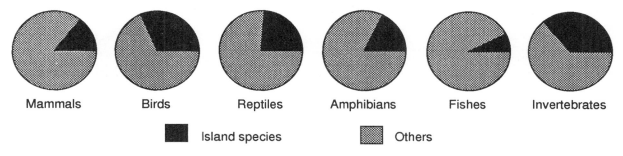

Figure 4. Pie charts to show approximate numbers of threatened species restricted to islands as opposed to 'others' - those occurring on continents or continents plus islands. Madagascar, Japan (main group), Borneo, Sumatra and Java have not been counted as islands for the purposes of this estimation.

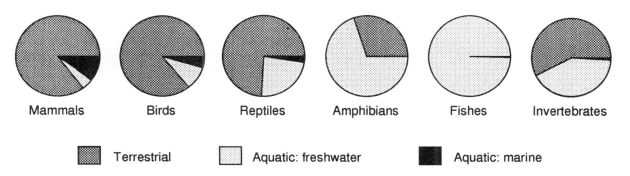

Figure 5. Pie charts to show approximate numbers of threatened species present in terrestrial or aquatic habitats. Aquatic species include cetaceans and a few other mammals, waterbirds, seabirds, sea turtles and water snakes, most amphibians, invertebrates with an aquatic stage in the life cycle, and of course all fishes. The aquatic species are divided into freshwater and marine.

A high, but not the greater, proportion of threatened species are restricted to islands; see Figure 4 (islands, for the purposes of this very broad overview, exclude Madagascar, Borneo, Japan, Sumatra but include most others). A high proportion of threatened species are aquatic; see Figure 5. These comprise both fully aquatic forms and those, including most of the amphibians and many invertebrates, with an obligatory aquatic stage in the life cycle. Few of the aquatic forms listed are marine species; cetaceans comprise the majority of these.

There is good reason to believe that historical records of extinctions since around 1600 AD are heavily biased geographically and taxonomically. The data that are available indicate that around 75% of recorded extinctions in this period have occurred on islands; almost all bird and mollusc extinctions have been recorded on islands. Very few species extinctions have been recorded in continental tropical forest habitats, where mass extinction events have been predicted to be underway. The patchy and similarly biased time-series data that can be assembled indicate that island extinctions in this period began some 200 years earlier than continental extinctions, and that rates in both areas have increased rapidly from around the middle of the last century to the middle of the present century. Extended discussion of extinct species and rates of extinction is provided in WCMC (1992: chapter 16).

ACKNOWLEDGEMENTS

The assistance of many people has been essential during the compilation of this document. We thank in particular the many SSC Specialist Group chairpersons and other members, and the many other field scientists who have provided data and opinions for this revision, usually adding to an already heavy workload. We hope not to have overlooked anyone in the list below, and trust that those who have made especially valuable contributions will not object to our alphabetical sequence. Particular thanks are due to Georgina Mace for agreeing to prepare the Guest Essay for this edition, an essay that will ensure that a wide audience gains insight into the new status categories and the considerations that went into their revision. The successful execution of this project was dependent on the timely liaison carried out by Simon Stuart (Head, Species Survival Programme), for which we are also grateful.

D. Agosti, R. Albuquerque de Matos, G.R. Allen, R. Alonso, C. Andrews, G. Archibald, J.M. Ayres, G. Bauer, C. Bibby, K. Bjorndal, A. Bogan, P. Bouchet, J. Bratton, M. Brooks, W.C. Brown, A.A. Burbidge, E. Cameron, R. Cameron, J.A. Campbell, R.R. Campbell, H. Campos, R. Chung, D. Clarke, H.G. Cogger, A.F. Coimbra-Filho, N. Collar, K. Corbett, D. Corke, J. Cortes, R. Cowie, A.J. Crivelli, R. Crombie, I. Das, M. Day, S. Dowell, R. East, S.K. Eltringham, F. Encarnación, A.A. Eudey, S.F. Ferrari, C. FitzGibbon, G. Fonseca, G. Foster, P. Foster-Turley, P.J. Garson, A. Gascoigne, R. Gerald, J. Gerlach, J.R. Ginsberg, A.R. Glatston, J. van Goethem, V. Goryachev, M. Green, O. Griffiths, S. Hedges, H. Hoeck, S. Hochwald, P. Horwitz, A.M. Hutson, M. Ibanez, P. Jackson, A. Jeffs, M.D. Jenkins, M.W. Klemens, V. Kessner, Mohd Khan bin Momin Khan, R.T. Klocek, Kunio Kikuchi, T.B. Larsen, M. Lazaridou-Dimitriadou, H. Marsh, S. Matola, D.E. McAllister, R. McDowall, S.L. Mendes, S.P. Mickleburgh, G. Mills, R.A. Mittermeier, J. Moore, N.W. Moore, T.R. New, M. Nicoll, J.F. Oates, J. Økland, K.A. Økland, W.L.R. Oliver, M.E. Oliveira, T.J. O'Shea, C. Padua, C. Peres, I.V. Pinto, W. Ponder, V.I. Prikhodko, Z. Pucek, A.I. Queiroz, P.J.H. Reijnders, J. Robinson, J.P. Ross, B. Roth, J. Ruetschi, H. Ruhberg, A.B. Rylands, M.J. Samways, I.B. Santos, A. Savage, P. Schembri, M. Seddon, D. Shackleton, M. Shea, G. Sherley, P.S. Skelton, S. Slack-Smith, A.T. Smith, B.D. Smith, B.J. Smith, M. Speight, J. Stanisic, J. Steffek, H. Stephenson, C. Stevanovitch, M.L.J. Stiassny, R. Sukumar, S. Tonge, H. Walden, T. Waller, S.M. Wells, Ø. Wiig, J.E. Williams, R. Wirth, D. Woodruff, Kazuhiro Yamase, Chen Yiyu, D. Zevin.

WCMC Credits

Research and compilation: Neil Cox, Brian Groombridge, Tim Inskipp, Martin Jenkins, Chris Magin, Helen Smith. Data processing and camera-ready preparation by Helen Corrigan. Data entry and word-processing by Esther Byford, Lorraine Collins, Helen Corrigan and Julie Reay. Graphics by Helen Smith. Andrea Cole, Mary Cordiner, Daniella Pitts and Lindsay Simpson provided varied assistance. Project development by Tim Johnson, assisted by Crawford Allan.

The database from which this list is produced is constantly being updated, with changes arising as new studies are undertaken or as groups not previously assessed are examined. It is inevitable in a publication of this nature that readers will find entries that require correction or updating. We would be most grateful if any relevant information could be sent to the address below.

Requests for sub-sets of data (geopolitical or taxonomic) for educational or conservation applications may be directed to Information Services at the address below.

Brian Groombridge, PhD
Species Unit
World Conservation Monitoring Centre
219 Huntingdon Road
Cambridge CB3 0DL
United Kingdom

Telephone: +44 223 277314
Fax: +44 223 277136
e-mail: redlist@wcmc.org.uk

REFERENCES

IUCN and IUCN/ICBP global Red Data Books, Action Plans[1] and lists

Collar, N.J. and Andrew, P. 1988. *Birds to Watch.* The ICBP World Checklist of Threatened Birds. ICBP Technical Publication No. 8. International Council for Bird Preservation.

Collar, N.J., Gonzaga, L.P., Krabbe, N., Madroño Nieto, A., Naranjo, L.G., Parker, T.A. and Wege, D.C. 1992. *Threatened Birds of the Americas. The ICBP/IUCN Red Data Book.* 3rd edition, part 2. International Council for Bird Preservation (now BirdLife International), Cambridge, UK.

Collins, N.M. and Morris, M.G. 1985. *Threatened Swallowtail Butterflies of the World. The IUCN Red Data Book.* IUCN, Gland and Cambridge.

Duncan, P. (ed). 1992. *Zebras, Asses, and Horses: an Action Plan for the conservation of Wild Equids.* IUCN, Gland.

Groombridge, B. 1982. *The IUCN Amphibia-Reptilia Red Data Book. Part 1, Testudines, Crocodylia, Rhynchocephalia.* IUCN, Gland.

Honegger, R. 1975/1979. *Red Data Book, Vol. 3 - Amphibia and Reptilia.* Second Edition. IUCN, Gland.

Klinowska, M. 1991. *Dolphins, Porpoises and Whales of the World. The IUCN Red Data Book.* IUCN, Gland, Switzerland and Cambridge, UK.

Mickleburgh, S.P., Hutson, A.M. and Racey, P.A. (eds). 1992. *Old World Fruit Bats: an Action Plan for their conservation.* IUCN, Gland.

Miller, R.R. 1977. *Red Data Book, Vol. 4 - Pisces.* Second Edition. IUCN, Morges.

New, T.R. (ed). 1993. *Conservation Biology of Lycaenidae (Butterflies).* Occasional Paper of the IUCN Species Survival Commission No. 8. IUCN, Gland, Switzerland.

Thornback, J. and Jenkins, M. 1982. *The IUCN Mammal Red Data Book. Part 1. The Americas and Australasia.* IUCN, Gland.

Wells, S.M., Pyle, R.M. and Collins, N.M. 1983. *The IUCN Invertebrate Red Data Book.* IUCN, Gland.

National Red Data Books[2] and lists

Anon. 1991. *Draft Red List of Threatened Animals of Turkey.* Prime Ministry Undersecretariat for Environment. Ankara. (unpublished).

Anon. 1991. *Livro Vermelho dos Vertebrados de Portugal.* Serviço Nacional de Parques, Reservas e Conservaçao da Natureza. Ministério do Ambiente e dos Recursos Naturais. Lisbon.

Anon. 1991. *Red Data Book of Japan.* 2 volumes: vertebrates, invertebrates. Japanese Wildlife Research Centre. (in Japanese)

Anon. (Ministry of Science, Technology and Environment). 1992. *Red Data Book of Vietnam. Volume 1. Animals.* Science and Technics Publishing House, Hanoi. (in Vietnamese).

Anon. 1992. *Endangered and Threatened Wildlife and Plants.* US Fish and Wildlife Service, Department of the Interior.

Bell, B.D. 1986. *The Conservation Status of New Zealand Wildlife.* New Zealand Wildlife Service, Wellington. Occasional Publication No. 12.

Bernardes, A.T., Machado, A.B.M. and Rylands, A.B. 1990. *Fauna Brasileira Ameaçada de Extinçao.* Belo Horizonte: Fundaçao da Diversidade Biològica.

Blanco, J.C. & González, J.L. (eds). 1992. *Libro Rojo de los Vertebrados de España.* Ministerio de Agricultura Pesca y Alimentacion.

Branch, W.R. (ed.) 1988. *South African Red Data Book - Reptiles and Amphibians.* South African National Scientific Programmes Report 151.

Garnett, S. 1992. *The Action Plan for Australian Birds.* Australian National Parks and Wildlife Service, Endangered Species Program, Project Number 121. Canberra.

Glade, A.A. (ed). 1988. *Red List of Chilean Terrestrial Vertebrates.* Chilean Forest Service (CONAF), Santiago.

Horwitz, P. 1990. *The Conservation Status of Australian Freshwater Crustacea*. Report no. 14, Australian National Parks and Wildlife Service, Canberra.

Karandinós, M. (ed) 1992. *The Red Data Book of Threatened Vertebrates of Greece*. Athens: Hellenic Zoological Society & Hellenic Ornithological Society.

Kennedy, M. (ed). 1992. *Australian Marsupials and Monotremes: an Action Plan for their conservation*. IUCN, Gland.

Maruyama, T. & Hiratsuka, J. 1992. *Vanishing Fishes of Japan*. Osaka: Freshwater Fish Protection Association of Japan, 1-10.

Nabhitibhata, Jarujin. 1989. Species diversity of Thai herpetofauna. In: *Biodiversity in Thailand*. Science Society of Bangkok, pp. 169-204. (in Thai) (not seen; data from Woodruff [1990] and *in litt.* 1993).

Severinghaus, L.L. and Liu, V.T. 1990. *The Endangered Plants and Animals of Taiwan*. Council of Agriculture and National Parks Association, Taiwan.

Skelton, P.H. 1987. *South African Red Data Book - Fishes*. South African National Scientific Programmes Report 137.

Wagner, R. & Jackson, P. 1993. *The Action Plan for Australian Freshwater Fishes*. Canberra: Australian Nature Conservation Agency, Endangered Species Program, Project Number 147. Canberra.

Woodruff, D.S. 1990. Review of: Endangered Animals of Thailand. *Natural History Bulletin of the Siam Society* 38:163-177. (Appendix: List of the Threatened Vertebrate Animals of Thailand, pp. 168-177).

Global taxonomic sources

Corbet, G.B. and Hill, J.E. 1980. *A World List of Mammalian Species*. British Museum (Natural History) and Cornell University Press.

Eschmeyer, W. N. 1990. *Catalog of the Genera of Recent Fishes*. San Francisco: California Academy of Sciences. 697pp.

Frost, D.R. 1985. *Amphibian Species of the World: A Taxonomic and Geographical Reference*. Allen Press Inc. and the Association of Systematics Collections, Lawrence, Kansas. I-V, 1-732.

Honacki, J.H., Kinman, K.E. and Koeppl, J.W. 1982. *Mammal Species of the World: a taxonomic and geographic reference*. Allen Press Inc. and the Association of Systematics Collections, Kansas.

Iverson, J.B. 1992. *A Checklist with Distribution Maps of the Turtles of the World*. Second edition. Published by the author; Richmond, Indiana.

Morony, J.J., Bock, W.J. and Farrand, J. 1975. *Reference list of the Birds of the World*. Department of Ornithology, American Museum of Natural History, New York

Parker, S.B. 1982. *Synopsis and Classification of Living Organisms*. McGraw-Hill, New York.

Sibley, C.G. and Monroe, B.L. 1990. *Distribution and Taxonomy of Birds of the World*. Yale University Press, New Haven.

Sibley, C.G. and Monroe, B.L. 1993. *A Supplement to Distribution and Taxonomy of Birds of the World*. Yale University Press, New Haven.

Tsuda, S. 1991. *A Distributional List of World Odonata*. Published by the author, Osaka.

Vaughan, K.C. 1989 (editors Abbott, R.T. and Boss, K.J). *A Classification of the Living Mollusca*. American Malacologists, Inc., Florida.

Wilson, D.E. and Reeder, D.M. (eds). 1993. *Mammal Species of the World: a taxonomic and geographic reference*. Second edition. Smithsonian Institution Press. Washington and London.

Other sources: status, taxonomy, distribution[3]

Anon. (Societas Europaea Herpetologica - Conservation Committee). 1990. Threatened reptiles in Europe requiring special conservation measures. Unpublished report to the Council of Europe. T-PVS (90) 57.

Anon. (Societas Europaea Herpetologica - Conservation Committee). 1991. Threatened amphibians in Europe requiring special habitat protection measures. Unpublished report to the Council of Europe. T-PVS (91) 72.

Anon. (Societas Europaea Herpetologica - Conservation Committee). 1992. Data sheets of species of amphibians and reptiles for possible amendment of Appendix II. Unpublished report to the Council of Europe. T-PVS (92) 75.

Allen, G.R. 1991. *Field Guide to the Freshwater Fishes of New Guinea*. Publication No. 9 of the Christensen Research Institute.

Blanc, M., Gaudet, J. L., Banarescu, P. and Hureau, J. C. 1971. *European Inland Water Fish: A Multilingual Catalogue*. London: F.A.O. & Fishing News Books.

Campbell, J.A. and Frost, D. 1993. Anguid Lizards of the genus *Abronia*: revisionary notes, description of four new species, a phylogenetic analysis and key. *Bulletin of American Natural History*. 216:1-121.

Collins, N.M. and Wells, S.M. 1987. *Invertebrates in need of special protection in Europe*. Council of Europe Nature and Environment Series No. 35. Strasbourg.

Corbet, G.B., & Hill, J.E. 1992. *The Mammals of the Indomalayan Region: a systematic review*. London: British Museum (Natural History). Oxford: Oxford University Press. 488pp.

Daugherty, C.H., Cree, A, Hay, J.M. and Thompson, M.B. 1990. Neglected taxonomy and continuing extinctions of tuatara (*Sphenodon*). *Nature*. 347:177-179.

Heath, J. 1981. *Threatened Rhopalocera (Butterflies) in Europe*. Council of Europe 'Nature and Environment Series' No. 23. Strasbourg.

Hedges, S.B. 1993. Global amphibian declines: a perspective from the Caribbean. *Biodiversity and Conservation*. 2:290-303.

Kottelat, M. and Xin-Luo, C. 1988. Revision of *Yunnanilus* with descriptions of a minature species flock and six new species from China (Cypriniformes: Homalopteridae). *Environmental Biology of Fishes*. 23(1-2), 65-93.

Kuru, M. 1980. *Türkiye Tatlisu Baliklari Katalogu*. Hacettepe Üniversitesi Fen Fakültesi Yayinlari, Yardimci Kitaplar, Dizisi: 1

Lee, D. S., Platania, S. P. & Burgess, G. H. 1983. *Atlas of North American Freshwater Fishes 1983 Supplement*. (Freshwater fishes of the Greater Antilles). Occasional Papers of the North Carolina Biological Survey. Contribution No. 1983-6.

Peters, J.A. and Donoso-Barros, R. (revised by P.E. Vanzolini). 1986. *Catalogue of the Neotropical Squamata. Part II. Lizards and Amphisbaenians*. Smithsonian Institution Press. Washington D.C.

Reyes, L. M. & Estrada, J. L. 1992. Estado Actual Del Mejoramiento Genetico Y Recomendaciones Para La Conservacian De Los Recursos Geneticos En Colombia. In:Halffter, G. (ed) *La Diversidad Biológica de Iberoamérica*. Mexico: Instituto de Ecología, A. C. 203-236.

Schlitter, D.A. 1985. Preliminary List - African Rodents of Special Concern. Unpublished Report to IUCN.

Schwartz, A. and Henderson, R.W. 1991. *Amphibians and Reptiles of the West Indies: Descriptions, Distributions, and Natural History*. University of Florida Press, Gainesville.

Simonetta, A. M. & Magnoni, M. L. 1986. Status and Conservation Problems of Somali Lower Vertebrates. *Rivista di Agricoltura Subtropicale e Tropicale*, 80(3). 405-432.

Stiassny, M. L. J. 1990. Notes on the Anatomy and Relationships of the Bedotiid Fishes of Madagascar, with a Taxonomic Revision of the Genus *Rheocles* (Atherinomorpha: Bedotiidae). *American Museum Novitates* New York: American Museum of Natural History. 2979.

Stiassny, M. L. J. 1993. Cichlids are Different!. *Tropical Fish Hobbyist*. March 1993.

Stiassny, M. L. J. & Reinthal, P. N. 1991. The Freshwater Fishes of Madagascar: A Study of an Endangered Fauna with recommendations for a Conservation Strategy. *Conservation Biology* 5(2): 231-243

Thorpe, R.S. 1980. Microevolution and taxonomy of European reptiles with particular reference to the grass snake *Natrix natrix* and the wall lizards *Podarcis sicula* and *P. melisellensis*. *Biological Journal of the Linnean Society*. 14: 215-233.

Thorpe, R.S. 1984. Geographic variation in the Western grass snake (*Natrix natrix helvetica*) in relation to hypothesized phylogeny and conventional subspecies. *Journal of Zoology, London*. 203: 345-355.

Tzeng, C. S. 1986. Distribution of the Freshwater Fishes of Taiwan. *Journal of the Taiwan Museum* 39 (2), 127-146

Vu Van Dung, Pham Mong Giao, Nguyen Ngoc Chinh, Do Tuoc, Arctander, P. and MacKinnon, J. 1993. A new species of living bovid from Vietnam. *Nature* 363: 443-445.

Wijesinghe, L.C.A. de S., Gunatilleke, I.A.U.N., Jayawardana, S.D.G., Kotagama, S.W. and Gunatilleke, C.V.S. 1989. *Biological Conservation in Sri Lanka (A national status report)*. Natural Resources, Energy and Science Authority of Sri Lanka, Colombo.

Witte, F., Goldschmidt, T., Wanink, J., van Oijen, M., Goudswaard, K., Witte-Maas, E. and Bouton, N. 1992. The destruction of an endemic species flock: quantitative data on the decline of the haplochromine cichlids of Lake Victoria. *Environmental Biology of Fishes* 34: 1-28.

World Conservation Monitoring Centre. 1992. *Global Biodiversity: Status of the Earth's Living Resources*. Chapman and Hall, London.

[1] the Action Plans listed include only published documents not used in the 1990 Red List; it excludes the draft Cat Action Plan, used in provisional form for the present Red List, and excludes those used in draft form for the 1990 Red List which have since been published.

[2] this is not a bibliography of country Red Data Books; it only includes sources from which single-country endemic species have been extracted for the 1994 IUCN Red List.

[3] excluding those cited in the 1990 Red List and not consulted for this revision.

EXPLANATORY NOTES

NOTES ON THE LISTS AND TABLES

Each entry includes: a single letter (E, V, I, K) or two (Ex, Ex?, CT) indicating the IUCN status category, the scientific name, and geopolitical distribution. Many entries also include a common name. Some marine species have a general distribution rather than a list of countries. The following annotated examples should aid interpretation of the taxon entries.

E[1]   ***Eulemur mongoz***[2]
         (*Lemur mongoz*)[3]
         Mongoose Lemur[4]
                 Comoros[5]: Mwali[6], Nzwani; Madagascar[7]

I   ***Pterodroma hasitata***
         Black-capped Petrel
                 Cuba; Dominican Republic; Haiti. *[8] Caribbean and western North Atlantic

R   ***Syrmaticus reevsii***
         Reeve's Pheasant
                 China
                 [Czechoslovakia[9]][10]

[1] IUCN status category

[2] Scientific name.

[3] Alternative scientific name (synonym).

[4] Common name (usually English).

[5] First country of occurrence.

[6] Island (or other area) within first country.

[7] Second country of occurrence (countries separated by semi-colon).

[8] Within birds only, an asterisk separates breeding range (left) from non-breeding range (right); vagrant records are excluded.

[9] Recent political events are reflected as accurately as possible but there are some entries for the former Czechoslovakia and USSR that have not been resolved in terms of new boundaries, and many entries for the former Yugoslavia retain the name of the old federation.

[10] Square brackets indicate introduced populations; populations that have been reintroduced within their former range are denoted by appropriate text.

List 1. Threatened species

This list includes those populations recognised at the species level by the taxonomic sources used that have been assessed and assigned to one of the current (non-revised) IUCN status categories. These categories are named and defined below.

Only species regarded as globally threatened are included. This has the regrettable but unavoidable consequence that no attention is drawn to purely local or national problems. For example, there is great concern in India about the Grizzled Giant Squirrel *Ratufa macroura*; the population, restricted to the southern states of Tamil Nadu and Kerala, has been estimated at only 300 animals. However, the species also occurs in Sri Lanka, where it widespread at a variety of altitudes and in different habitats, and is not listed as threatened in the country (Wijesinghe *et al.*, 1989). Because it is not globally threatened it is not listed in the present Red List. This is just one example among very many.

All species have been assigned to a single category except those from *Threatened Birds of the Americas* (Collar *et al*, 1992) that were given a dual category in that book (the reader is referred to the introduction of that volume for discussion). Very many species are given a mixed R/K category in the provisional draft of the Action Plan for Australian Reptiles made available to us, but given a policy of not using mixed categories and a recommendation not to include all potential K species from the draft, we have omitted them from this list.

Confusion and possible inconsistency exists over the position of 'Insufficiently Known' (K) taxa. Some texts include this category with others which collectively denote threatened status, other texts exclude it from that group. Insufficiently Known species are commonly regarded as threatened species even though while insufficient data are available to make a firm determination they remain only *suspected* of being threatened, and so by definition have not actually been identified as threatened species. We feel it would have been very useful clearly to distinguish such taxa from species known to be threatened, but have retained 'K' species in the main listing, largely in deference to common usage, which tends to class 'K' species with those more certainly threatened (R, I, V and E categories). As noted above, Insufficiently Known species are in the draft new category system explicitly not to be understood as threatened species.

The few 'T' designations given in past editions, indicating that different populations of the species in question had been assigned different status categories, have all been modified by us to reflect a provisional category for the species as a whole.

As noted above, it has jointly been decided by the SSC and BirdLife International that the bird listing will remain substantially the same as in the 1990 Red List (which gave categories to species listed in *Birds to Watch* (Collar and Andrew, 1988). The list has been revised to take account of *Threatened Birds of the Americas* (Collar *et al.* 1992), which entailed the removal of many species and the addition of others. There are a few other differences between the present list and the 1990 Red List. One bird species (*Dasyornis brachypterus*) inadvertently omitted from the 1990 list has been included, with the status category given in *The Action Plan for Australian Birds* (Garnett, 1992). In two cases, populations previously treated as subspecies of species themselves categorised as 'Rare' (R) (*Phalacrocorax carunculatus, Polyplectron malacense*) have been elevated to species rank in Sibley and Monroe (1992) and are here provisionally listed as 'R'. Similarly, a few taxa formerly treated at species level are given subspecific rank in Sibley and Monroe, and this is followed herein. This has had two effects on the present lists. Where other conspecifics were previously listed in the 1990 Red List there is now an appropriate revised entry in the main threatened species list (eg. *Gallinula nesiotis*, for the Tristan da Cunha form *nesiotis*, regarded as extinct, plus the Gough Island form *comeri*, previously listed as Rare). Where conspecifics were not listed previously there is now an entry in the subspecies list (eg. *Pterodroma hasitata caribbaea* for the probably extinct Jamaica Petrel, treated as E/Ex at species level *P. caribbaea* in Collar *et al.* 1992).

List 2. Extinct and probably extinct species

This list includes species that have been assigned to the IUCN status category Extinct (Ex) in previous editions of the Red List and in Red Data Books. This category includes species that have not definitely been located in the wild during the past 50 years. Many species have not been seen within this period, but nor have they been looked for, and there has been no attempt to list all such species here. A subset of this category (Ex?) includes species that have been seen within the past 50 years but are believed with near certainty to be extinct. Similar species that are only possibly extinct should according to the current definitions be listed as Endangered.

We have also included here species that are known or believed to have become extinct since 1600 AD or thereabouts (WCMC, 1992) and which have never appeared in previous Red Lists nor been given a status category. To distinguish these they remain without a category in the list. For many of these latter species (and some of those with a category) the date shown in parentheses indicates variously the last collection, the last observation in the wild, or the time of extinction.

There are 23 bird taxa which have been given the joint category 'E/Ex' by BirdLife International. Those that are treated at species level by Sibley and Monroe (1990) (not the Magdalena Tinamou or Jamaica Petrel [see notes to List 1 above]) are listed in the main threatened species list even though at least seven of the 21 species are almost certainly extinct. None is included in the Extinct species list. The full species are counted as Endangered in the tables.

In almost all cases there is no positive evidence of extinction, only an accumulation of negative evidence; several species once thought recently extinct have been rediscovered and doubtless others will be in future. On the other hand, there are good grounds for believing that many species have become extinct unnoticed and sometimes undescribed. Note that changes in species level taxonomy have a significant effect on this list; a few extinct populations formerly treated as full species are now treated as conspecific with extant populations, and so do not appear below (the reverse is also possible).

List 3. Entries for genera and other higher taxa

This list includes entries for genera or higher taxa, entire or in part, that appeared in the 1990 Red List or earlier publications and that have not been resolved to the single species level. Some previous group entries have been so resolved and now appear in the main threatened species list. The category assigned to the Lake Victoria cichlid fishes has been changed from Endangered (E) to Indeterminate (I) in the absence of adequately detailed species-specific population data for the lake as a whole (Indeterminate is an inclusive category covering inadequately known taxa that may have recently become extinct, or which are seriously declining or which may simply be Rare; see status category definitions below). There is no doubt that a very marked decline in cichlid abundance has occurred in Lake Victoria (Witte *et al.*, 1992) linked to the introduction of a large predator (Nile Perch *Lates* sp.) and probably to over-fishing, but it is not possible to determine which individual species are actually Endangered. Where possible, the relevant number of species within the groups listed here are included in the tabulations.

List 4. Threatened and extinct subspecies

Previous editions of the Red List mixed full species and subspecies in a single list. This led to some minor confusion. Threatened populations at subspecies rank are by most standards (and all else being equal) of lesser priority than threatened species, assuming reasonable taxonomic consistency between taxa being compared. It is also evident that subspecies descriptions are not infrequently based on minor superficial features; in several cases subspecies names in common use have been demonstrated to accord only poorly with genetic differentiation assessed by biochemical and other tools. These several considerations have led us to list subspecies separately from species.

In the subspecies list we have made no attempt to add subspecies other than those suggested by contributors. We have tried to ensure that, if appropriate, an entry exists in the full species list whenever all described subspecies have been proposed as threatened. The list therefore consists largely of taxa previously listed, and while some nomenclature has been revised, some outdated names and other inconsistencies are likely to remain.

Subspecies have been excluded from all tables.

List 5. Commercially Threatened species

This contains species categorised as Commercially Threatened (CT). These species should not be regarded as threatened with extinction in the same sense that those in the main species list categorised as

Endangered, Vulnerable, Indeterminate or Rare are believed to be. The CT category means that the species were considered to be threatened as a sustainable commercial resource; pending further evaluation of the full implications of listing such species we have thought it advisable to distinguish them clearly from other listed species. All species (with the exception of the Pigtail Macaque, proposed in 1993 for listing as V or CT) were previously listed as Commercially Threatened in the 1990 Red List or earlier publications and have not been critically evaluated since. We have not attempted to update nomenclature or resolve marine distribution at country level.

Commercially Threatened species have been excluded from all tables.

Distribution information

Distribution is generally given in terms of country names; it is geopolitical not purely geographic. Unless geographically very remote from each other, islands and other territories are included with the parent country; the Hawaiian Islands have been recorded separately. Many distribution entries include within-country information. This is usually when a species occurs on a few islands of an island state; occasionally when otherwise restricted, a mountain or river system is named.

Although we have given general distribution information for all marine species, including cetaceans, we have not given country distribution records for cetaceans other than the freshwater and estuarine or coastal species with a relatively restricted range. In most other cases, country records for cetaceans reflect the distribution of research or whaling activity more fully than the presumed world distribution of the species. We have attempted to give complete country records for other marine animals. All country records are included in the summary tabulations above.

Countries where a species is known to have become extinct in recent decades are not included. In several cases, a country name is followed by the annotation: (ex?). This indicates a significant possibility that the species is extinct in that country; this ancilliary information should not be confused with the IUCN status category.

Geopolitical events during recent years have led to some inconsistency and possible errors. In the absence at the time of writing of internationally recognised boundaries and names within the former Yugoslavia, we have continued to use that name in the distribution information and in the country tabulations. Of the component republics of the former federation of Yugoslavia, only Slovenia has been distinguished herein, although there are likely to be some species occurring there for which only Yugoslavia appears in the distribution section. For most species within the boundaries of the former USSR, we have been able to determine with reasonable confidence which new state they are present in. Some unresolved USSR entries remain in the invertebrate section. Similarly, there are a few entries for the former Czechoslovakia in cases where we have been unable to determine whether a particular species occurs in the Czech Republic or Slovakia, or both.

Notes on tables

All the tables cover taxa of species rank only; subspecies are excluded. The tables cover species that have been assigned to one of the standard IUCN-SSC status categories; the Commercially Threatened taxa (CT) set out in List 5 are excluded.

Tables 2, 3 and 6 for simplicity use the same major geopolitical units as in the distribution entries in the species lists. This results in loss of geographical resolution of some biological interest; in particular it should be noted that island territories of mainland countries are in most cases included with their parent countries. For example, the Canary Islands, which feature prominently in the mollusc lists, are included with Spain in the tables. However, the distribution entries in the species lists will indicate "Spain: Canary Islands", so the relevant information can be retrieved. The same applies to Madeira, the Azores, and several other islands. Tristan da Cunha is included with St Helena. The Hawaiian Islands have a separate entry.

In the distribution entries in the lists below, unconfirmed occurrence of a species is indicated by "?" after the relevant country. All such unconfirmed occurrences are counted in the tables.

Note that a few species, mainly cosmopolitan marine forms, have distribution indicated in a generalised format, not country names; these are not included in the country-based tables (Tables 2 and 3). This applies to most cetaceans, three elasmobranch fishes, and very few invertebrates. It also applies to a larger number of species included in the genera recorded in List 3 (entries for genera and Lake Victoria cichlid fishes) for which country-specific data are lacking. We have retained the figure of 250 haplochromine and 2 tilapiine cichlid fishes in Lake Victoria cited in the 1990 Red List, although recent estimates suggest more than 300 haplochromine species are present, of which around 200 may be critically threatened. All these species (except in two genera for which we have no count of species number) are included in the taxonomic summary tables (Tables 1, 4 and 5).

In all relevant tables we have treated the 21 E/Ex and the 78 V/R bird species given mixed categories as categories E and V, respectively.

IUCN THREATENED SPECIES CATEGORIES

EXTINCT (Ex)

Species not definitely located in the wild during the past 50 years (criterion as used by the Convention on International Trade in Endangered Species of Wild Fauna and Flora).

N.B. On a few occasions, the category Ex? has been assigned; this denotes that it is virtually certain that the taxon has recently become extinct.

ENDANGERED (E)

Taxa in danger of extinction and whose survival is unlikely if the causal factors continue operating.

Included are taxa whose numbers have been reduced to a critical level or whose habitats have been so drastically reduced that they are deemed to be in immediate danger of extinction. Also included are taxa that may be extinct but have definitely been seen in the wild in the past 50 years.

VULNERABLE (V)

Taxa believed likely to move into the 'Endangered' category in the near future if the causal factors continue operating.

Included are taxa of which most or all the populations are decreasing because of over-exploitation, extensive destruction of habitat or other environmental disturbance; taxa with populations that have been seriously depleted and whose ultimate security has not yet been assured; and taxa with populations that are still abundant but are under threat from severe adverse factors throughout their range.

N.B. In practice, 'Endangered' and 'Vulnerable' categories may include, temporarily, taxa whose populations are beginning to recover as a result of remedial action, but whose recovery is insufficient to justify their transfer to another category.

RARE (R)

Taxa with small world populations that are not at present 'Endangered' or 'Vulnerable', but are at risk.

These taxa are usually localised within restricted geographical areas or habitats or are thinly scattered over a more extensive range.

INDETERMINATE (I)

Taxa *known* to be 'Endangered', 'Vulnerable' or 'Rare' but where there is not enough information to say which of the three categories is appropriate.

INSUFFICIENTLY KNOWN (K)

Taxa that are *suspected* but not definitely known to belong to any of the above categories, because of lack of information.

THREATENED (T)

Threatened is a general term to denote species which are 'Endangered', 'Vulnerable', 'Rare', 'Indeterminate', or 'Insufficiently Known' and should not be confused with the use of the same term by the U.S. Office of Endangered Species. In previous volumes it is has been used to identify taxa comprised of several sub-taxa which have differing status categories.

COMMERCIALLY THREATENED (CT)

Taxa not currently threatened with extinction, but most or all of whose populations are threatened as a sustainable commercial resource, or will become so, unless their exploitation is regulated.

This category applies only to taxa whose populations are assumed to be relatively large.

N.B. In practice, this category has only been used for marine species of commercial importance that are being overfished in several parts of their ranges.

Table 1. Threatened species: totals for higher taxa by status category

	E	V	R	I	SUBTOTAL[1]	K	TOTAL
Class: MAMMALIA							
ARTIODACTYLA	31	34	3	7	75	6	81
CARNIVORA	15	29	4	15	63	36	99
CETACEA	5	7	0	1	13	64	77
CHIROPTERA	16	22	18	8	64	8	72
DASYUROMORPHIA	6	2	2	0	10	0	10
DIPROTODONTIA	16	17	4	0	37	2	39
HYRACOIDEA	0	0	0	1	1	0	1
INSECTIVORA	3	4	9	11	27	46	73
LAGOMORPHA	8	3	1	7	19	4	23
MACROSCELIDEA	0	1	1	0	2	0	2
MONOTREMATA	1	0	0	0	1	0	1
PERAMELEMORPHIA	3	2	1	1	7	1	8
PERISSODACTYLA	8	4	0	0	12	0	12
PRIMATES	43	48	9	5	105	8	113
PROBOSCIDEA	1	1	0	0	2	0	2
RODENTIA	19	19	37	12	87	31	118
SIRENIA	0	4	0	0	4	0	4
XENARTHRA	2	2	0	0	4	2	6
Subtotal	177	199	89	68	533	208	741
Class: AVES							
ANSERIFORMES	3	9	2	1	15	3	18
APODIFORMES	6	15	5	8	34	2	36
APTERYGIFORMES	0	1	0	0	1	0	1
CAPRIMULGIFORMES	2	0	1	4	7	2	9
CHARADRIIFORMES	3	6	9	8	26	5	31
CICONIIFORMES	7	4	2	3	16	2	18
COLUMBIFORMES	7	16	14	12	49	0	49
CORACIIFORMES	0	5	10	4	19	1	20
CUCULIFORMES	2	3	2	3	10	1	11
FALCONIFORMES	7	8	13	2	30	4	34
GALLIFORMES	16	20	21	4	61	3	64
GRUIFORMES	10	13	8	14	45	7	52
PASSERIFORMES	85	107	136	87	415	63	478
PELECANIFORMES	1	2	5	1	9	1	10
PICIFORMES	5	2	1	3	11	3	14
PODICIPEDIFORMES	3	0	0	0	3	1	4
PROCELLARIIFORMES	11	5	2	5	23	1	24
PSITTACIFORMES	18	23	19	6	66	5	71
SPHENISCIFORMES	0	1	0	0	1	1	2
STRIGIFORMES	1	0	7	7	15	2	17
TINAMIFORMES	1	1	0	3	5	1	6
TROGONIFORMES	0	0	0	1	1	0	1
Subtotal	188	241	257	176	862	108	970
Class: REPTILIA							
CROCODYLIA	7	5	0	0	12	0	12
RHYNCHOCEPHALIA	1	0	1	0	2	0	2
SAURIA	18	47	45	18	128	21	149
SERPENTES	10	15	24	11	60	11	71
TESTUDINES	11	21	9	14	55	27	82
Subtotal	47	88	79	43	257	59	316
Class: AMPHIBIA							
ANURA	27	26	36	10	99	31	130
CAUDATA	5	6	19	4	34	5	39
Subtotal	32	32	55	14	133	36	169

Table 1. Threatened species: totals for higher taxa by status category (continued)

	E	V	R	I	SUBTOTAL[1]	K	TOTAL
Class: CEPHALASPIDOMORPHI							
PETROMYZONTIFORMES	0	1	2	0	3	2	5
Subtotal	0	1	2	0	3	2	5
Class: ELASMOBRANCHII							
ORECTOLOBIFORMES	0	0	0	1	1	2	3
Subtotal	0	0	0	1	1	2	3
Class: ACTINOPTERYGII							
ACIPENSERIFORMES	3	5	1	0	9	0	9
ATHERINIFORMES	5	25	41	4	75	6	81
BELONIFORMES	5	6	3	0	14	0	14
CHARACIFORMES	1	5	0	0	6	0	6
CLUPEIFORMES	0	0	1	0	1	1	2
CYPRINIFORMES	44	64	66	17	191	5	196
CYPRINODONTIFORMES	34	24	12	10	80	3	83
GASTEROSTEIFORMES	2	2	0	0	4	0	4
OPHIDIIFORMES	2	0	0	1	3	0	3
OSTEOGLOSSIFORMES	0	0	2	0	2	2	4
PERCIFORMES	25	58	88	261	432	16	448
PERCOPSIFORMES	1	2	0	0	3	0	3
SALMONIFORMES	17	14	12	2	45	2	47
SCORPAENIFORMES	1	2	5	0	8	0	8
SILURIFORMES	16	16	13	6	51	5	56
SYNBRANCHIFORMES	2	0	0	0	2	1	3
SYNGNATHIFORMES	0	1	0	2	3	0	3
Subtotal	158	224	244	303	929	41	970
Class: SARCOPTERYGII							
COELACANTHIFORMES	0	1	0	0	1	0	1
Subtotal	0	1	0	0	1	0	1
Class: ANTHOZOA							
ACTINIARIA	1	1	0	0	2	0	2
GORGONACEA	0	0	0	0	0	1	1
Subtotal	1	1	0	0	2	1	3
Class: TURBELLARIA							
TRICLADIDA	2	0	1	0	3	0	3
Subtotal	2	0	1	0	3	0	3
Class: ENOPLA							
HOPLONEMERTEA	2	0	4	0	6	0	6
Subtotal	2	0	4	0	6	0	6
Class: GASTROPODA							
ARCHAEOGASTROPODA	0	12	5	1	18	0	18
BASOMMATOPHORA	5	2	0	20	27	0	27
MESOGASTROPODA	53	174	16	176	419	2	421
STYLOMMATOPHORA	206	224	117	56	603	27	630
Subtotal	264	412	138	253	1067	29	1096
Class: BIVALVIA							
UNIONOIDA	45	8	1	54	108	1	109
VENEROIDA	0	2	0	5	7	3	10
Subtotal	45	10	1	59	115	4	119

Table 1. Threatened species: totals for higher taxa by status category (continued)

	E	V	R	I	SUBTOTAL[1]	K	TOTAL
Class: POLYCHAETA							
EUNICIDA	0	0	0	0	0	1	1
Subtotal	0	0	0	0	0	1	1
Class: HIRUDINEA							
ARHYNCHOBDELLAE	0	0	0	1	1	0	1
Subtotal	0	0	0	1	1	0	1
Class: OLIGOCHAETA							
HAPLOTAXIDA	2	145	1	0	148	0	148
Subtotal	2	145	1	0	148	0	148
Class: MEROSTOMATA							
XIPHOSURA	0	0	0	0	0	4	4
Subtotal	0	0	0	0	0	4	4
Class: ARACHNIDA							
ARANEAE	2	1	4	7	14	1	15
OPILIONES	0	1	0	0	1	0	1
PSEUDOSCORPIONIDA	1	0	0	1	2	0	2
Subtotal	3	2	4	8	17	1	18
Class: CRUSTACEA							
AMPHIPODA	1	0	0	49	50	0	50
ANASPIDACEA	0	1	0	2	3	2	5
ANOSTRACA	0	0	0	3	3	5	8
CALANOIDA	0	0	3	0	3	0	3
CLADOCERA	0	0	4	0	4	0	4
DECAPODA	7	4	16	17	44	4	48
HARPACTICOIDA	0	0	0	0	0	8	8
ISOPODA	2	1	5	9	17	9	26
MYODOCOPINA	0	0	0	0	0	3	3
PODOCOPINA	0	0	0	0	0	1	1
THORACICA	0	0	0	2	2	0	2
Subtotal	10	6	28	82	126	32	158
Class: INSECTA							
ANOPLURA	1	0	0	0	1	0	1
BLATTARIA	0	0	0	1	1	0	1
COLEOPTERA	190	24	8	154	376	2	378
COLLEMBOLA	0	0	0	6	6	0	6
DERMAPTERA	1	0	0	0	1	0	1
DIPTERA	3	0	0	15	18	0	18
EPHEMEROPTERA	0	0	1	13	14	0	14
GRYLLOBLATTARIA	0	1	0	0	1	0	1
HEMIPTERA	1	0	0	25	26	0	26
HOMOPTERA	0	3	0	18	21	0	21
HYMENOPTERA	11	5	0	70	86	3	89
LEPIDOPTERA	25	61	158	79	323	19	342
MANTODEA	1	0	0	0	1	0	1
MECOPTERA	0	0	0	1	1	0	1
NEUROPTERA	0	0	0	7	7	0	7
ODONATA	15	17	46	50	128	10	138
ORTHOPTERA	3	8	26	35	72	0	72
PLECOPTERA	1	0	2	12	15	0	15
THYSANURA	0	0	0	2	2	0	2
TRICHOPTERA	0	0	0	49	49	0	49

Table 1. Threatened species: totals for higher taxa by status category (continued)

	E	V	R	I	SUBTOTAL[1]	K	TOTAL
ZORAPTERA	0	0	0	1	1	0	1
Subtotal	252	119	241	538	1150	34	1184
Class: ONYCHOPHORA							
ONYCHOPHORA	1	7	4	0	12	0	12
Subtotal	1	7	4	0	12	0	12
Class: ECHINOIDEA							
ECHINOIDA	0	0	0	0	0	1	1
Subtotal	0	0	0	0	0	1	1
TOTAL	**1184**	**1488**	**1148**	**1546**	**5366**	**563**	**5929**

[1] Subtotal includes species categorised E, V, R or I; these are known to be threatened species. Category K comprises those suspected to be threatened.

This table does not include beetles of the genera *Itodacnus* and *Oodemas* in List 3 from the Hawaiian Islands for which we do have an estimate of species number.

We have used the figure of 250 haplochromine and 2 tilapiine cichlid fishes in Lake Victoria given in the 1990 Red List, although recent estimates suggest >300 species are present of which some 200 may be critically threatened.

Classes are in the same taxonomic sequence as List 1; Order within Classes are in alphabetical sequence.

Table 2. Threatened species: country totals by taxonomic group

	MAMMALS	BIRDS	REPTILES	AMPHIBIANS	FISHES	INVERTS
AFRICA						
Algeria	14	9	0	0	0	5
Angola	21	13	5	0	0	3
Ascension	0	1	1	0	0	0
Benin	8	1	2	0	0	1
Botswana	8	6	0	0	0	0
Burkina Faso	9	1	1	0	0	0
Burundi	8	6	0	0	0	1
Cameroon	34	15	3	1	0	3
Cape Verde	1	3	3	0	0	0
Central African Republic	13	2	1	0	0	1
Chad	16	3	1	0	0	0
Comoros	3	6	2	0	0	4
Congo	17	2	2	0	0	3
Côte d'Ivoire	23	9	4	1	0	1
Djibouti	6	3	2	0	0	0
Egypt	11	11	4	0	0	10
Equatorial Guinea	16	2	3	1	0	3
Eritrea	3	0	0	0	0	0
Ethiopia	32	16	2	0	0	2
Gabon	22	5	3	0	0	2
Gambia	6	0	1	0	0	0
Ghana	17	9	4	0	0	1
Guinea	18	4	3	1	0	1
Guinea-Bissau	6	1	3	0	0	1
Kenya[1]	23	16	4	0	2+	4
Lesotho[2]	2	5	1	2	0	1+
Liberia	19	9	3	1	0	2
Libya	11	4	2	0	0	0
Madagascar	46	27	13	0	0	19
Malawi	7	7	0	0	0	2
Mali	14	5	1	0	0	0
Mauritania	15	3	3	0	0	0
Mauritius	3	8	6	0	0	20
Mayotte	0	2	2	0	0	0
Morocco	12	14	1	0	0	6
Mozambique	10	12	6	1	0	4
Namibia	13	8	4	1	0	0
Niger	16	1	0	0	0	1
Nigeria	28	9	3	0	0	1
Rwanda	20	6	0	0	0	2
Réunion	0	2	2	0	0	22
Saint Helena	0	6	0	0	0	5
São Tomé and Príncipe	2	7	2	0	0	4
Senegal	16	5	6	0	0	0
Seychelles	1	7	4	4	0	6
Sierra Leone	16	7	3	0	0	3
Somalia	20	7	2	0	0	1
South Africa[2]	31	13	37	16	0	178+
Sudan	23	9	2	0	0	2
Swaziland	4	4	2	1	0	0
Tanzania[1]	25	23	5	0	2+	11
Togo	12	1	3	0	0	1
Tunisia	7	9	1	0	0	3
Uganda[1]	22	13	0	0	2+	2
Western Sahara	5	3	2	0	0	0
Zaire	45	28	3	0	0	5
Zambia	8	8	1	0	0	1
Zimbabwe	10	5	0	0	0	2

	MAMMALS	BIRDS	REPTILES	AMPHIBIANS	FISHES	INVERTS
ANTARCTICA						
Falkland Islands	5	0	0	0	0	0
French Southern and Antarctic Territories	3	2	0	0	0	0
ASIA						
Afghanistan	12	15	1	1	0	2
Armenia	2	8	2	0	0	16
Azerbaijan	3	12	1	0	0	15
Bahrain	3	2	0	0	0	0
Bangladesh	24	24	18	0	0	0
Bhutan	24	12	1	0	0	4
British Indian Ocean Territory	0	0	2	0	0	2
Brunei	17	13	4	0	0	1
Cambodia	28	18	9	0	0	0
China	59	88	12	1	0	17
Cyprus	2	5	3	0	0	0
Georgia	4	10	6	1	0	18
Hong Kong	2	10	1	0	0	0
India	53	69	23	3	0	22
Indonesia	77	123	19	0	0	69
Iran	15	19	7	0	0	9
Iraq	8	14	0	0	0	6
Israel	11	10	4	0	0	5
Japan	20	30	10	11	0	70
Jordan	9	3	0	0	0	4
Kazakhstan	12	17	0	0	0	19
Korea D.P.R.	10	20	0	0	0	0
Korea Republic	9	20	0	0	0	0
Kuwait	5	3	2	0	0	0
Kyrgyzstan	6	7	0	0	0	3
Laos	33	23	5	0	0	0
Lebanon	5	4	1	0	0	3
Malaysia	32	36	15	0	0	21
Maldives	0	1	2	0	0	2
Mongolia	10	15	0	0	0	6
Myanmar	29	40	18	0	0	9
Nepal	28	24	9	0	0	2
Oman	10	5	4	0	0	2
Pakistan	17	25	8	0	0	1
Papua New Guinea	38	22	8	0	0	26
Philippines	31	43	8	2	0	31
Qatar	3	2	2	0	0	0
Russia	23	42	3	0	0	40
Saudi Arabia	10	8	2	0	0	8
Singapore	7	5	1	0	0	7
Sri Lanka	9	8	9	0	0	6
Syria	4	8	1	0	0	6
Taiwan	9	13	2	0	0	8
Tajikistan	7	12	1	0	0	3
Thailand	33	38	21	4	0	9
Turkey	5	20	12	5	0	19
Turkmenistan	12	15	1	0	0	5
Ukraine	5	9	1	0	0	33
United Arab Emirates	4	3	2	0	0	0
Uzbekistan	9	14	1	0	0	3
Viet Nam	35	40	12	1	0	7
Yemen	7	8	2	0	0	1

Table 2. Threatened species: country totals by taxonomic group (continued)

	MAMMALS	BIRDS	REPTILES	AMPHIBIANS	FISHES	INVERTS
former USSR	0	0	0	0	0	1
EUROPE						
Albania	3	10	3	0	0	8
Andorra	1	0	0	0	0	2
Austria	3	8	0	0	0	67
Belarus	5	4	0	0	0	22
Belgium	3	2	0	0	0	33
Bulgaria	5	12	2	0	0	27
Czech Republic	3	0	0	0	0	37
former Czechoslovakia	0	6	0	0	0	1
Denmark	2	4	0	0	0	21
Estonia	5	2	0	0	0	19
Finland	4	3	0	0	0	27
France	6	8	2	2	0	97
Germany	3	5	0	0	0	63
Gibraltar	0	3	0	0	0	2
Greece	5	13	5	1	0	19
Hungary	2	11	0	0	0	42
Iceland	2	1	0	0	0	1
Ireland	1	1	0	0	0	7
Italy	4	10	4	9	0	47
Latvia	4	6	0	0	0	22
Liechtenstein	1	2	0	0	0	7
Lithuania	4	4	0	0	0	24
Luxembourg	2	2	0	0	0	10
Malta	2	1	1	0	0	6
Moldova	1	8	0	0	0	20
Netherlands	3	3	0	0	0	24
Norway	6	3	0	0	0	21
Poland	5	6	0	0	0	41
Portugal	7	11	2	1	0	85
Romania	4	13	1	0	0	34
Slovakia	3	0	0	0	0	39
Slovenia	3	0	0	2	0	0
Spain	8	17	6	3	0	86
Sweden	4	4	0	0	0	35
Switzerland	2	4	0	1	0	50
United Kingdom	2	4	0	0	0	21
former Yugoslavia	4	13	2	1	0	37
NORTH AND CENTRAL AMERICA						
Anguilla	0	0	5	0	0	0
Antigua and Barbuda	0	1	5	0	0	0
Aruba	1	1	2	0	0	1
Bahamas	3	3	6	0	0	1
Barbados	0	1	2	0	0	0
Belize	7	2	5	0	0	1
Bermuda	0	2	0	0	0	1
British Virgin Islands	0	2	5	1	0	0
Canada	10	4	0	0	0	13
Cayman Islands	0	1	2	0	0	0
Costa Rica	12	7	7	1	0	10
Cuba	11	14	8	0	0	5
Dominica	0	2	4	0	0	0
Dominican Republic	4	9	11	1	0	8
El Salvador	4	0	6	0	0	1

Table 2. Threatened species: country totals by taxonomic group (continued)

	MAMMALS	BIRDS	REPTILES	AMPHIBIANS	FISHES	INVERTS
Greenland	5	1	0	0	0	0
Grenada	0	1	4	0	0	0
Guadeloupe	1	0	7	0	0	0
Guatemala	8	5	9	0	0	5
Haiti	4	9	7	2	0	6
Honduras	6	3	7	0	0	2
Jamaica	3	4	10	4	0	8
Martinique	0	2	5	0	0	0
Mexico	30	28	20	3	0	42
Montserrat	0	0	5	0	0	0
Netherlands Antilles	1	1	6	0	0	0
Nicaragua	8	2	7	0	0	0
Panama	15	6	7	0	0	2
Puerto Rico	1	6	9	3	0	2
Saint Kitts-Nevis	0	0	5	0	0	0
Saint Lucia	0	3	6	0	0	0
Saint Vincent	0	1	4	0	0	0
Trinidad and Tobago	2	2	5	0	0	1
Turks and Caicos Islands	0	3	4	0	0	0
USA	29	14	26	18	174	701
USA: Hawaiian Islands[3]	0	28	2	0	0	653
Virgin Islands of the United States	0	2	4	0	0	0
OCEANIA						
American Samoa	2	1	2	0	0	8
Australia	49	36	43	37	0	403
Christmas Island	0	3	2	0	0	0
Cocos (Keeling) Islands	0	1	0	0	0	1
Cook Islands	0	5	2	0	0	1
Federated States of Micronesia	5	3	2	0	0	60
Fiji	4	5	6	1	0	6
French Polynesia	0	19	2	0	0	14
Guam	3	4	2	0	0	57
Kiribati	0	1	2	0	0	4
Line Islands	0	0	1	0	0	0
Marshall Islands	0	1	2	0	0	6
Nauru	0	1	0	0	0	0
New Caledonia	4	5	4	0	0	10
New Zealand	5	24	18	3	0	46
Niue	0	0	1	0	0	0
Northern Marianas	2	3	2	0	0	17
Palau	3	2	3	0	0	62
Papau New Guinea	0	0	0	0	0	0
Pitcairn Islands	0	2	0	0	0	3
Solomon Islands	6	15	6	0	0	12
Tokelau	0	0	2	0	0	2
Tonga	0	2	3	0	0	5
Tuvalu	0	0	2	0	0	6
USA Pacific Islands	0	0	1	0	0	1
Vanuatu	4	2	3	0	0	6
Western Samoa	2	2	2	0	0	4
SOUTH AMERICA						
Argentina	33	37	8	5	0	2
Bolivia	27	22	5	1	0	2
Brazil	54	100	16	8	0	17
Chile	19	15	22	21	0	0

Table 2. Threatened species: country totals by taxonomic group (continued)

	MAMMALS	BIRDS	REPTILES	AMPHIBIANS	FISHES	INVERTS
Colombia	30	58	15	0	0	0
Ecuador	27	48	12	0	0	30
French Guiana	9	2	6	0	0	3
Guyana	11	2	7	0	0	1
Paraguay	12	26	5	0	0	0
Peru	38	65	9	1	0	4
Suriname	9	2	5	0	0	1
Uruguay	9	11	1	0	0	1
Venezuela	18	20	12	0	0	1

[1] The figure for fishes does not include 252 cichlids in Lake Victoria for which we have insufficient data on the range of individual species. These species are included in Table 4. The total of 250 haplochromine and 2 tilapiine cichlid fishes in Lake Victoria is given in the 1990 Red List, but recent estimates suggest >300 haplochromine species are present of which some 200 may be critically threatened.

[2] The figure for invertebrates does not include 62 earthworms of the genera *Microscolex* and *Udeina* in List 3 which occur in Lesotho and South Africa but for which we have insufficient data on the range of individual species.

[3] The invertebrate total does not include species of the insect genera *Itodacnus* and *Oodemus* for which we have been unable to determine the number of recognised species.

Widespread marine cetaceans lacking full country-specific range data are excluded. All the tables cover taxa of species rank only; subspecies are excluded. The tables cover species that have been assigned to one of the standard IUCN-SSC status categories; the Commercially Threatened taxa (CT) set out in List 5 are excluded.

Tables 2, 3 and 6 for simplicity use the same major geopolitical units as in the distribution entries in the species lists. This results in loss of geographical resolution of some biological interest; in particular it should be noted that island territories of mainland countries are in most cases included with their parent countries. For example, the Canary Islands, which feature prominently in the mollusc lists, are included with Spain in the tables. However, the distribution entries in the species lists will indicate "Spain: Canary Islands", so the relevant information can be retrieved. Tristan da Cunha is included with St Helena. The Hawaiian Islands have a separate entry. All unconfirmed occurrences (indicated in the lists by "?" after the country name) are counted in the tables.

Table 3. Threatened species: country totals by status category

	E	V	R	I	SUBTOTAL[1]	K	TOTAL
AFRICA							
Algeria	9	8	5	3	25	4	29
Angola	5	12	9	7	33	9	42
Ascension	1	0	1	0	2	0	2
Benin	3	6	2	0	11	1	12
Botswana	2	4	6	1	13	1	14
Burkina Faso	2	5	1	0	8	3	11
Burundi	1	6	3	2	12	3	15
Cameroon	9	27	19	4	59	17	76
Cape Verde	3	1	1	0	5	2	7
Central African Republic	2	7	3	0	12	5	17
Chad	6	8	1	1	16	4	20
Comoros	4	3	6	1	14	2	16
Congo	3	11	4	0	18	6	24
Côte d'Ivoire	8	16	4	2	30	8	38
Djibouti	3	3	2	0	8	3	11
Egypt	4	12	5	10	31	6	37
Equatorial Guinea	4	12	3	2	21	4	25
Eritrea	0	3	0	0	3	0	3
Ethiopia	11	10	11	4	36	16	52
Gabon	5	10	3	1	19	13	32
Gambia	0	4	0	0	4	3	3
Ghana	5	13	7	0	25	6	31
Guinea	5	14	2	0	21	6	27
Guinea-Bissau	2	6	1	1	10	1	11
Kenya[1]	9	13	9	4+	35+	12	47+
Lesotho[2]	1	1+	8	1	11+	1	12+
Liberia	6	15	2	3	26	8	34
Libya	3	7	3	1	14	3	17
Madagascar	21	20	34	18	93	34	127
Malawi	3	4	5	1	13	3	16
Mali	4	9	2	1	16	4	20
Mauritania	6	7	2	1	16	5	21
Mauritius	18	6	7	5	36	1	37
Mayotte	2	0	1	0	3	1	4
Morocco	6	13	5	2	26	8	34
Mozambique	7	6	13	3	29	6	35
Namibia	5	8	12	1	26	5	31
Niger	4	5	2	1	12	6	18
Nigeria	9	16	9	0	34	7	41
Rwanda	2	10	8	1	21	7	28
Réunion	9	11	2	3	25	1	26
Saint Helena	3	1	6	1	11	0	11
São Tomé and Príncipe	2	2	3	7	14	1	15
Senegal	5	12	1	0	18	9	27
Seychelles	8	0	11	1	20	2	22
Sierra Leone	5	14	3	2	24	5	29
Somalia	5	8	3	2	18	13	31
South Africa[2]	20	121+	123	34	298+	13	311+
Sudan	7	10	6	3	26	10	36
Swaziland	2	2	6	1	11	0	11
Tanzania[1]	8	18	21	2+	49+	15	64+
Togo	4	7	2	0	13	4	17
Tunisia	5	6	4	1	16	4	20
Uganda[1]	1	13	10	3+	27+	10	37+
Western Sahara	4	3	2	0	9	1	10
Zaire	5	17	23	5	50	32	82
Zambia	2	6	5	2	15	3	18
Zimbabwe	2	4	8	1	15	3	18

	E	V	R	I	SUBTOTAL[1]	K	TOTAL
ANTARCTICA							
Falkland Islands	0	1	0	0	1	4	5
French South'n Antarctic Terr.	1	1	0	0	2	3	5
ASIA							
Afghanistan	4	13	7	0	24	7	31
Armenia	6	8	6	2	22	6	28
Azerbaijan	6	9	9	2	26	5	31
Bahrain	0	2	2	0	4	2	6
Bangladesh	11	22	9	13	55	11	66
Bhutan	10	11	8	4	33	8	41
British Indian Ocean Terr.	2	0	0	1	3	1	4
Brunei	5	10	7	4	26	11	37
Cambodia	15	19	8	6	48	13	61
China	34	49	46	33	162	32	194
Cyprus	2	5	3	0	10	0	10
Georgia	8	8	12	3	31	8	39
Hong Kong	1	5	4	1	11	2	13
India	26	49	45	28	148	24	172
Indonesia	38	80	120	78	316	38	354
Iran	7	18	11	3	39	13	52
Iraq	2	9	12	1	24	6	30
Israel	5	12	6	2	25	5	30
Japan	42	42	47	11	142	9	151
Jordan	3	8	3	1	15	1	16
Kazakhstan	10	18	10	3	41	8	49
Korea D.P.R.	5	13	4	4	26	4	30
Korea Republic	3	13	6	3	25	4	29
Kuwait	2	3	2	0	7	3	10
Kyrgyzstan	2	6	6	0	14	2	16
Laos	14	16	14	10	54	11	65
Lebanon	2	6	4	1	13	0	13
Malaysia	14	23	20	27	84	26	110
Maldives	2	0	1	1	4	1	5
Mongolia	5	15	7	0	27	4	31
Myanmar	17	27	20	15	79	18	97
Nepal	16	20	6	12	54	9	63
Oman	3	7	6	1	17	6	23
Pakistan	9	21	8	4	42	9	51
Papua New Guinea	14	40	60	17	131	11	142
Philippines	15	39	41	26	121	16	137
Qatar	2	1	1	0	4	3	7
Russia	23	38	19	12	92	20	112
Saudi Arabia	2	7	5	6	20	8	28
Singapore	2	5	1	4	12	9	31
Sri Lanka	10	25	7	2	44	7	51
Syria	4	9	5	1	19	0	19
Taiwan	6	14	3	4	27	6	33
Tajikistan	3	10	7	0	20	3	23
Thailand	20	24	24	18	86	32	118
Turkey	14	17	19	18	68	11	79
Turkmenistan	2	15	9	0	26	8	34
Ukraine	14	17	6	5	42	9	51
United Arab Emirates	2	3	2	0	7	2	9
Uzbekistan	3	13	7	0	23	4	27
Viet Nam	19	25	18	17	79	20	99
Yemen	3	4	3	3	13	5	18

	E	V	R	I	SUBTOTAL[1]	K	TOTAL
former USSR	0	1	0	0	1	0	1

EUROPE

	E	V	R	I	SUBTOTAL	K	TOTAL
Albania	5	9	8	1	23	2	25
Andorra	0	1	1	1	3	0	3
Austria	28	31	8	4	71	9	80
Belarus	9	12	1	4	26	5	31
Belgium	14	15	1	3	33	6	39
Bulgaria	9	21	8	1	39	8	47
Czech Republic	17	16	1	3	37	5	42
former Czechoslovakia	0	1	5	0	6	1	7
Denmark	8	10	2	4	24	4	28
Estonia	8	10	1	5	24	3	27
Finland	10	14	4	5	33	3	36
France	21	29	21	39	110	8	118
Germany	28	26	6	6	66	9	75
Gibraltar	0	0	3	1	4	1	5
Greece	15	20	15	3	53	7	60
Hungary	16	18	9	3	46	10	56
Iceland	1	2	0	0	3	2	5
Ireland	2	5	2	0	9	2	11
Italy	15	33	17	4	69	7	76
Latvia	8	13	2	5	28	5	33
Liechtenstein	4	2	2	0	8	2	10
Lithuania	10	12	1	5	28	5	33
Luxembourg	5	6	1	1	13	1	14
Malta	3	3	3	0	9	1	10
Moldova	10	10	4	2	26	5	31
Netherlands	7	12	2	4	25	6	31
Norway	4	16	3	4	27	5	32
Poland	17	18	7	6	48	7	55
Portugal	25	33	41	9	108	9	117
Romania	14	21	8	2	45	10	55
Slovakia	13	21	3	1	38	6	44
Slovenia	0	5	0	0	5	0	5
Spain	29	43	38	14	124	12	136
Sweden	12	18	4	6	40	5	45
Switzerland	13	28	6	5	52	8	60
United Kingdom	5	14	3	1	23	6	29
former Yugoslavia	17	22	13	3	55	7	62

NORTH AND CENTRAL AMERICA

	E	V	R	I	SUBTOTAL	K	TOTAL
Anguilla	3	2	0	0	5	0	5
Antigua and Barbuda	4	2	0	0	6	0	6
Aruba	1	0	1	1	3	2	5
Bahamas	3	4	3	4	14	0	14
Barbados	1	1	0	1	3	0	3
Belize	2	9	0	1	12	3	15
Bermuda	2	1	0	0	3	0	3
British Virgin Islands	4	4	0	0	8	0	8
Canada	12	17	6	7	42	5	47
Cayman Islands	0	3	0	0	3	0	3
Costa Rica	8	11	2	11	32	5	37
Cuba	12	10	4	11	37	1	38
Dominica	4	1	1	0	6	0	6
Dominican Republic	5	9	6	8	28	5	33
El Salvador	5	3	0	1	9	2	11

Table 3. Threatened species: country totals by status category (continued)

	E	V	R	I	SUBTOTAL[1]	K	TOTAL
Greenland	0	3	0	0	3	3	6
Grenada	4	1	0	0	5	0	5
Guadeloupe	3	4	0	1	8	0	8
Guatemala	4	12	0	7	23	4	27
Haiti	3	8	5	9	25	3	28
Honduras	5	9	0	2	16	2	18
Jamaica	6	8	5	8	27	2	29
Martinique	6	1	0	0	7	0	7
Mexico	63	78	34	27	202	20	222
Montserrat	3	1	0	1	5	0	5
Netherlands Antilles	3	3	0	0	6	2	8
Nicaragua	4	8	1	1	14	3	17
Panama	6	13	2	4	25	5	30
Puerto Rico	8	5	3	4	20	1	21
Saint Kitts-Nevis	3	2	0	0	5	0	5
Saint Lucia	6	2	1	0	9	0	9
Saint Vincent	3	0	2	0	5	0	5
Trinidad and Tobago	6	2	0	1	9	1	10
Turks and Caicos Islands	3	2	1	1	7	0	7
USA	146	129	108	549	932	30	962
USA: Hawaiian Islands[3]	270	7	7	160	444	1	445
Virgin Islands of the US	4	2	0	0	6	0	6

OCEANIA

	E	V	R	I	SUBTOTAL[1]	K	TOTAL
American Samoa	6	3	0	3	12	1	13
Australia	115	213	161	58	547	94	641
Christmas Island	1	4	0	0	5	0	5
Cocos (Keeling) Islands	0	2	0	0	2	0	2
Cook Islands	3	1	3	0	7	1	8
Fed. States of Micronesia	6	59	2	2	69	1	70
Fiji	6	7	1	5	19	3	22
French Polynesia	17	7	7	3	34	1	35
Guam	8	55	0	1	64	2	66
Kiribati	3	1	0	2	6	1	7
Line Islands	1	0	0	0	1	0	1
Marshall Islands	2	4	0	2	8	1	9
Nauru	1	0	0	0	1	0	1
New Caledonia	4	6	2	10	22	1	23
New Zealand	16	50	19	9	94	8	102
Niue	1	0	0	0	1	0	1
Northern Marianas	5	14	1	2	22	2	24
Palau	2	61	2	3	68	2	70
Papau New Guinea	0	0	1	0	1	0	1
Pitcairn Islands	0	0	4	0	4	1	5
Solomon Islands	6	5	12	11	34	5	39
Tokelau	2	0	0	1	3	1	4
Tonga	2	4	0	2	8	2	10
Tuvalu	2	2	0	2	6	2	8
USA Pacific Islands	1	0	0	0	1	1	2
Vanuatu	2	5	2	4	13	2	15
Western Samoa	3	4	0	2	9	1	10

SOUTH AMERICA

	E	V	R	I	SUBTOTAL[1]	K	TOTAL
Argentina	10	39	4	11	64	22	86
Bolivia	8	24	2	10	44	14	58
Brazil	54	79	10	27	170	34	204
Chile	26	39	17	5	87	19	106

Table 3. Threatened species: country totals by status category (continued)

	E	V	R	I	SUBTOTAL[1]	K	TOTAL
Colombia	24	39	5	21	89	17	106
Ecuador	56	31	6	10	103	14	117
French Guiana	5	8	0	1	14	6	20
Guyana	6	9	0	1	16	6	22
Paraguay	7	23	1	3	34	9	43
Peru	28	47	3	11	89	29	118
Suriname	5	7	0	1	13	4	17
Uruguay	1	7	0	6	14	8	22
Venezuela	15	23	0	3	41	10	51

[1] The figures for Indeterminate category species in Kenya, Tanzania and Uganda do not include 252 cichlid fishes in Lake Victoria for which we have insufficient data on the range of individual species. These species are included in Table 4. The figure of 250 haplochromine and 2 tilapiine cichlid fishes in Lake Victoria was given in the 1990 Red List, but recent estimates suggest >300 species are present.

[2] The figures for Vulnerable category species in Lesotho and South Africa do not include 62 earthworms of the genera *Microscolex* and *Udeina* in List 3 for which we have insufficient data on the range of individual species.

[3] The invertebrate total does not include species of the insect genera *Itodacnus* and *Oodemus* for which we have been unable to determine the number of recognised species.

Widespread marine cetaceans lacking full country-specific range data are excluded. All the tables cover taxa of species rank only; subspecies are excluded. The tables cover species that have been assigned to one of the standard IUCN-SSC status categories; the Commercially Threatened taxa (CT) set out in List 5 are excluded.

Tables 2, 3 and 6 for simplicity use the same major geopolitical units as in the distribution entries in the species lists. This results in loss of geographical resolution of some biological interest; in particular it should be noted that island territories of mainland countries are in most cases included with their parent countries. For example, the Canary Islands, which feature prominently in the mollusc lists, are included with Spain in the tables. However, the distribution entries in the species lists will indicate "Spain: Canary Islands", so the relevant information can be retrieved. Tristan da Cunha is included with St Helena. The Hawaiian Islands have a separate entry. Unconfirmed occurrence of a species (indicated in the lists by "?" after the relevant country) are counted in the tables.

Birdlife International have assigned mixed categories to many birds. There are 21 E/Ex and 78 V/R species included in the tables; in Tables 2 and 3 E/Ex categories are counted as E and V/R as V.

Table 4. Threatened species: summary by group and status category

	E	V	R	I	SUBTOTAL[1]	K	TOTAL
MAMMALS	177	199	89	68	533	208	741
BIRDS[2]	188	241	257	176	862	108	970
REPTILES	47	88	79	43	257	59	316
AMPHIBIANS	32	32	55	14	133	36	169
FISHES[3]	158	226	246	304	934	45	979
INVERTEBRATES[4]	582	702	422	941	2647	107	2754
TOTAL	1184	1488	1148	1546	5366	563	5929

[1] Subtotal includes species categorised E, V, R or I; these are known to be threatened species. Category K comprises those suspected to be threatened.

[2] BirdLife International have given mixed categories to many birds. In Tables 2 and 3 the 21 E/Ex species are treated as E, and 78 V/R as V.

[3] Includes 252 species of Lake Victoria cichlids in List 3 with category I. The figure of 250 haplochromine and 2 tilapiine cichlid fishes in Lake Victoria was given in the 1990 Red List, but recent estimates suggest >300 species are present.

[4] Includes 160 category E insects, 143 category V earthworms and 78 category I insects in List 3.

Table 5. Threatened species: totals by group in 1990 and 1994

	1990	1994
MAMMALS	535	741
BIRDS	1026	970
REPTILES	169	316
AMPHIBIANS	57	169
FISHES	713	979
INVERTEBRATES	1977	2754
TOTAL	4477	5929

The figures for 1990 (1990 Red List) and 1994 (this book) are not exactly comparable; 1990 figures exclude Ex species but include Ex? and include 182 Commercially Threatened (CT) invertebrates, 1994 figures exclude all these.

Table 6. Extinct species: country totals by group

	MAMMALS	BIRDS	REPTILES	AMPHIBIANS	FISHES	INVERTS
AFRICA						
Algeria	1	0	0	0	0	0
Cape Verde	0	0	1	0	0	0
Kenya	0	0	0	1	0	0
Madagascar	0	2	0	0	0	0
Mauritius	1	21	8	0	0	16
Mayotte	0	0	0	0	0	5
Réunion	1	10	2	0	0	3
Saint Helena	0	0	0	0	0	23
Seychelles	0	1	0	0	0	1
South Africa	2	0	1	0	1	2
Tanzania	1	0	0	0	0	0
Togo	1	0	0	0	0	0
ANTARCTICA						
Falkland Islands	1	0	0	0	0	0
ASIA						
China	0	0	0	0	1	0
India	0	2	0	0	0	0
Indonesia	0	1	0	0	0	0
Israel	0	0	0	1	1	0
Japan	2	4	0	0	0	24
Myanmar	0	1	0	0	0	0
Nepal	0	1	0	0	0	0
Papua New Guinea	0	1	0	0	0	1
Philippines	3	0	0	0	0	0
Russia	1	2	0	0	0	0
Thailand	1	0	0	0	0	0
Viet Nam	1	0	0	0	0	0
EUROPE						
Austria	0	0	0	0	0	5
Denmark	0	1	0	0	0	0
France	1	0	0	0	0	2
Germany	1	0	0	0	0	2
Iceland	0	1	0	0	0	0
Italy	1	0	0	0	0	1
Portugal	0	0	0	0	0	13
Spain	0	1	0	0	0	0
United Kingdom	0	2	0	0	0	0
Yugoslavia	0	0	0	0	0	1
NORTH AND CENTRAL AMERICA						
Bahamas	1	1	0	0	0	0
Barbados	1	0	0	0	0	0
Canada	0	2	0	0	2	0
Cayman Islands	3	1	0	0	0	0
Cuba	5	1	0	0	0	0
Dominican Republic	7	0	0	0	0	0
Greenland	0	1	0	0	0	0
Guadeloupe	1	0	1	0	0	0
Guatemala	0	1	0	0	0	0
Haiti	8	0	0	0	0	0
Honduras	1	0	0	0	0	0
Jamaica	1	0	1	0	0	0

Table 6. Extinct species: country totals by group (continued)

	MAMMALS	BIRDS	REPTILES	AMPHIBIANS	FISHES	INVERTS
Martinique	1	0	2	0	0	0
Mexico	3	2	0	1	11	0
Puerto Rico	1	0	0	0	0	0
Saint Lucia	1	0	0	0	0	0
Saint Vincent	1	0	0	0	0	0
USA	2	5	1	1	17	61
USA: Hawaiian Islands	0	13	0	0	0	101
Virgin Islands of the United States	0	0	1	0	0	0
OCEANIA						
American Samoa	0	0	0	0	0	1
Australia	19	7	0	0	1	4
Christmas Island	2	0	0	0	0	0
Cook Islands	0	0	0	0	0	14
Federated States of Micronesia	0	3	0	0	0	0
French Polynesia	0	5	0	0	0	76
Guam	1	0	0	0	0	2
New Caledonia	0	3	0	0	0	4
New Zealand	1	13	1	0	1	3
Norfolk Island	0	1	0	0	0	0
Palau	1	0	0	0	0	0
Solomon Islands	1	2	0	0	0	0
Tonga	0	0	1	0	0	0
Western Samoa	0	1	0	0	0	0
SOUTH AMERICA						
Argentina	0	0	0	0	0	1
Brazil	0	0	0	0	0	2
Colombia	1	0	0	0	1	0
Ecuador: Galapagos Islands	1	0	0	0	0	0
Unknown	0	1	0	0	0	0

The figures include species listed as Ex and Ex? They also include species that are known or believed to have become extinct since 1600AD or thereabouts (WCMC, 1992) and which have never appeared in previous Red Lists nor been given a status category.

GUEST ESSAY

The status of proposals to redefine the IUCN threatened species categories

Georgina M. Mace

Introduction

The threatened species categories now used in Red Data Books and Red Lists have been in place, with some modification, for almost 30 years (see Scott, Burton & Fitter 1987). Since their inception they have become recognised internationally, and they are now used in a whole range of publications and listings, not only those produced by IUCN. Their value is that they provide an easily comprehended method for highlighting those species at risk of extinction, in order to focus attention on conservation measures designed to protect them. Nowadays, with the increasing recognition that the resources available for conservation are finite and limited, the categories have become applied more frequently to setting priorities for conservation action. It is this change in emphasis that has provoked recent moves to redefine the categories.

The application of threatened species categories

To play an effective role in conservation planning the categories need to have a number of characteristics. They need to be equally applicable across broad taxonomic groups whose basic biology and life histories differ in fundamental ways. They also need to be applicable to taxonomic levels below that of species, and to regional or national subsets. Because the amount of information about species varies widely from almost nothing (in the vast majority of cases) to full life history and distribution data (in a very few) the system used for placing taxa into categories also needs to make best use of data that are available, but should not preclude listing when information is sparse. Finally, and most importantly, the system should be based around an evaluation of how likely the taxon in question is to go extinct.

In this context, the current system has some drawbacks. The definitions are merely stated in terms of ".. in danger of extinction..". Without any reference to a time frame, or to the likelihood of extinction within this time frame, the definition can be interpreted in different ways by different authorities. This can result in the same species being classified quite differently, or in different taxa or different regional floras and faunas being judged by quite different standards. If conservation action is to be based upon them, threatened species categories will require an approach that is better validated. A more objective system that can be challenged and judged against an accepted set of rules is needed.

A second drawback of the current system is that a number of different kinds of variables are embedded in the definitions, which complicates their application to setting priorities. Thus while *Endangered* and *Vulnerable* measure the likelihood of extinction, *Rare* is defined in terms of the kind of distribution a species has. Species can be rare in a number of different ways: some have always had very restricted distributions (eg. some endemic island forms), others have been reduced from a formerly wide range; some are always found in small but scattered populations, others are widely distributed but limited to very specific habitat types (see Rabinowitz *et al*. 1986). The relationship between these different forms of rarity and extinction risk is not simple or well understood. *Insufficiently Known* is a category that simply describes the quality and quantity of information about a particular species and thus has no direct relationship to the severity of threat. Other categories that appear in some publications also measure different characteristics. For example, *Commercially Threatened* is a statement primarily about the cause of the extinction risk.

Many other threatened species classification schemes exist, focusing on particular regional or taxonomic groups, but most use definitions that are broadly similar in nature to the IUCN ones (Munton 1987).

The publication of Red Data Books and Lists has other implications. Diamond (1987), among others, has discussed how this immediately puts a limit on the number of taxa that are recognised as being under threat of extinction because only described species can be listed, and once a list exists conservationists and survey expeditions focus especially on those species. Little attention is paid to taxa that are not listed, either because they have not been described or are not listed as threatened, and their plight worsens. In addition, once a taxonomic or regional list is produced, there is an implicit message that all described taxa in that group or region have been evaluated. This is often far from the case. Even among the vertebrates only a proportion of all the described species have been evaluated by IUCN. The birds have been fully reviewed; but only a proportion of other taxa have (see Introduction above and WCMC, 1992). Despite these difficulties, threatened species categories are widely used and recognised, especially at an international level. If the existing level of credibility given to them is to continue, they need to be more soundly based and more consistently applied.

New Proposals

In 1990, the IUCN/SSC began a process to redefine the categories of threat used in Red Data Books. Russ Lande and I (Mace and Lande, 1991) proposed a new basis for the categories where the definitions were given explicitly and solely in terms of the estimated probability of extinction. The definitions we proposed were for three threat categories which we named *Critical*, *Endangered* and *Vulnerable*, which had decreasing probabilities of extinction over increasing time frames:

CRITICAL: 50% probability of extinction within 5 years or 2 generations, whichever is the longer.

ENDANGERED: 20% probability of extinction within 20 years or 10 generations, whichever is the longer.

VULNERABLE: 10% probability of extinction in 100 years

We chose to vary both time scale and extinction probability for a variety of reasons. First, a shorter time scale for the most threatened forms would focus attention on the immediacy of the problem and hopefully stimulate appropriately prompt action. But such short time scales would not be appropriate for the less threatened forms which might then seem to have very low extinction probabilities. The longest time scale for the lowest level of threat was set at 100 years which seems to be generally agreed as about the longest period for effective foresight and planning of human activities while a 5 or 10% chance of extinction within this period is about the highest level that conservation biologists have recommended (eg. see Shaffer, 1981).

We recognised that these definitions would be inadequate to classify species because there are no simple rules to translate from basic ecological information to extinction risk. We therefore also suggested a set of quantitative criteria which might be used operationally. The criteria that we proposed were based around population size, population structure and sub-structure, and observed or projected rates of decline. Although only a proposal, the Mace-Lande criteria (as they have become known) have been applied to a large number of species over the last couple of years, mainly through the Conservation and Assessment Management Plans (CAMPs) undertaken by the IUCN/SSC Captive Breeding Specialist Group and various taxon specialist groups of the SSC (Seal *et al.*, 1993). This has provided invaluable material for assessing the proposal. A number of positive and negative aspects have emerged. On the positive side it is clear that with the informed input of specialists in the CAMP workshops, it is possible to classify the majority of species using the quantitative criteria. In the latest summary tables compiled by CBSG, 3130 out of 3559 (88%) of vertebrates species were classified as Safe or in one of the three new threat categories (Seal *et al.*, 1993). With the comprehensive review procedure that is characteristic of CAMPs the proportion of described species that are listed as threatened increases substantially from previous levels. Of the 3130 vertebrate taxa classified by CAMPs, 1345 (43%) are listed as threatened. This is much higher than the levels previously seen in IUCN Red Lists. There are some factors that may in part explain this increase. First, CAMPs have tended to focus on higher order taxa that contain many species which are of conservation concern; a higher proportion of threatened forms might therefore be expected in this subset. Second, by necessity, many CAMP classifications are made on the basis of very little information, and group dynamics in workshop sessions are likely to lead to the more conservative estimates being accepted. Thus there may be a tendency for over-listing in this context, especially in the lower risk categories. Finally, CAMPs have routinely classified many sub-species which may, through restricted range and number, be more threatened than are species. However, a systematic examination of the data suggests that the increase is not simply an artefact of sub-species listing (Mace, in press).

Although widely used for vertebrates it soon became clear that there were difficulties in applying the Mace-Lande criteria to other taxa. Some of the terminology used was especially inappropriate for plants and invertebrates. With this background data available, the process for developing new categories continued in 1992 and 1993.

IUCN proposed criteria
During the summer of 1992 a number of discussion papers were prepared presenting alternative methods for classifying species according to severity of threat. Among these was an investigation of the potential for using distribution and habitat data, and an alternative method based around management. These and some other papers provided the framework for a workshop held in November 1992, at which about 30 people representing a wide diversity of interests met to discuss the different proposals. In general, the technical workshop approved the general kinds of definitions that we had earlier proposed, but felt that additional kinds of information needed to be incorporated in the criteria. In order to formulate criteria for major taxonomic groups, four working groups were set up with responsibility for higher vertebrates, lower vertebrates, plants and invertebrates. Using the background papers as a starting point, they developed criteria appropriate for each major taxonomic grouping. At the end of the technical workshop there were four sets of criteria, all based around the categories Critical, Endangered, Vulnerable and a new lower risk category called Susceptible. The criteria drafted for plants included both population and distribution-based criteria, those for lower vertebrates and invertebrates were based around the number and status of known and suitable locations and populations, and the higher vertebrate criteria were largely population-based.

A drafting group was then formed to assimilate all these criteria into a single coherent proposal. The drafting group included at least one person from each of the taxonomic working groups, and for practical reasons most were based in the UK. The group produced an interim report in March 1993 which was subsequently published in *Species* (Mace *et al.*, 1992). This proposal was presented as a draft for discussion and evaluation and is reproduced in summary form here for general information (see Figures 6 and 7). Since its distribution a large number of comments have been received and a number of species have been classified. As this Red List goes to press, the precise proposal is still under active development and refinement. We expect that there will be some modifications to the criteria, to the notes for guidance and to the definitions of terms used, all of which form an integral part of the proposal. The formulation presented here should therefore be taken as a *general* description only, and should not be applied without reference to the full document (Mace *et al.*, 1992); the final version of the system will be available in early 1994.

One of the more controversial aspects of the working group's report was the decision to merge all the criteria from the different taxonomic working groups into a single consolidated set. This decision is worth explaining in detail. The reason that different criteria are needed for different major taxa is that there are broad life history differences between them. Thus, for example, population size can rarely be measured for a number of invertebrate groups, and even if it could be it may not provide a good predictor of extinction risk, which for many invertebrate species is more likely to be a function of a limited habitat availability. In general therefore, it is appropriate to have different criteria for different groups. However, there is not a complete correspondence between major taxonomic grouping and life history. For example, some plants and invertebrates have life histories more similar to higher vertebrates and some lower vertebrates have life histories more characteristic of plants. With the taxonomically split criteria it seemed likely that those species that were untypical for their group would be judged by inappropriate criteria. An alternative

1

strategy, to group the criteria by broad kinds of life history patterns, was felt to be unworkable because of the difficulties of making judgements about which set of criteria to judge any particular species by. In fact, on closer inspection, the criteria provided by each of the major taxon working groups could be seen to be generally quite similar. With little substantial change it was found that it was possible to include almost all of these criteria in a single list, and this seemed to be the most conservative solution to the problem. Using this approach, a species has only to qualify under any one criterion to be listed, and the fact that other criteria are not met, or even that they are wildly inappropriate, does not matter. For example, the fact that the home range size of a single large carnivorous mammal may exceed the qualifying range area for a threat category does not invalidate the range size criterion. The large carnivorous mammals are much more appropriately judged by their population size and status, so that what matters in terms of validating the criteria is whether any one is met, not whether all are appropriate.

Once the draft criteria were published, a period of about 6 months was available for comments to be submitted from all interested parties, and for trial classifications to be made using the criteria. There are still more comments coming in as this book goes to press but several major points have already emerged.

The IUCN review
One evident concern is over the extent to which the proposed system relies on the ability of the person undertaking the evaluation to make appropriate estimations, inferences and projections about the status of the taxon in question. The system is quantitative so that all taxa are judged against a common standard, but we recognise that sufficient data of high quality rarely exist. Therefore it will be necessary to use available information to make explicit judgements. For example, known or estimated areas for current distributions along with characteristic population densities for similar species can be used to judge whether or not the taxon is likely to have a population size falling below the numbers specified in the criteria A or B for any category, and future decline rates calculated from estimated rates of habitat loss can be used to see whether the taxon will qualify under D for any category. This kind of reasoning does not come easily to many field biologists, but as the CAMP workshops have shown, it can be done for a majority of species once the context and methodology is understood. It is however an essential component of the system we have proposed, and it is clear that we need to give more guidance on how this should be done. We are also concerned to ensure that explicit reasoning should always accompany classifications.

A second issue relates to the many species that are now substantially reduced in numbers from historical levels, but which are now held relatively stable at moderate population sizes by continuing management. Depending on their current status, these species will sometimes not be listed because the category is a statement of current status and extinction risk, not a relative measure of current status compared to some previous level. We are looking at ways of highlighting these species, while recognising that effective management has limited the extent to which they are now threatened. Other systems will be needed to highlight those species that particular management authorities believe should be in greater numbers or distributed over wider areas.

A third issue concerns the general applicability of the range size values under criterion C which is now under special study for different taxa as well as for aquatic species.

Conclusions
Some of the consequences and side-benefits that we expect to result from application of the proposed system are as follows:

1.   Because the new categories are based around explicit definitions, the reasons for listing will be evident. Thus classifications will be accompanied by an indication of which criteria and sub-criteria (Figure 7) were operative. This will enable judgements to be understood, and if necessary challenged and refined.

2.   With appropriate input, and informed use of estimation, inference and projection, it will be

possible to classify the great majority of taxa into one of the new categories. The new set of categories should be more applicable to conservation planning as they are more explicit about what is being measured and what actions are therefore appropriate. Where there is really very little data, taxa can be classified as *Insufficiently known*. This is now not a threatened category but a separate status assessment indicating those species for which additional information is needed. Another category, again measuring a different status variable, is Not Evaluated. This is allocated to species that have not been evaluated at all against the categories. With effective use of all these categories it should be possible to arrive at useful and reliable data on many species, and summary data for particular taxa and regions should give a better idea of the status of species generally.

3. On the basis of the validations carried out so far, the proportion of threatened species in major taxa is likely to rise, although to what extent is not yet clear. The correspondence between species classified as highly threatened under the proposed and existing systems is high, but there are differences among the *Vulnerable* taxa. Some taxa previously listed as threatened will no longer qualify and *vice versa*.

4. A major benefit will be that data on fundamental species biology (population size and structure, geographical range area and decline rates) will become available. These data exist in a variety of forms and locations for many species, but are rarely collated into a useful form. The application of the new categories will result in these data being collected, stored and maintained over time, thus enabling monitoring of the status of many species. This is a fundamental pre-requisite for effective species conservation.

The new categories measure the severity of threat being faced by particular taxa. But this is only one aspect of setting priorities. In practice, priority assessment needs to include an assessment of logistical, political and financial factors, as well as incorporating other aspects of biodiversity. The taxonomic distinctiveness of the species and the number of other species that will benefit from its protection are both important biological components. There is a need to develop rational methods to incorporate all this information in decision-making processes.

ACKNOWLEDGEMENTS

Nigel Collar and Kevin Gaston made helpful comments on an earlier draft of this essay. Along with the other members of the drafting group (Justin Cooke, Josh Ginsberg, Nigel Leader-Williams, Mike Maunder and E.J. Milner-Gulland) they have provided a great deal towards the development of the proposals. The process has been guided throughout by Simon Stuart. I am grateful to the Pew Scholars Program in Conservation and the Environment for financial support.

Georgina M. Mace, PhD
Institute of Zoology
Zoological Society of London
Regent's Park, London NW1 4RY, UK.

GUEST ESSAY: REFERENCES

Diamond, J.M. 1987. Extant unless proven extinct? Or extinct unless proven extant? *Conservation Biology*, 1(1):77-79.

Mace, G.M. 1994. An investigation into methods for categorising the conservation status of species. In *Large scale ecology and conservation biology* (in press).

Mace, G.M., Collar, N., Cooke, J., Gaston, K., Ginsberg, G., Leader-Williams, N., Maunder, M., Milner-Gulland, E.J. 1992. The development of new criteria for listing species on the IUCN Red List. *Species*, 19(Dec.):16-22.

Mace, G.M., & Lande, R. 1991. Assessing extinction threats: toward a re-evaluation of IUCN threatened species categories. *Conservation Biology*, 5(2):148-157.

Munton, P. 1987. Concepts of threat to the survival of species used in Red Data Books and similar compilations. In R. Fitter, & M. Fitter (Ed.), *The Road to Extinction* (pp. 71-111). IUCN, Gland.

Rabinowitz, D., Cairns, S., & Dillon, T. 1986. Seven forms of rarity and their frequency in the flora of the British Isles. In M.E. Soule (Ed.), *Conservation Biology*: the Science of Scarcity and Diversity (pp. 182-204). Sinauer Assoc, Inc., Sunderland, Mass.

Scott, P., Burton, J.A., & Fitter, R. 1987. Red Data Books: the historical background. In R. Fitter, & M. Fitter (Eds.), *The Road to Extinction* (pp. 1-6). IUCN, Gland.

Seal, U.S., Ellis, S.A., Foose, T.J., & Byers, A.P. 1993. Conservation assessment and management plans (CAMPs) and global captive action plans (GCAPs). 4(2):5-10.

Shaffer, M.L. 1981. Minimum population sizes for species conservation. *BioScience*, 31:131-134.

World Conservation Monitoring Centre. 1992. *Global Biodiversity: Status of the Earth's Living Resources*. Chapman & Hall, London.

Figure 6. NEW DRAFT DEFINITIONS FOR THREATENED SPECIES CATEGORIES

EXTINCT

A taxon is *Extinct* when there is no reasonable doubt that the last individual has died. A taxon is presumed extinct when exhaustive surveys in known and/or expected habitat, at appropriate times, throughout its historic range have failed to record an individual. Surveys should be over a time frame appropriate to the taxon's life cycle and life form.

EXTINCT IN THE WILD

A taxon is *Extinct in the wild* when it is known only to survive in cultivation, in captivity, or as a naturalised population (or populations) outside the historical range.

CRITICAL

A taxon is *Critical* when it is facing an extremely high probability of extinction in the wild in the immediate future. A taxon is defined as Critical by any of the quantitative criteria (A-E) (see Figure 7).

ENDANGERED

A taxon is *Endangered* when it is not Critical but is facing a very high probability of extinction in the wild in the near future. A taxon is defined as *Endangered* by any of the quantitative criteria (A-E) (see Figure 7).

VULNERABLE

A taxon is *Vulnerable* when it is not Critical or Endangered but is facing a high probability of extinction in the wild in the medium-term future. A taxon is defined as Vulnerable by any of the quantitative criteria (A-E) (see Figure 7).

SUSCEPTIBLE

A taxon is *Susceptible* when it does not qualify for any of the categories above, but is of concern because its range area is restricted (typically less than 100 km^2, and/or it is found at few locations, which render it prone to the effects of human activities.

SAFE/LOW RISK

A taxon is *Safe/Low Risk* when it has been evaluated and found not to qualify for any of the threatened categories above.

Figure 7. OUTLINE OF DRAFT CRITERIA FOR QUANTITATIVE CATEGORIES

Any one of ↓		CRITICAL	ENDANGERED	VULNERABLE
A	**VERY SMALL POPULATION SIZE** number of mature individuals	≤50	≤250	≤1,000
B	**SMALL POPULATION SIZE** number of mature individuals and either all populations small or small no. sub-pops and declining	≤250 ≤50 ≤1 any rate	≤2,500 ≤250 ≤1 any rate	≤10,000 ≤1,000 ≤1 any rate
C	**SMALL DISTRIBUTION** either geographical extent or range area	≤100km² ≤10km²	≤5,000km² ≤500km²	≤20,000km² ≤2,000km²

	and 2 of: - declining
	     - either fragmented
	       or small no. sub-pops
	     - fluctuating
		any rate
		+
		≤1
		>1 order/mag.
			any rate
			+
			≤2
			>1 order/mag.
				any rate
				+
				≤5
				>1 order/mag.

D	**DECLINE RATE** population decline rate at least
	
	in any of: - observed rates
	             - inferred rates
	             - projected rates
		25%pa over 5yrs	50% in 5 yrs or 2 generations[*]	50% in 10 yrs or 3 generations[*]

E	**QUANTITATIVE ANALYSIS** showing the probability of extinction in the wild is expected to be at least	50% in 5 yrs or 2 generations[*]	20% in 20 yrs or 5 generations[*]	10% in 100 yrs[*]

[*] whichever is the longer.

Note that this table is for reference purposes only. To apply the criteria refer to the full document which provides definitions for terms used.

List 1

THREATENED SPECIES

Class MAMMALIA

Order MONOTREMATA

Family TACHYGLOSSIDAE

E   *Zaglossus bruijni*
    Long-beaked Echidna
        Indonesia: Irian Jaya; Papua New Guinea

Order DASYUROMORPHIA

Family MYRMECOBIIDAE

E   *Myrmecobius fasciatus*
    Numbat
        Australia

Family DASYURIDAE

E   *Dasycercus byrnei*
    Kowari
        Australia

V   *Dasycercus cristicauda*
    Mulgara
        Australia

E   *Dasyurus geoffroii*
    Chuditch
        Australia

E   *Parantechinus apicalis*
    (*Antechinus apicalis*)
    Dibbler
        Australia

E   *Phascogale calura*
    Red-tailed Phascogale
        Australia

R   *Sminthopsis aitkeni*
    Kangaroo Island Dunnart
        Australia

R   *Sminthopsis butleri*
    Carpentarian Dunnart
        Australia

E   *Sminthopsis douglasi*
    Julia Creek Dunnart
        Australia

V   *Sminthopsis psammophila*
    Sandhill Dunnart
        Australia

Order PERAMELEMORPHIA

Family PERAMELIDAE

E   *Isoodon auratus*
    Golden Bandicoot
        Australia

V   *Macrotis lagotis*
    Bilby
        Australia

E   *Perameles bougainville*
    Western Barred Bandicoot
        Australia: Bernier Island, Dorre Island

V   *Perameles gunnii*
    Eastern Barred Bandicoot
        Australia

Family PERORYCTIDAE

R   *Echymipera clara*
    Clara Bandicoot
        Indonesia: Irian Jaya

K   *Echymipera echinista*
    Fly River Bandicoot
        Papua New Guinea

E   *Peroryctes broadbenti*
    Giant Bandicoot
        Papua New Guinea

I   *Rhynchomeles prattorum*
    Ceram Bandicoot
        Indonesia: Ceram

Order DIPROTODONTIA

Family VOMBATIDAE

E   *Lasiorhinus krefftii*
    Northern Hairy-nosed Wombat
        Australia

Family PHALANGERIDAE

V   *Phalanger lullulae*
    Woodlark Island Cuscus
        Papua New Guinea: Woodlark Island

V   *Phalanger matanim*
    Telefomin Cuscus
        Papua New Guinea

V   *Phalanger rothschildi*
    Obi Cuscus
        Indonesia: Pulau Obi Besar

R   *Phalanger vestitus*
    Stein's Cuscus
        Indonesia: Irian Jaya; Papua New Guinea

R   *Spilocuscus kraemeri*
    (may be a subspecies of *S. maculatus*)
    Manus Island Spotted Cuscus
        Papua New Guinea: Manus Island

R   *Spilocuscus papuensis*
    Waigeo Spotted Cuscus
        Indonesia: Irian Jaya (Waigeo Island)

V   *Spilocuscus rufoniger*
(*Phalanger rufoniger*)
Black-spotted Cuscus
   Indonesia: Irian Jaya; Papua New Guinea

Family POTOROIDAE

E   *Bettongia lesueur*
Boodie
   Australia: Bernier Island, Dorre Island, Barrow
   Island

E   *Bettongia penicillata*
Woylie
Australia

E   *Bettongia tropica*
(may be included in *B. penicillata*)
Northern Bettong
Australia

E   *Potorous longipes*
Long-footed Potoroo
Australia

Family MACROPODIDAE

V   *Dendrolagus dorianus*
Doria's Tree-kangaroo
   Indonesia: Irian Jaya; Papua New Guinea

E   *Dendrolagus goodfellowi*
Goodfellow's Tree-kangaroo
Papua New Guinea

V   *Dendrolagus inustus*
Grizzled Tree-kangaroo
   Indonesia: Irian Jaya; Papua New Guinea

V   *Dendrolagus matschiei*
Matschie's Tree-kangaroo
Papua New Guinea

E   *Dendrolagus scottae*
Scott's Tree-kangaroo
Papua New Guinea

V   *Dendrolagus spadix*
Lowland Tree-kangaroo
Papua New Guinea

V   *Dendrolagus ursinus*
White-throated Tree-kangaroo
Indonesia: Irian Jaya

V   *Dorcopsis atrata*
Black Dorcopsis Wallaby
   Papua New Guinea: Goodenough Island

V   *Dorcopsulus macleayi*
(*Dorcopsis macleayi*)
Macleay's Dorcopsis
   Papua New Guinea

E   *Lagorchestes hirsutus*
Mala
Australia

E   *Lagostrophus fasciatus*
Banded Hare-wallaby
   Australia: Bernier Island, Dorre Island, Dirk
   Hartog Island

R   *Macropus parma*
Parma Wallaby
Australia
[New Zealand: Kawau Island]

E   *Onychogalea fraenata*
Bridled Nailtail Wallaby
Australia

V   *Petrogale lateralis*
Black-footed Rock-wallaby
Australia

V   *Petrogale penicillata*
Brush-tailed Rock-wallaby
Australia

E   *Petrogale persephone*
Prosperine Rock-wallaby
Australia

V   *Thylogale bruinii*
Southern Bush Wallaby
   Indonesia: Irian Jaya, Aru Islands; Papua New
   Guinea

E   *Thylogale calabyi*
Alpine Wallaby
   Papua New Guinea

Family BURRAMYIDAE

E   *Burramys parvus*
Mountain Pygmy-possum
Australia

Family PSEUDOCHEIRIDAE

K   *Pseudocheirus caroli*
Weyland Ringtail
   Indonesia: Irian Jaya

V   *Pseudocheirus occidentalis*
(*P. peregrinus occidentalis*)
Western Ringtail
Australia

K   *Pseudocheirus schlegeli*
Arfak Ringtail
   Indonesia: Irian Jaya

Family PETAURIDAE

V **Dactylopsila megalura**
Great-tailed Troik
Indonesia: Irian Jaya; Papua New Guinea

E **Dactylopsila tatei**
Fergusson Island Striped Possum
Papua New Guinea: Fergusson Island

E **Gymnobelideus leadbeateri**
Leadbeater's Possum
Australia

V **Petaurus abidi**
Northern Glider
Papua New Guinea

E **Petaurus gracilis**
Mahogany Glider
Australia

Order XENARTHRA

Family BRADYPODIDAE

E **Bradypus torquatus**
Maned Sloth
Brazil

Family DASYPODIDAE

K **Chlamyphorus retusus**
(**Burmeisteria retusa**)
Greater Pichi Ciego
Argentina; Bolivia; Paraguay

K **Chlamyphorus truncatus**
Lesser Pichi Ciego
Argentina

V **Priodontes maximus**
(**P. giganteus**)
Giant Armadillo
Argentina; Bolivia; Brazil; Colombia; French
Guiana; Guyana; Paraguay; Peru; Suriname;
Venezuela

E **Tolypeutes tricinctus**
Brazilian Three-banded Armadillo
Brazil

Family MYRMECOPHAGIDAE

V **Myrmecophaga tridactyla**
(**M. jubata**)
Giant Anteater
Argentina; Belize (ex?); Bolivia; Brazil;
Colombia; Costa Rica; Ecuador?; French
Guiana; Guyana; Honduras; Nicaragua;
Panama; Paraguay; Peru; Suriname; Uruguay;
Venezuela

Order INSECTIVORA

Family SOLENODONTIDAE

E **Solenodon cubanus**
Cuban Solenodon
Cuba

E **Solenodon paradoxus**
Haitian Solenodon
Dominican Republic; Haiti

Family TENRECIDAE

K **Geogale aurita**
Large-eared Tenrec
Madagascar

I **Limnogale mergulus**
Aquatic Tenrec
Madagascar

K **Microgale brevicaudata**
(includes *M. occidentalis*)
Short-tailed Shrew-tenrec
Madagascar

K **Microgale gracilis**
Gracile Shrew-tenrec
Madagascar

K **Microgale longicaudata**
(includes *M. majori*)
Lesser Long-tailed Shrew-tenrec
Madagascar

K **Microgale parvula**
Pygmy Shrew-tenrec
Madagascar

K **Microgale pulla**
(may be synonymous with *M. parvula*)
Dusky Shrew-tenrec
Madagascar

K **Microgale thomasi**
Thomas's Shrew-tenrec
Madagascar

E **Micropotamogale lamottei**
Nimba Otter-shrew
Côte d'Ivoire; Guinea; Liberia

I **Micropotamogale ruwenzorii**
Ruwenzori Otter-shrew
Uganda; Zaire

Family CHRYSOCHLORIDAE

I **Amblysomus gunningi**
Gunning's Golden Mole
South Africa

I   *Amblysomus iris*
Zulu Golden Mole
South Africa

I   *Amblysomus julianae*
Juliana's Golden Mole
South Africa

R   *Calcochloris obtusirostris*
(*Chlorotalpa obtusirostris*)
Yellow Golden Mole
Mozambique; South Africa; Zimbabwe

R   *Chlorotalpa duthieae*
Duthie's Golden Mole
South Africa

I   *Chlorotalpa sclateri*
Sclater's Golden Mole
South Africa

I   *Chlorotalpa tytonis*
Somali Golden Mole
Somalia

I   *Chrysochloris visagiei*
Visagie's Golden Mole
South Africa

R   *Chrysospalax trevelyani*
Giant Golden Mole
South Africa

V   *Chrysospalax villosus*
Rough-haired Golden Mole
South Africa

I   *Cryptochloris wintoni*
De Winton's Golden Mole
South Africa

I   *Cryptochloris zyli*
Van Zyl's Golden Mole
South Africa

R   *Eremitalpa granti*
Grant's Golden Mole
Namibia; South Africa

Family ERINACEIDAE

R   *Ateleric frontalis*
(*Erinaceus frontalis*)
South African Hedgehog
Angola; Botswana; Lesotho; Namibia; South Africa; Zimbabwe

V   *Podogymnura truei*
Mindanao Gymnure
Philippines: Mindanao

Family SORICIDAE

K   *Congosorex polli*
(*Myosorex polli*)
Zaire

K   *Crocidura ansellorum*
Zambia

K   *Crocidura baileyi*
Ethiopia

K   *Crocidura congobelgica*
Zaire

K   *Crocidura crenata*
Gabon

K   *Crocidura eisentrauti*
Cameroon

K   *Crocidura glassi*
Ethiopia

K   *Crocidura grassei*
Cameroon; Central African Republic; Gabon

K   *Crocidura kivuana*
Zaire

K   *Crocidura lanosa*
Rwanda; Zaire

K   *Crocidura latona*
Zaire

K   *Crocidura longipes*
Nigeria

K   *Crocidura lucina*
Ethiopia

K   *Crocidura ludia*
(*C. dolichura ludia*)
Zaire

K   *Crocidura manengubae*
Cameroon

K   *Crocidura maquassiensis*
Makwassie Musk Shrew
South Africa; Zimbabwe

K   *Crocidura monax*
Kenya; Tanzania; Zaire

K   *Crocidura nimbae*
Côte d'Ivoire; Guinea; Liberia

R   *Crocidura orii*
Orii's Shrew
Japan: Sado

K   *Crocidura phaeura*
Ethiopia

K   *Crocidura polia*
(*C. dolichura polia*)
Zaire

K   *Crocidura raineyi*
(*C. luna raineyi*)
Kenya

K   *Crocidura selina*
(*C. luna selina*)
Uganda

K   *Crocidura stenocephala*
(*C. littoralis stenocephala*)
Zaire

K   *Crocidura tansaniana*
Tanzania

K   *Crocidura telfordi*
Tanzania

K   *Crocidura thalia*
Ethiopia

K   *Crocidura thomensis*
(*C. poensis thomensis*)
São Tomé and Príncipe: São Tomé

K   *Crocidura usambarae*
Tanzania

K   *Crocidura wimmeri*
Cameroon; Côte d'Ivoire; Gabon; Liberia

R   *Crocidura zimmermanni*
Greece: Crete

R   *Sorex sadonis*
Sado Shrew
Japan: Sado

K   *Myosorex eisentrauti*
Cameroon; Equatorial Guinea

K   *Myosorex geata*
Tanzania

K   *Myosorex longicaudatus*
Long-tailed Forest Shrew
South Africa

K   *Myosorex schalleri*
Zaire

K   *Paracrocidura graueri*
Zaire

K   *Paracrocidura maxima*
Rwanda; Uganda; Zaire

I   *Ruwenzorisorex suncoides*
(*Sylvisorex suncoides*)
Burundi; Rwanda; Uganda; Zaire

K   *Suncus remyi*
Gabon Dwarf Shrew
Gabon

K   *Sylvisorex howelli*
Tanzania

K   *Sylvisorex ollula*
Cameroon; Gabon; Nigeria; Zaire

K   *Sylvisorex vulcanorum*
Burundi; Rwanda; Uganda; Zaire

Family TALPIDAE

V   *Desmana moschata*
Russian Desman
Belarus; Estonia; Kazakhstan; Latvia; Lithuania; Russia; Turkmenistan; Ukraine

V   *Galemys pyrenaicus*
Pyrenean Desman
Andorra?; France; Portugal; Spain

R   *Mogera tokudae*
Sado Mole
Japan: Sado

Order CHIROPTERA

Family PTEROPODIDAE

E   *Acerodon jubatus*
Golden-capped Fruit Bat
Philippines

I   *Aethalops alecto*
Pygmy Fruit Bat
Brunei; Malaysia; Indonesia

R   *Alionycteris paucidentata*
Philippines: Mindanao

E   *Aproteles bulmerae*
Bulmer's Fruit Bat
Papua New Guinea

R   *Dobsonia minor*
Lesser Naked-backed Fruit Bat
Indonesia: Irian Jaya, Sulawesi; Papua New Guinea

I   *Dobsonia peronii*
Western Naked-backed Fruit Bat
Indonesia

R   *Dyacopterus spadiceus*
Dyak Fruit Bat
Brunei; Indonesia: Sumatra; Malaysia; Philippines: Luzon, Mindanao

R   *Epomophorus angolensis*
Angolan Epauletted Fruit Bat
Angola; Namibia

R **Epomophorus grandis**
(*Micropteropus grandis*)
Lesser Angolan Epauletted Fruit Bat
Angola; Congo

V **Epomops buettikoferi**
Buettikofer's Epauletted Fruit Bat
Cote d'Ivoire; Ghana; Guinea; Liberia;
Nigeria; Sierra Leone

V **Haplonycteris fischeri**
Fischer's Pygmy Fruit Bat
Philippines

R **Latidens salimalii**
India

R **Megaerops kusnotoi**
Javan Tail-less Fruit Bat
Indonesia: Java

R **Micropteropus intermedius**
Hayman's Epauletted Fruit Bat
Angola; Zaire

V **Myonycteris brachycephala**
São Tomé Collared Fruit Bat
São Tomé and Príncipe: São Tomé

V **Myonycteris relicta**
East African Collared Fruit Bat
Kenya; Tanzania

R **Neopteryx frosti**
Small-toothed Fruit Bat
Indonesia: Sulawesi

I **Notopteris macdonaldii**
Long-tailed Fruit Bat
Fiji; New Caledonia; Vanuatu

R **Nyctimene aello**
Broad-striped Tube-nosed Fruit Bat
Indonesia: Irian Jaya; Papua New Guinea

I **Nyctimene cyclotis**
Round-eared Tube-nosed Fruit Bat
Indonesia: Irian Jaya; Papua New Guinea

R **Nyctimene draconilla**
Indonesia: Irian Jaya; Papua New Guinea

E **Nyctimene rabori**
Philippines Tube-nosed Fruit Bat
Philippines: Negros

I **Otopteropus cartilagonodus**
Philippines: Luzon

R **Paranyctimene raptor**
Lesser Tube-nosed Fruit Bat
Indonesia: Irian Jaya; Papua New Guinea

R **Plerotes anchietae**
d'Anchieta's Fruit Bat
Angola; Zaire; Zambia

E **Pteralopex acrodonta**
Fiji

E **Pteralopex anceps**
Papua New Guinea: Bougainville; Solomon
Islands

E **Pteralopex atrata**
Cusp-toothed Fruit Bat
Solomon Islands

E **Pteralopex pulchra**
Solomon Islands: Guadalcanal

I **Pteropus anetianus**
White Flying-fox
Vanuatu

E **Pteropus dasymallus**
Ryukyu Flying-fox
Japan: Ryukyu Islands; Taiwan

E **Pteropus insularis**
Chuuk Flying-fox
Federated States of Micronesia: Chuuk

V **Pteropus leucopterus**
Philippines

E **Pteropus livingstonei**
Comoro Black Flying-fox
Comoros: Mwali (Mohéli) and Nzwani
(Anjouan)

V **Pteropus mahaganus**
Lesser Flying-fox
Papua New Guinea: Bougainville; Solomon
Islands: Santa Isabel

V **Pteropus mariannus**
Marianas Flying-fox
Federated States of Micronesia; Guam; Japan:
Ryukyu Islands; Northern Mariana Islands;
Palau

E **Pteropus molossinus**
Pohnpei Flying-fox
Federated States of Micronesia: Chuuk,
Pohnpei

V **Pteropus niger**
Greater Mascarene Flying-fox
Mauritius

I **Pteropus ornatus**
New Caledonia

E **Pteropus phaeocephalus**
(probably a subspecies of *P. insularis*)
Mortlock Islands Flying-fox
Federated States of Micronesia: Chuuk

V **Pteropus pselaphon**
Japan: Kazan-retto (Volcano Islands),
Ogasawara-shoto (Bonin Islands)

V **Pteropus pumilus**
Little Golden-mantled Flying-fox
Indonesia: Miangas; Philippines

E **Pteropus rodricensis**
Rodrigues Flying-fox
Mauritius: Rodrigues

V **Pteropus samoensis**
Samoa Flying-fox
American Samoa; Fiji; Western Samoa

R **Pteropus speciosus**
Indonesia: Laut Kecil, Masalembu Besar;
Philippines

R **Pteropus vetulus**
New Caledonia

E **Pteropus voeltzkowi**
Pemba Flying-fox
Tanzania: Pemba

R **Syconycteris hobbit**
Moss-forest Blossom Bat
Papua New Guinea

Family CRASEONYCTERIDAE

R **Craseonycteris thonglongyai**
Kitti's Hog-nosed Bat
Thailand

Family EMBALLONURIDAE

E **Coleura seychellensis**
Seychelles Sheath-tailed Bat
Seychelles

K **Emballonura furax**
Greater Sheath-tailed Bat
Indonesia: Irian Jaya; Papua New Guinea

K **Emballonura raffrayana**
Raffray's Sheath-tailed Bat
Indonesia: Irian Jaya, Kai Islands, Seram,
Sulawesi; Papua New Guinea; Solomon Islands

V **Emballonura semicaudata**
American Samoa (ex?); Fiji; Guam; Northern
Mariana Islands; Palau; Samoa (ex?); Vanuatu

Family MEGADERMATIDAE

V **Macroderma gigas**
Ghost Bat
Australia

Family RHINOLOPHIDAE

R **Hipposideros papua**
Geelvinck Bay Leaf-nosed Bat
Indonesia: Biak, Irian Jaya, northern Moluccas

V **Hipposideros ridleyi**
Ridley's Leaf-nosed Bat
Malaysia: Peninsular Malaysia, Sabah;
Singapore

K **Rhinonicteris aurantia**
Orange Leaf-nosed Bat
Australia

Family PHYLLOSTOMIDAE

K **Leptonycteris curasoae**
(includes *L. yerbabuenae* = *L. sanborni*)
Aruba; Colombia; Netherlands Antilles:
Bonaire, Curacao; El Salvador; Guatemala;
Mexico; USA; Venezuela

V **Leptonycteris nivalis**
Big Long-nosed Bat
Guatemala; Mexico; USA

K **Phyllonycteris aphylla**
Jamaican Flower Bat
Jamaica

K **Phyllonycteris poeyi**
Cuban Flower Bat
Cuba; Dominican Republic; Haiti

Family MYZOPODIDAE

V **Myzopoda aurita**
Sucker-footed Bat
Madagascar

Family VESPERTILIONIDAE

K **Glischropus javanus**
Javan Thick-thumbed Bat
Indonesia: Java

V **Myotis capaccinii**
Long-fingered Bat
Algeria; Austria; Bulgaria; France; Greece;
Iraq; Iran; Israel; Italy; Jordan; Lebanon;
Malta; Morocco; Slovenia; Spain: including
Balearic Islands; Turkey; Uzbekistan;
Yugoslavia

V   *Myotis dasycneme*
Pond Bat
Austria; Belarus; Belgium; China; Czech Republic; Denmark; Estonia; France; Germany; Hungary; Kazakhstan; Latvia; Lithuania; Luxembourg; Netherlands; Poland; Russia; Slovakia; Sweden; Switzerland; Ukraine

E   *Myotis grisescens*
Grey Bat
USA

V   *Myotis myotis*
Greater Mouse-eared Bat
Albania; Austria; Azores; Belarus; Belgium; Bulgaria; Cyprus; Czech Republic; France; Germany; Greece; Hungary; Israel; Italy; Jordan; Lebanon; Liechtenstein; Luxembourg; Malta; Netherlands; Poland; Portugal; Romania; Slovakia; Slovenia; Spain; Switzerland; Syria; Turkey; Ukraine; United Kingdom (ex?); Yugoslavia

V   *Myotis sodalis*
Indiana Bat
USA

I   *Plecotus townsendii*
Townsend's Big-eared Bat
Canada; Mexico; USA

Family MYSTACINIDAE

V   *Mystacina tuberculata*
New Zealand Lesser Short-tailed Bat
New Zealand

Family MOLOSSIDAE

K   *Otomops formosus*
Javan Mastiff Bat
Indonesia: Java

V   *Otomops wroughtoni*
Wroughton's Free-tailed Bat
India

Order PRIMATES

Family CHEIROGALEIDAE

E   *Allocebus trichotis*
(*Cheirogaleus trichotis*)
Hairy-eared Dwarf Lemur
Madagascar

V   *Microcebus coquereli*
(*Mirza coquereli*)
Coquerel's Mouse-lemur
Madagascar

R   *Phaner furcifer*
Fork-marked Lemur
Madagascar

Family LEMURIDAE

E   *Eulemur coronatus*
(*Eulemur mongoz coronatus*; often included in *Lemur*)
Crowned Lemur
Madagascar

V   *Eulemur macaco*
(*Lemur macaco*)
Black Lemur
Madagascar

E   *Eulemur mongoz*
(*Lemur mongoz*)
Mongoose Lemur
Comoros: Mwali (Mohéli) and Nzwani (Anjouan); Madagascar

V   *Eulemur rubriventer*
(*Lemur rubriventer*)
Red-bellied Lemur
Madagascar

E   *Hapalemur aureus*
Golden Bamboo Lemur
Madagascar

E   *Hapalemur simus*
Broad-nosed Gentle Lemur
Madagascar

V   *Lemur catta*
Ring-tailed Lemur
Madagascar

E   *Varecia variegata*
Ruffed Lemur
Madagascar

Family MEGALADAPIDAE

V   *Lepilemur dorsalis*
(*L. mustelinus dorsalis*)
Grey-backed Sportive Lemur
Madagascar

R   *Lepilemur edwardsi*
(*L. mustelinus edwardsi*)
Milne-Edwards' Sportive Lemur
Madagascar

R   *Lepilemur leucopus*
(*L. mustelinus leucopus*)
White-footed Sportive Lemur
Madagascar

R **Lepilemur microdon**
(*L. mustelinus microdon*)
Light-necked Sportive Lemur
Madagascar

R **Lepilemur mustelinus**
Greater Sportive Lemur
Madagascar

R **Lepilemur ruficaudatus**
(*L. mustelinus ruficaudatus*)
Red-tailed Sportive Lemur
Madagascar

V **Lepilemur septentrionalis**
(*L. mustelinus septentrionalis*)
Northern Sportive Lemur
Madagascar

Family INDRIDAE

V **Avahi laniger**
(*Lichanotus laniger*)
Woolly Lemur
Madagascar

E **Indri indri**
Indri
Madagascar

E **Propithecus diadema**
Diademed Sifaka
Madagascar

E **Propithecus tattersalli**
Golden-crowned Sifaka
Madagascar

V **Propithecus verreauxi**
Verreaux's Sifaka
Madagascar

Family DAUBENTONIIDAE

E **Daubentonia madagascariensis**
Aye-aye
Madagascar

Family LORIDAE

V **Arctocebus calabarensis**
Golden Potto
Angola; Cameroon; Central African Republic?;
Congo; Equatorial Guinea; Gabon; Nigeria;
Zaire?

V **Nycticebus pygmaeus**
Pygmy Loris
Cambodia?; China; Laos; Viet Nam

Family GALAGONIDAE

V **Galago matschiei**
(*G. inustus*, sometimes referred to *Euoticus*)
Eastern Needle-clawed Galago
Rwanda?; Uganda; Zaire

K **Galagoides thomasi**
(*G. demidoff thomasi*, often included in *Galago*)
Thomas's Galago
Angola?; Cameroon; Kenya?; Malawi?;
Nigeria?; Tanzania?; Uganda; Zaire

V **Galagoides zanzibaricus**
(*G. senegalensis zanzibaricus*, often included in
Galago)
Zanzibar Galago
Kenya; Malawi; Mozambique; Somalia;
Tanzania: including Zanzibar; Zimbabwe

Family TARSIIDAE

I **Tarsius dianae**
Indonesia: Sulawesi

I **Tarsius pumilus**
(*T. spectrum pumilus*)
Lesser Spectral Tarsier
Indonesia: Sulawesi

K **Tarsius spectrum**
Spectral Tarsier
Indonesia: Peleng, Sangir, Savu, Seleyar,
Sulawesi

Family CALLITRICHIDAE

R **Callimico goeldii**
Goeldi's Marmoset
Bolivia; Brazil; Colombia; Ecuador?; Peru

E **Callithrix aurita**
(*C. jacchus aurita*)
Buffy-tufted-ear Marmoset
Brazil

V **Callithrix chrysoleuca**
(*C. humeralifer chrysoleuca*)
Golden-white Tassel-ear Marmoset
Brazil

E **Callithrix flaviceps**
(*C. jacchus flaviceps*)
Buffy-headed Marmoset
Brazil

V **Callithrix geoffroyi**
(*C. jacchus geoffroyi*)
Geoffroy's Tufted-ear Marmoset
Brazil

V **Callithrix intermedia**
(*C. argentata intermedia, C. humeralifer intermedia*)
Aripuanã Marmoset
Brazil

V **Callithrix kuhli**
(may be included in *C. jacchus*)
Wied's Marmoset
Brazil

V **Callithrix nigriceps**
(*C. argentata nigriceps*)
Black-headed Marmoset
Brazil

E **Leontopithecus caissara**
(*L. rosalia caissara*, may be a form of *L. [rosalia] chrysopygus*)
Black-faced Lion Tamarin
Brazil

E **Leontopithecus chrysomelas**
(*L. rosalia chrysomelas*)
Golden-headed Lion Tamarin
Brazil

E **Leontopithecus chrysopygus**
(*L. rosalia chrysopygus*)
Golden-rumped Lion Tamarin
Brazil

E **Leontopithecus rosalia**
(*L. rosalia rosalia*)
Golden Lion Tamarin
Brazil

E **Saguinus leucopus**
White-footed Tamarin
Colombia

E **Saguinus oedipus**
Cotton-top Tamarin
Colombia

K **Saguinus tripartitus**
Golden-mantled Saddle-back Tamarin
Ecuador; Peru

Family CEBIDAE

V **Alouatta fusca**
(*A. guariba*, includes *A. beniensis*)
Brown Howler
Argentina; Bolivia; Brazil

K **Alouatta pigra**
(*A. villosa*)
Guatemalan Howler
Belize; Guatemala; Mexico

V **Aotus brumbacki**
Brumback's Night Monkey
Colombia

V **Aotus miconax**
(*A. trivirgatus miconax*)
Andean Night Monkey
Peru

V **Ateles belzebuth**
Long-haired Spider Monkey
Brazil; Colombia; Ecuador; Peru; Venezuela

V **Ateles fusciceps**
Brown-headed Spider Monkey
Colombia; Ecuador; Panama

V **Ateles geoffroyi**
Geoffroy's Spider Monkey
Belize; Colombia?; Costa Rica; El Salvador; Guatemala; Honduras; Mexico; Nicaragua; Panama

V **Ateles paniscus**
(includes *A. chamek*)
Black Spider Monkey
Bolivia; Brazil; French Guiana; Guyana; Peru; Suriname

E **Brachyteles arachnoides**
Muriqui
Brazil

E **Cacajao calvus**
(includes *C. rubicundus*)
Bald Uakari
Brazil; Peru

E **Cacajao melanocephalus**
Black Uakari
Brazil; Colombia; Venezuela

V **Callicebus oenanthe**
Andean Titi Monkey
Peru

I **Callicebus olallae**
Beni Titi Monkey
Bolivia

V **Callicebus personatus**
Masked Titi
Brazil

E **Cebus kaapori**
(*C. apella kaapori*)
Ka'apor Capuchin Monkey
Brazil

V **Chiropotes albinasus**
White-nosed Bearded Saki
Brazil

E   *Lagothrix flavicauda*
(*L. hendeei*)
Yellow-tailed Woolly Monkey
   Ecuador?; Peru

V   *Lagothrix lagothricha*
Common Woolly Monkey
   Bolivia; Brazil; Colombia; Ecuador; Peru

V   *Pithecia aequatorialis*
Equatorial Saki
   Ecuador; Peru

E   *Saimiri oerstedii*
Central American Squirrel Monkey
   Costa Rica; Panama

V   *Saimiri vanzolinii*
(*S. boliviensis vanzolinii*)
Blackish Squirrel Monkey
   Brazil

Family CERCOPITHECIDAE

K   *Allenopithecus nigroviridis*
(*Cercopithecus nigroviridis*)
Allen's Swamp Monkey
   Angola?; Congo; Zaire

V   *Cercopithecus diana*
(includes *C. roloway*)
Diana Guenon
   Côte d'Ivoire; Ghana; Guinea; Liberia; Sierra Leone; Togo

K   *Cercopithecus dryas*
(*C. salongo*)
Salongo Guenon
   Zaire

E   *Cercopithecus erythrogaster*
Red-bellied Guenon
   Benin?; Nigeria; Togo

V   *Cercopithecus erythrotis*
Russet-eared Guenon
   Cameroon; Equatorial Guinea: Bioko

V   *Cercopithecus hamlyni*
Owl-faced Guenon
   Rwanda; Uganda; Zaire

V   *Cercopithecus lhoesti*
(includes *C. thomasi*)
L'Hoest's Monkey
   Burundi; Rwanda; Uganda; Zaire

E   *Cercopithecus preussi*
(*C. lhoesti preussi*)
Preuss's Guenon
   Cameroon; Equatorial Guinea: Bioko

E   *Cercopithecus sclateri*
White-throated Guenon
   Nigeria

E   *Cercopithecus solatus*
Sun-tailed Guenon
   Gabon

V   *Colobus polykomos*
Western Black-and-white Colobus
   Côte d'Ivoire; Gambia; Guinea; Guinea Bissau; Liberia; Senegal; Sierra Leone.

V   *Colobus satanas*
Black Colobus
   Cameroon; Congo; Equatorial Guinea: including Bioko; Gabon

V   *Colobus vellerosus*
(*Colobus polykomos vellerosus*)
Geoffroy's Black-and-white Colobus
   Benin; Côte d'Ivoire; Ghana; Nigeria; Togo

K   *Macaca arctoides*
Stump-tailed Macaque
   Bangladesh; Cambodia; China; India; Laos; Malaysia; Myanmar; Thailand; Viet Nam

V   *Macaca cyclopis*
(*M. mulatta cyclopis*)
Taiwan Macaque
   Taiwan
   [Japan]

V   *Macaca fuscata*
Japanese Macaque
   Japan

V   *Macaca maura*
(*M. nigra maura*)
Moor Macaque
   Indonesia: Sulawesi

I   *Macaca nigra*
Celebes Black Macaque
   Indonesia: Sulawesi

E   *Macaca silenus*
Lion-tailed Macaque
   India

V   *Macaca sylvanus*
Barbary Macaque
   Algeria; Morocco
   [Gibraltar]

K   *Macaca thibetana*
Tibetan Macaque
   China

E *Mandrillus leucophaeus*
(*Papio leucophaeus*)
Drill
Cameroon; Equatorial Guinea: Bioko; Gabon?;
Nigeria

V *Mandrillus sphinx*
(*Papio sphinx*)
Mandrill
Cameroon; Congo; Equatorial Guinea; Gabon

E *Nasalis concolor*
(*Simias concolor*)
Pig-tailed Snub-nosed Monkey
Indonesia: Mentawai Islands

V *Nasalis larvatus*
Proboscis Monkey
Brunei; Indonesia: Kalimantan; Malaysia:
Sabah, Sarawak

E *Presbytis comata*
(*P. aygula*)
Grizzled Leaf Monkey
Indonesia: Java

E *Presbytis potenziani*
Mentawai Leaf Monkey
Indonesia: Mentawai Islands

V *Procolobus verus*
(*Colobus verus*)
Olive Colobus
Benin?; Côte d'Ivoire; Ghana; Guinea; Liberia;
Nigeria; Sierra Leone; Togo?

E *Pygathrix avunculus*
(*Rhinopithecus avunculus*)
Tonkin Snub-nosed Monkey
Viet Nam

E *Pygathrix brelichi*
(*P. roxellana brelichi*, sometimes referred to
Rhinopithecus)
Guizhou Snub-nosed Monkey
China

E *Pygathrix nemaeus*
Douc Monkey
Cambodia; China: Hainan; Laos; Viet Nam

V *Pygathrix roxellana*
(*Rhinopithecus roxellana*)
Golden Snub-nosed Monkey
China; India?: Arunachal Pradesh, Manipur

R *Theropithecus gelada*
Gelada Baboon
Ethiopia

E *Trachypithecus francoisi*
(*Presbytis francoisi, Semnopithecus francoisi*)
François' Leaf Monkey
China; Laos; Viet Nam

R *Trachypithecus geei*
(possibly a subspecies of *T. pileatus*, sometimes
referred to *Presbytis* or *Semnopithecus*)
Golden Leaf Monkey
Bhutan; India

I *Trachypithecus johnii*
(*Presbytis johnii, Semnopithecus johnii*)
Nilgiri Leaf Monkey
India

Family HYLOBATIDAE

E *Hylobates concolor*
(includes *H. leucogenys*)
Black Gibbon
Cambodia; China; Laos; Viet Nam

E *Hylobates hoolock*
Hoolock Gibbon
Bangladesh; China; India; Laos?; Myanmar

E *Hylobates klossii*
Mentawai Gibbon
Indonesia: Mentawai Islands

E *Hylobates moloch*
(*H. lar moloch*)
Silvery Gibbon
Indonesia: Java

E *Hylobates pileatus*
(*H. lar pileatus*)
Pileated Gibbon
Cambodia; Laos; Thailand

Family HOMINIDAE

V *Gorilla gorilla*
Gorilla
Angola; Burundi (ex?); Cameroon; Central
African Republic; Congo; Equatorial Guinea;
Gabon; Nigeria; Rwanda; Uganda; Zaire

V *Pan paniscus*
Dwarf Chimpanzee
Congo?; Zaire

V *Pan troglodytes*
Chimpanzee
Angola; Burundi; Cameroon; Central African
Republic; Congo; Côte d'Ivoire; Equatorial
Guinea; Gabon; Ghana; Guinea; Guinea-Bissau
(ex?); Liberia; Mali; Nigeria; Rwanda (ex?);
Senegal; Sierra Leone; Sudan; Tanzania;
Uganda; Zaire
[Reintroduced in Gambia]

E **Pongo pygmaeus**
Orang-utan
Brunei?; Indonesia: Kalimantan, Sumatra;
Malaysia: Sabah, Sarawak

Order CARNIVORA

Family CANIDAE

V **Canis lupus**
Grey Wolf
Afghanistan; Albania; Armenia; Azerbaijan;
Bangladesh (ex?); Belarus; Bhutan; Bulgaria;
Canada; China; Czech Republic?; Estonia;
Egypt; Finland; Greece; Greenland; India; Iran;
Iraq; Israel; Italy; Jordan; Kazakhstan; Korea
D.P.R; Korea Republic?; Kuwait; Kyrgyzstan;
Latvia; Lebanon; Libya; Lithuania; Mexico;
Moldova; Mongolia; Myanmar (ex?); Nepal;
Norway; Oman; Pakistan; Poland; Portugal;
Romania; Russia; Saudi Arabia; Slovakia;
Slovenia; Spain; Sweden; Syria; Tajikistan;
Turkey; Turkmenistan; Ukraine; USA;
Uzbekistan; Viet Nam; Yemen; Yugoslavia

E **Canis rufus**
(*C. niger*)
Red Wolf
USA

E **Canis simensis**
Ethiopian Wolf
Ethiopia

V **Chrysocyon brachyurus**
Maned Wolf
Argentina; Bolivia; Brazil; Paraguay; Peru

V **Cuon alpinus**
Asiatic Wild Dog
Bangladesh; Bhutan; Cambodia; China; India;
Indonesia: Java, Sumatra; Kazakhstan?; Korea
D.P.R?; Korea Republic?; Kyrgyzstan?; Laos;
Malaysia: Peninsular Malaysia; Mongolia;
Myanmar; Nepal; Russia; Sri Lanka (ex?);
Tajikistan?; Thailand; Uzbekistan?; Viet Nam

V **Dusicyon griseus**
(*Pseudalopex griseus*, includes *D. fulvipes*)
Grey Zorro, Argentine Grey Fox
Argentina; Chile; Falkland Islands; Peru

K **Dusicyon microtis**
(*Atelocynus microtis*)
Small-eared Dog
Bolivia?; Brazil; Colombia; Ecuador; Peru

K **Dusicyon sechurae**
(*Pseudalopex sechurae*)
Sechuran Zorro
Ecuador; Peru

K **Dusicyon vetulus**
(*Pseudalopex vetulus*)
Hoary Zorro
Brazil

K **Fennecus zerda**
(*Vulpes zerda*)
Fennec Fox
Algeria; Burkina Faso?; Chad; Egypt; Israel;
Kuwait; Libya; Mauritania; Morocco; Niger;
Oman; Sudan; Tunisia; Western Sahara

E **Lycaon pictus**
Wild Dog
Algeria (ex?); Angola; Benin (ex?); Botswana;
Burkina Faso; Burundi (ex?); Cameroon;
Central African Republic; Chad; Congo (ex?);
Côte d'Ivoire; Ethiopia; Gabon (ex?); Ghana
(ex?); Guinea; Kenya; Malawi; Mali (ex?);
Mauritania?; Mozambique; Namibia; Niger;
Nigeria; Rwanda (ex?); Senegal; Sierra Leone;
Somalia; South Africa; Sudan; Swaziland;
Tanzania; Togo (ex?); Uganda (ex?); Zaire
(ex?); Zambia; Zimbabwe

V **Speothos venaticus**
Bush Dog
Argentina; Bolivia; Brazil; Colombia; Ecuador;
French Guiana; Guyana; Panama; Paraguay;
Peru; Suriname; Venezuela

R **Urocyon littoralis**
(probably conspecific with *U. cinereoargentatus*)
Island Grey Fox
USA: islands off California

I **Vulpes bengalensis**
Bengal Fox
Bangladesh; India; Nepal; Pakistan

K **Vulpes cana**
Blanford's Fox
Afghanistan; Iran; Israel; Oman; Pakistan;
Turkmenistan

K **Vulpes corsac**
Corsac Fox
Afghanistan; China; Kazakhstan; Kyrgyzstan;
Mongolia; Russia; Turkmenistan

K **Vulpes pallida**
Pale Fox
Burkina Faso; Cameroon; Chad; Guinea;
Libya; Mali; Niger; Nigeria; Senegal; Sudan

K **Vulpes rueppelli**
Rueppell's Fox
Afghanistan; Algeria; Chad; Egypt; Ethiopia;
Iraq; Iran; Libya; Morocco; Niger; Saudi
Arabia; Somalia; Sudan; Yemen

Family FELIDAE

V *Acinonyx jubatus*
Cheetah
Afghanistan (ex?); Algeria (ex?); Angola; Benin; Botswana; Burkina Faso; Cameroon; Chad; Ethiopia; Iran; Jordan (ex?); Kenya; Libya; Malawi; Mali; Mauritania; Morocco (ex?); Mozambique; Namibia; Niger; Nigeria; Pakistan (ex?); Saudi Arabia (ex?); Senegal; Somalia; South Africa; Sudan; Swaziland; Tanzania; Turkmenistan; Uganda; Western Sahara (ex?); Zaire; Zambia; Zimbabwe

K *Catopuma badia*
(*Felis badia*)
Bay Cat
Brunei; Indonesia: Kalimantan; Malaysia: Sabah, Sarawak

I *Catopuma temmincki*
(*Felis temmincki*)
Asiatic Golden Cat
Bangladesh; Bhutan; Cambodia; China; India; Indonesia: Sumatra; Laos; Malaysia: Peninsular Malaysia; Myanmar; Nepal; Thailand; Viet Nam

K *Felis bieti*
Chinese Desert Cat
China

K *Felis margarita*
Sand Cat
Algeria; Egypt; Iran; Israel; Jordan; Kazakhstan; Morocco; Niger; Oman; Pakistan; Qatar; Saudi Arabia; Senegal; Turkmenistan; Uzbekistan; Yemen

K *Leopardus tigrinus*
(*Felis tigrina*)
Little Spotted Cat
Argentina; Brazil; Colombia; Costa Rica; Ecuador; French Guiana; Guyana; Nicaragua?; Paraguay?; Peru?; Suriname; Venezuela

K *Leopardus wiedii*
(*Felis wiedii*)
Margay
Argentina; Belize; Bolivia; Brazil; Colombia; Costa Rica; Ecuador; El Salvador; French Guiana?; Guatemala; Guyana; Honduras; Mexico; Nicaragua; Panama; Paraguay; Peru; Suriname; Uruguay; Venezuela

E *Lynx pardinus*
(*L. lynx pardinus*, sometimes included in *Felis*)
Spanish Lynx
Portugal; Spain

V *Neofelis nebulosa*
Clouded Leopard
Bangladesh (ex?); Bhutan; Brunei; Cambodia?; China; India; Indonesia: Kalimantan, Sumatra; Laos; Malaysia: Peninsular Malaysia, Sabah, Sarawak; Myanmar; Nepal; Taiwan; Thailand; Viet Nam

I *Oncifelis colocolo*
(*Felis colocolo*)
Pampas Cat, Chilean Pampas Cat
Argentina; Bolivia; Brazil; Chile; Ecuador; Paraguay; Peru; Uruguay

I *Oncifelis guigna*
(*Felis guigna*)
Kodkod, Chilean Cat
Argentina; Chile

K *Oreailurus jacobita*
(*Felis jacobita*)
Andean Cat
Argentina; Bolivia; Chile; Peru

K *Otocolobus manul*
(*Felis manul*)
Pallas's Cat
Afghanistan; Armenia; China; India; Iran; Kazakhstan; Kyrgyzstan; Mongolia; Pakistan; Russia; Tajikistan; Turkmenistan; Uzbekistan

E *Panthera tigris*
Tiger
Afghanistan (ex?); Bangladesh; Bhutan; Cambodia; China; India; Indonesia: Java, Sumatra; Kazakhstan; Korea D.P.R (ex?); Kyrgyzstan; Laos; Malaysia: Peninsular Malaysia; Myanmar; Nepal; Russia; Tajikistan; Thailand; Turkmenistan; Uzbekistan; Viet Nam

K *Pardofelis marmorata*
(*Felis marmorata*)
Marbled Cat
Bangladesh?; Bhutan?; Brunei; Cambodia; China; India; Indonesia: Kalimantan, Sumatra; Laos; Malaysia: Peninsular Malaysia, Sabah, Sarawak; Myanmar; Nepal; Thailand; Viet Nam

K *Prionailurus planiceps*
(*Felis planiceps*)
Flat-headed Cat
Brunei; Indonesia: Kalimantan, Sumatra; Malaysia: Peninsular Malaysia, Sabah, Sarawak; Thailand

K *Prionailurus rubiginosa*
(*Felis rubiginosa*)
Rusty-spotted Cat
India; Sri Lanka

K   *Prionailurus viverrinus*
    (*Felis viverrinus, F. viverrina*)
    Fishing Cat
        Bangladesh; Bhutan; Cambodia; China; India;
        Indonesia: Bali, Java, Sumatra; Laos;
        Malaysia: Peninsular Malaysia; Nepal;
        Pakistan; Sri Lanka; Taiwan; Thailand; Viet
        Nam

K   *Profelis aurata*
    (*Felis aurata*)
    African Golden Cat
        Angola; Burkina Faso; Burundi; Cameroon;
        Central African Republic; Congo; Côte
        d'Ivoire; Equatorial Guinea; Gabon; Gambia;
        Ghana; Guinea?; Kenya; Liberia; Niger?;
        Rwanda; Senegal; Sierra Leone; Togo?;
        Uganda; Zaire

E   *Uncia uncia*
    (*Panthera uncia*)
    Snow Leopard
        Afghanistan; Bhutan; China; India;
        Kazakhstan; Kyrgyzstan; Mongolia; Nepal;
        Pakistan; Russia; Tajikistan; Uzbekistan

Family HERPESTIDAE

K   *Bdeogale jacksoni*
    Jackson's Mongoose
        Kenya; Uganda

I   *Galidictis fasciata*
    Broad-striped Mongoose
        Madagascar

R   *Galidictis grandidieri*
    (*G. grandidiensis*)
    Giant-striped Mongoose
        Madagascar

E   *Liberiictis kuhni*
    Liberian Mongoose
        Liberia; Côte d'Ivoire; Guinea

V   *Mungotictis decemlineata*
    Narrow-striped Mongoose
        Madagascar

K   *Salanoia concolor*
    Brown-tailed Mongoose
        Madagascar

Family HYAENIDAE

V   *Hyaena brunnea*
    Brown Hyaena
        Angola; Botswana; Mozambique; Namibia;
        South Africa; Zimbabwe

Family MUSTELIDAE

K   *Aonyx cinerea*
    Oriental Small-clawed Otter
        Bangladesh; Bhutan; Brunei; Cambodia;
        China; India; Indonesia: Java, Kalimantan,
        Sumatra; Laos; Malaysia: Peninsular Malaysia,
        Sabah, Sarawak; Myanmar; Nepal; Philippines:
        Palawan; Singapore; Sri Lanka; Thailand;
        Viet Nam

V   *Gulo gulo*
    Wolverine
        Canada; Estonia; Finland; Mongolia; Norway;
        Russia; Sweden; USA

V   *Lutra felina*
    (*Lontra felina*)
    Marine Otter
        Argentina; Chile; Peru

K   *Lutra perspicillata*
    Smooth-coated Otter
        Bangladesh; Bhutan; Cambodia; China; India;
        Indonesia: Java, Kalimantan, Sumatra; Iraq;
        Laos; Malaysia: Peninsular Malaysia, Sabah,
        Sarawak; Myanmar; Nepal; Pakistan; Thailand;
        Viet Nam

V   *Lutra provocax*
    Southern River Otter
        Argentina; Chile

K   *Lutra sumatrana*
    Hairy-nosed Otter
        Brunei; Cambodia; Indonesia: Bangka,
        Kalimantan, Sumatra; Laos?; Malaysia:
        Peninsular Malaysia, Sabah, Sarawak;
        Singapore; Thailand; Viet Nam

V   *Martes gwatkinsii*
    (*M. flavigula gwatkinsii*)
    Nilgiri Marten
        India

K   *Melogale everetti*
    Kinabalu Ferret-badger
        Malaysia: Sabah

I   *Mustela africana*
    Tropical Weasel
        Brazil; Colombia?; Ecuador; Peru

E   *Mustela felipei*
    Colombian Weasel
        Colombia; Ecuador

E *Mustela lutreola*
European Mink
   Belarus; Estonia; Finland (ex?); France;
   Georgia; Latvia; Lithuania; Poland (ex?);
   Romania; Russia; Spain

K *Mustela lutreolina*
Indonesian Mountain Weasel
   Indonesia: Java, Sumatra

E *Mustela nigripes*
Black-footed Ferret
   [Reintroduced in USA]

K *Mustela strigidorsa*
Back-striped Weasel
   Bhutan; China; India; Laos; Myanmar;
   Thailand; Viet Nam

K *Mydaus marchei*
Palawan Stink Badger
   Philippines: Palawan, Calamian Islands

V *Pteronura brasiliensis*
Giant Otter
   Argentina; Bolivia; Brazil; Colombia; Ecuador;
   French Guiana; Guyana; Paraguay; Peru;
   Suriname; Uruguay (ex?); Venezuela

Family OTARIIDAE

V *Arctocephalus philippii*
Juan Fernandez Fur Seal
   Chile: Juan Fernandez Archipelago

V *Arctocephalus townsendi*
Guadalupe Fur Seal
   Mexico; USA

V *Eumetopias jubatus*
Steller's Sea Lion
   Canada; Japan?; Russia; USA

R *Neophoca cinerea*
Australian Sea Lion
   Australia

V *Phocarctos hookeri*
Hooker's Sea Lion
   New Zealand: Aukland Islands

Family PHOCIDAE

E *Monachus monachus*
Mediterranean Monk Seal
   Albania; Algeria; Bulgaria; Cyprus (ex?);
   Greece; Italy: Sardinia (ex?); Lebanon (ex?);
   Libya; Mauritania; Morocco; Portugal:
   Madeira, Desertas Islands; Spain: Canary
   Islands (ex?), Chafarinas Islands; Syria (ex?);
   Tunisia: La Galite (ex?); Turkey; Western
   Sahara; Yugoslavia

E *Monachus schauinslandii*
Hawaiian Monk Seal
   USA: Hawaiian Islands

V *Phoca caspica*
Caspian Seal
   (Caspian Sea)
   Azerbaijan; Iran; Kazakhstan; Russia;
   Turkmenistan

Family PROCYONIDAE

K *Bassaricyon beddardi*
   Brazil?; Guyana; Venezuela?

I *Bassaricyon gabbii*
   Colombia; Costa Rica; Ecuador; Nicaragua;
   Panama

I *Bassaricyon lasius*
   Costa Rica

I *Bassaricyon pauli*
   Panama

V *Bassariscus sumichrasti*
   Belize; Costa Rica; El Salvador; Guatemala;
   Honduras?; Mexico; Nicaragua; Panama

I *Nasua nelsoni*
   (*N. narica nelsoni*)
Cozumel Island Coati
   Mexico: Cozumel Island

K *Nasuella olivacea*
   Colombia; Ecuador; Venezuela

I *Procyon insularis*
   (*P. lotor insularis*)
   Mexico: Tres Marias Is (Maria Madre, Maria
   Magdalena)

I *Procyon maynardi*
   (*P. lotor maynardi*)
   Bahamas: Nassau

I *Procyon minor*
   (*P. lotor minor*)
   Guadeloupe

K *Procyon pygmaeus*
   (*P. lotor pygmaeus*)
Cozumel Island Raccoon
   Mexico: Cozumel Island

Family URSIDAE

E *Ailuropoda melanoleuca*
Giant Panda
   China

V *Ailurus fulgens*
Lesser Panda
   Bhutan; China; India; Laos; Myanmar; Nepal

V **Helarctos malayanus**
(*Ursus malayanus*)
Sun Bear
Brunei; Cambodia; China; India; Indonesia: Kalimantan, Sumatra; Laos; Malaysia: Peninsular Malaysia, Sabah, Sarawak; Myanmar; Thailand; Viet Nam

V **Melursus ursinus**
(*Ursus ursinus*)
Sloth Bear
Bangladesh; Bhutan?; India; Nepal; Sri Lanka

V **Selenarctos thibetanus**
(*Ursus thibetanus*)
Asiatic Black Bear
Afghanistan; Bangladesh; Bhutan; Cambodia; China; India; Iran; Japan; Korea D.P.R; Korea Republic; Laos; Malaysia?: Peninsular Malaysia; Mongolia; Myanmar; Nepal; Pakistan; Russia; Taiwan; Thailand; Viet Nam

V **Tremarctos ornatus**
Spectacled Bear
Argentina; Bolivia; Brazil; Colombia; Ecuador; Panama; Peru; Venezuela

V **Ursus maritimus**
(*Thalarctos maritimus*)
Polar Bear
Canada; Greenland; Norway: Svalbard and Jan Mayen Islands; Russia; USA

Family VIVERRIDAE

I **Chrotogale owstoni**
Owston's Palm Civet
China; Laos; Viet Nam

K **Cryptoprocta ferox**
Fossa
Madagascar

E **Cynogale bennettii**
(includes *C. lowei*)
Otter-civet
Brunei; Indonesia: Kalimantan, Sumatra; Malaysia: Peninsular Malaysia, Sabah, Sarawak; Singapore?; Thailand; Viet Nam

I **Diplogale hosei**
Hose's Palm Civet
Malaysia: Sabah, Sarawak

V **Eupleres goudotii**
(includes *E. major*)
Falanouc
Madagascar

V **Fossa fossa**
(*F. fossana*)
Malagasy Civet
Madagascar

K **Genetta abyssinica**
Abyssinian Genet
Djibouti; Ethiopia; Somalia

E **Genetta cristata**
(*G. servalina cristata*)
Crested Genet
Cameroon; Nigeria

K **Genetta johnstoni**
Johnston's Genet
Côte d'Ivoire; Liberia; Guinea

R **Macrogalidia musschenbroekii**
Sulawesi Palm Civet
Indonesia: Sulawesi

K **Mungos gambianus**
Gambian Mongoose
Côte d'Ivoire; Gambia; Ghana; Niger; Nigeria; Senegal; Sierra Leone; Togo

V **Paradoxurus jerdoni**
Jerdon's Palm Civet
India

Order CETACEA

Family BALAENIDAE

V **Balaena mysticetus**
Bowhead Whale
(Arctic Ocean, Beaufort, Barents and Chukchi Seas; North Atlantic - arctic waters; North Pacific - arctic waters, Japan, Okhotsk and Bering Seas)

V **Eubalaena australis**
(*E. glacialis australis*; sometimes included in *Balaena*)
Southern Right Whale
(Circumpolar in Southern Hemisphere from ca 20°S to 50°S)

E **Eubalaena glacialis**
(*Balaena glacialis*)
Northern Right Whale
(Northern temperate and sub-polar waters: North Atlantic from Florida to Greenland and from Spain to Svalbard; North Pacific from China Sea to Sea of Okhotsk and from California to Bering Sea, including Hawaiian Islands)

Family BALAENOPTERIDAE

K   *Balaenoptera acutorostrata*
Minke Whale
(Widespread in all oceans but rarer in the tropics; extends into polar pack ice; recorded from Baltic and Black Seas)

V   *Balaenoptera borealis*
Sei Whale
(Widespread in most oceans and seas, favouring temperate oceanic waters)

K   *Balaenoptera edeni*
Bryde's Whale
(Circum-equatorial in tropical and warm temperate waters between ca 40°N and 40°S)

E   *Balaenoptera musculus*
Blue Whale
(Occurs in all major oceans, especially cold and temperate waters)

V   *Balaenoptera physalus*
Fin Whale
(Occurs in all major oceans, extending to pack ice zones but rare in warmest waters at latitudes less than about 20°)

V   *Megaptera novaeangliae*
Humpback Whale
(Found in all major oceans from Arctic to Antarctic, but absent from pack ice zones)

Family NEOBALAENIDAE

K   *Caperea marginata*
Pygmy Right Whale
(Temperate waters of the Southern Hemisphere between ca 31°S and 52°S)

Family DELPHINIDAE

K   *Cephalorhynchus commersonii*
Commerson's Dolphin
(Coastal temperate waters off southern South America and some South Atlantic and southern Indian Ocean islands)
Argentina; Chile; Falkland Islands; French Southern and Antarctic Territories: Kerguelen Islands

K   *Cephalorhynchus eutropia*
Black Dolphin
(Cold, inshore waters of Chile, between 33°S and 55°S)
Chile

K   *Cephalorhynchus heavisidii*
Heaviside's Dolphin
(Cold, inshore waters of Benguela current, South Atlantic)
Angola?; Namibia; South Africa

I   *Cephalorhynchus hectori*
White-headed Dolphin, Hector's Dolphin
(Coastal waters of New Zealand)
New Zealand

K   *Delphinus delphis*
(includes *Delphinus tropicalis*)
Common Dolphin
(Recorded from all warm temperate and tropical waters, including the Mediterranean and Black Seas)

K   *Feresa attenuata*
(*F. occulta*)
Pygmy Killer Whale
(Recorded sporadically from warm temperate and tropical waters, including North and South Atlantic, Indian Ocean and North Pacific)

K   *Globicephala macrorhynchus*
(*G. sieboldii*)
Short-finned Pilot Whale
(Warm temperate and tropical waters, including Atlantic, Pacific and Indian Oceans)

K   *Globicephala melas*
(*Globicephala melaena*; includes *G. edwardii*)
Long-finned Pilot Whale
(Occurs in two separate populations, the southern being circumpolar in cool temperate waters of Atlantic, Pacific and Indian Oceans north of the Antarctic Convergence; the North Atlantic population extending from USA and the Mediterranean to the Barents Sea. Apparently absent from North Pacific)

K   *Grampus griseus*
Risso's Dolphin
(Worldwide distribution in tropical and warm temperate waters)

K   *Lagenodelphis hosei*
Fraser's Dolphin
(Circum-equatorial in oceanic tropical waters)

K   *Lagenorhynchus acutus*
Atlantic White-sided Dolphin
(Northern North Atlantic, including North and Baltic Seas; vagrants further south)

K   *Lagenorhynchus albirostris*
White-beaked Dolphin
(North Atlantic and western Arctic from the USA and Spain to Svalbard, including the Baltic, Davis Strait and Barents Sea)

K   *Lagenorhynchus australis*
Peale's Dolphin
(Cold, coastal waters of southern South America)
Argentina; Chile; Falkland Islands

K **Lagenorhynchus cruciger**
Hourglass Dolphin
(Circumpolar in Antarctic and sub-Antarctic, recorded from high southern latitudes to the edge of the pack ice)

K **Lagenorhynchus obliquidens**
Pacific White-sided Dolphin
(Temperate waters of the North Pacific)

K **Lagenorhynchus obscurus**
(includes *L. superciliosus*)
Dusky Dolphin
(Temperate and cold temperate circumpolar waters near land masses in the Southern Hemisphere)
Argentina; Chile; Falkland Islands; French Southern and Antarctic Territories: Kerguelen Islands; New Zealand: Campbell and Auckland Islands; Peru; South Africa

K **Lissodelphis borealis**
Northern Right Whale Dolphin
(Temperate waters of the North Pacific)

K **Lissodelphis peronii**
Southern Right Whale Dolphin
(Circumpolar in temperate waters of the Southern Hemisphere, extending to 19°S off Chile and to Indonesia)

K **Orcaella brevirostris**
Irrawaddy Dolphin
(Coastal waters from Bay of Bengal to South-east Asia and Australia, including major rivers - Ganges, Brahmaputra and Irrawaddy)
Australia; Bangladesh; Brunei?; Cambodia; India; Indonesia: Java, Kalimantan, Sumatra; Laos?; Malaysia: Sabah, Sarawak; Myanmar; Papua New Guinea; Philippines?; Singapore?; Thailand; Viet Nam

K **Orcinus orca**
(includes *O. glacialis*)
Killer Whale
(Reported from all sea areas, especially in cooler regions; extending well into the pack ice zone)

K **Peponocephala electra**
Melon-headed Whale
(Widespread scattered records from warm temperate and tropical seas)

K **Pseudorca crassidens**
False Killer Whale
(Widespread, mainly in warm waters but strandings as far north as the Baltic)

K **Sotalia fluviatilis**
(includes *S. brasiliensis*, *S. guianensis*)
Tucuxi
(All major rivers in the Amazon system, extending to Central America)
Bolivia?; Brazil; Colombia; Ecuador; French Guiana; Guyana; Panama; Peru; Suriname; Trinidad and Tobago; Venezuela

K **Sousa chinensis**
(includes *S. borneensis, S. lentiginosa, S. plumbea*)
Indo-Pacific Hump-backed Dolphin
(Coastal and inshore waters of the Indian and western Pacific Ocean, including Red Sea and Arabian Gulf to South-east Asia and south China coast; occurs in estuaries and occasionally lower reaches of rivers)
Australia; Bahrain; Bangladesh; Brunei; Cambodia; China; Djibouti; Egypt; Ethiopia; Hong Kong; India; Indonesia; Iran; Iraq; Israel; Kenya; Kuwait; Madagascar; Malaysia: Sarawak; Mozambique; Myanmar; Oman; Pakistan; Papua New Guinea; Philippines; Qatar; Saudi Arabia; Somalia; South Africa; Sri Lanka; Sudan; Taiwan; Tanzania; Thailand; United Arab Emirates; Viet Nam; Yemen

K **Sousa teuszii**
Atlantic Hump-backed Dolphin
(West coast of Africa, from Angola to Mauritania; enters rivers)
Angola?; Benin; Cameroon; Congo?; Côte d'Ivoire; Equatorial Guinea?; Gabon?; Gambia; Ghana; Guinea; Guinea-Bissau; Liberia; Mauritania; Nigeria; Senegal; Sierra Leone; Togo; Zaire?

K **Stenella attenuata**
Pantropical Spotted Dolphin
(Widespread in warm deep waters)

K **Stenella clymene**
Helmet Dolphin, Clymene Dolphin
(Tropical and subtropical waters of North Atlantic)

K **Stenella coeruleoalba**
(includes *S. styx*)
Striped Dolphin
(Widespread in tropical, subtropical and warm temperate waters)

K **Stenella frontalis**
(*S. plagiodon*, *S. attenuata frontalis*)
Atlantic Spotted Dolphin
(Tropical, subtropical and warm temperate Atlantic)

K *Stenella longirostris*
(includes *S. microps*, *S. roseiventris*)
Long-snouted Dolphin, Spinner Dolphin
(Circum-equatorial in tropical and subtropical waters, occasionally in warm temperate waters)

K *Steno bredanensis*
Rough-toothed Dolphin
(Widespread in tropical and warm temperate ocean areas, including Red, Caribbean, Mediterranean and North Seas)

K *Tursiops truncatus*
(includes *T. aduncus*, *T. gilli*, *T. nuuanu*)
Bottlenose Dolphin
(Known from all temperate and tropical marine areas)

Family MONODONTIDAE

K *Delphinapterus leucas*
White Whale, Beluga
(Circumpolar in Arctic and sub-Arctic with scattered records to France and Japan; often in estuaries)
Canada; Greenland; Norway: including Svalbard and Jan Mayen Islands; Russia; USA
(excludes vagrants)

K *Monodon monoceros*
Narwhal
(Circumpolar and virtually confined to limits of Arctic pack ice; vagrants as far south as the United Kingdom)
Canada; Greenland; Iceland; Norway: including Svalbard and Jan Mayen Islands; Russia; USA
(excludes vagrants)

Family PHOCOENIDAE

K *Australophocaena dioptrica*
(*Phocoena dioptrica*)
Spectacled Porpoise
(Coastal waters of southern South America and Southern Ocean islands)
Argentina; Australia: Macquarie Island; Chile; Falkland Islands: including South Georgia; French Southern and Antarctic Territories: Kerguelen Islands; New Zealand: Auckland Islands; Uruguay

K *Neophocaena phocaenoides*
Finless Porpoise
(Coastal and freshwater Indo-Pacific from China and Japan to the Gulf of Arabia, including South-East Asian archipelago)
Bahrain; Bangladesh; Brunei?; Cambodia; China; Hong Kong?; India; Indonesia; Iran; Iraq; Japan; Korea D.P.R; Korea Republic; Kuwait; Malaysia: Sabah, Sarawak; Myanmar; Oman; Pakistan; Philippines; Qatar; Saudi Arabia; Singapore?; South Africa?; Sri Lanka; Taiwan; Thailand; United Arab Emirates; Viet Nam

K *Phocoena phocoena*
(includes *P. vomerina*)
Common Porpoise, Harbour Porpoise
(Coastal waters of North Pacific, North Atlantic and Arctic Oceans, from Japan and California to Chukchi Sea, and from Baffin Island to west Africa, including Baltic, Mediterranean and Black Seas)
Belgium; Bulgaria; Canada; Cape Verde; China?; Denmark; Faeroe Islands; Finland; France; Germany; Georgia; Greenland; Iceland; Ireland; Japan; Korea D.P.R.; Korea Republic; Mauritania; Mexico; Morocco; Netherlands; Norway; Poland; Portugal: including Azores; Romania; Russia; Senegal; Spain; Sweden; Tunisia; Turkey; Ukraine; United Kingdom; USA

E *Phocoena sinus*
Vaquita
(Northern half of Gulf of California)
Mexico

K *Phocoena spinipinnis*
Burmeister's Porpoise
(Coastal South America)
Argentina; Brazil; Chile; Peru; Uruguay

K *Phocoenoides dalli*
Dall's Porpoise
(North Pacific from Japan and Mexico to Bering Sea)
Canada; Japan; Korea D.P.R; Korea Republic; Mexico; Russia; USA

Family PHYSETERIDAE

K *Kogia breviceps*
Pygmy Sperm Whale
(Recorded from nearly all temperate, subtropical and tropical waters)

K *Kogia simus*
Dwarf Sperm Whale
(Recorded from nearly all temperate, subtropical and tropical waters)

K *Physeter catodon*
(*P. macrocephalus*)
Sperm Whale
(Found in all major oceans, from Arctic to Antarctic, including semi land-locked seas such as Mediterranean)

Family PLATANISTIDAE

V **Inia geoffrensis**
Boto, Amazon River Dolphin
(Found in all major rivers of the Orinoco and Amazon systems)
Bolivia; Brazil; Colombia; Ecuador; Guyana?; Peru; Venezuela

E **Lipotes vexillifer**
Baiji, Yangtse River Dolphin
(Only found in the Chiangjiang River of China, may occasionally enter other rivers during times of flood)
China

V **Platanista gangetica**
Ganges River Dolphin
(Ganges and Brahmaputra river systems)
Bangladesh; Bhutan; India; Nepal

E **Platanista minor**
(*P. indi*, *P. gangetica minor*)
Indus River Dolphin
(Indus River)
Pakistan

K **Pontoporia blainvillei**
La Plata River Dolphin
(La Plata estuary and adjacent rivers and coasts)
Argentina; Brazil; Uruguay

Family ZIPHIIDAE

K **Berardius arnuxii**
Arnoux's Beaked Whale
(Cool temperate sub-Antarctic and Antarctic waters)

K **Berardius bairdii**
Baird's Beaked Whale
(Apparently confined to deep waters of North Pacific)

K **Hyperoodon ampullatus**
(*H. rostratus*)
Northern Bottlenose Whale
(Deep waters of the northern North Atlantic)

K **Hyperoodon planifrons**
Southern Bottlenose Whale
(Entire Southern Ocean north to ca 30°S)

K **Indopacetus pacificus**
(*Mesoplodon pacificus*)
Indo-Pacific Beaked Whale
(Probable Indo-Pacific distribution, known only from 2 skulls found on beaches in Australia and Somalia and a possible sighting in the Seychelles)

K **Mesoplodon bidens**
Sowerby's Beaked Whale
(Cold temperate waters of the North Atlantic, mostly around British Isles)

K **Mesoplodon bowdoini**
Splaytooth Beaked Whale, Andrews' Beaked Whale
(Temperate South Pacific and southern Indian Ocean)

K **Mesoplodon carlhubbsi**
(*M. bowdoini carlhubbsi*)
Arch-beaked Whale, Hubbs' Beaked Whale
(Cold temperate North Pacific)

K **Mesoplodon densirostris**
Blainville's Beaked Whale
(Circum-equatorial; temperate and tropical waters)

K **Mesoplodon europaeus**
Gervais' Beaked Whale
(North Atlantic, where population probably concentrated in south-west)

K **Mesoplodon ginkgodens**
Ginkgo-toothed Beaked Whale
(Warm temperate and tropical Pacific and Indian Oceans)

K **Mesoplodon grayi**
Gray's Beaked Whale
(Circumpolar in Southern Hemisphere, south of 30°S, but mainly around New Zealand)

K **Mesoplodon hectori**
Hector's Beaked Whale
(Temperate latitudes of Southern Hemisphere and temperate eastern North Pacific)

K **Mesoplodon layardii**
Layard's Beaked Whale, Strap-toothed Whale
(Circumpolar distribution in Southern Hemisphere between ca 30°S and Antarctic convergence)

K **Mesoplodon mirus**
True's Beaked Whale
(North Atlantic and temperate waters in Southern Hemisphere)

K **Mesoplodon peruvianus**
Lesser Beaked Whale
(Eastern South Pacific and eastern North Pacific: cold temperate to tropical waters)

K **Mesoplodon stejnegeri**
Stejneger's Beaked Whale
(Cold temperate waters of the North Pacific)

K   *Tasmacetus shepherdi*
Shepherd's Beaked Whale
(Cooler waters of the Southern Hemisphere
between 33°S and 50°S)

K   *Ziphius cavirostris*
Cuvier's Beaked Whale
(Widespread in all major oceans, but rarely
found in polar regions)

Order SIRENIA

Family DUGONGIDAE

V   *Dugong dugon*
Dugong
(Shallow tropical and subtropical coastal and
inland waters of the Indian and western Pacific
Oceans from east Africa and the Red Sea to
Vanuatu)
Australia; Bahrain; Bangladesh; Brunei?;
Cambodia; China; Comoros?; Djibouti; Egypt;
Ethiopia; Federated States of Micronesia: Yap;
Guam; India; Indonesia; Iran; Iraq; Israel;
Japan: Ryukyu Islands; Jordan; Kenya;
Kuwait; Madagascar; Malaysia: Peninsular
Malaysia, Sabah, Sarawak; Mauritius;
Mozambique; Myanmar; New Caledonia;
Oman; Pakistan; Palau; Papua New Guinea;
Philippines; Saudi Arabia; Singapore; Solomon
Islands; Somalia; South Africa; Sri Lanka;
Sudan; Taiwan; Tanzania; Thailand; United
Arab Emirates; Vanuatu; Viet Nam; Yemen

Family TRICHECHIDAE

V   *Trichechus inunguis*
Amazonian Manatee
(Major rivers of the Amazon drainage basin)
Brazil; Colombia; Ecuador; Peru; Venezuela

V   *Trichechus manatus*
Caribbean Manatee
(Tropical and subtropical coastal waters and
rivers of the Caribbean and Atlantic regions of
the Americas)
Bahamas; Belize; Brazil; Colombia; Costa
Rica; Cuba; Dominican Republic; French
Guiana; Guatemala; Guyana; Haiti; Honduras;
Jamaica; Mexico; Nicaragua; Panama; Puerto
Rico; Suriname; Trinidad and Tobago; USA;
Venezuela

V   *Trichechus senegalensis*
African Manatee
(River systems of West Africa)
Angola; Benin (ex?); Cameroon; Chad; Congo;
Côte d'Ivoire; Equatorial Guinea; Gabon;
Gambia; Ghana; Guinea?; Guinea-Bissau?;
Liberia; Mali; Mauritania; Niger; Nigeria;
Senegal; Sierra Leone; Togo; Zaire

Order PROBOSCIDEA

Family ELEPHANTIDAE

E   *Elephas maximus*
Indian Elephant
Bangladesh; Bhutan; Brunei; Cambodia;
China; India; Indonesia: Kalimantan, Sumatra;
Laos; Malaysia: Peninsular Malaysia, Sabah;
Myanmar; Nepal; Sri Lanka; Thailand;
Viet Nam

V   *Loxodonta africana*
African Elephant
Angola; Benin; Botswana; Burkina Faso;
Cameroon; Central African Republic; Chad;
Congo; Côte d'Ivoire; Equatorial Guinea;
Ethiopia; Gabon; Ghana; Guinea; Kenya;
Liberia; Malawi; Mali; Mauritania;
Mozambique; Namibia; Niger; Nigeria;
Rwanda; Senegal; Sierra Leone; Somalia;
South Africa; Sudan; Tanzania; Togo; Uganda;
Zaire; Zambia; Zimbabwe

Order PERISSODACTYLA

Family EQUIDAE

E   *Equus africanus*
(sometimes given the same name as the domestic
donkey or ass *E. asinus*)
African Wild Ass
Ethiopia; Somalia
(Free-living animals of uncertain pedigree
occur elsewhere in northern Africa)

E   *Equus grevyi*
Grevy's Zebra
Ethiopia; Kenya

V   *Equus hemionus*
Asian Wild Ass (Kulan, Khur, Onager,
Dziggetai)
China; India; Iran; Kazakhstan; Mongolia;
Turkmenistan
[Reintroduced in: Israel; Uzbekistan]

V   *Equus zebra*
Mountain Zebra
Angola; Namibia; South Africa

Family TAPIRIDAE

V   *Tapirus bairdii*
Central American Tapir
Belize; Colombia; Costa Rica; Ecuador;
Guatemala; Honduras; Mexico (ex?);
Nicaragua; Panama

E **Tapirus indicus**
Malayan Tapir
Indonesia: Sumatra; Laos; Malaysia: Peninsular Malaysia; Myanmar; Thailand; Viet Nam

E **Tapirus pinchaque**
(*T. roulini*)
Mountain Tapir
Colombia; Ecuador; Peru; Venezuela

Family RHINOCEROTIDAE

V **Ceratotherium simum**
White Rhinoceros
South Africa; Zaire
[Reintroduced in: Botswana; Kenya; Namibia; Swaziland; Zambia (ex?); Zimbabwe]

E **Dicerorhinus sumatrensis**
(*Didermocerus sumatrensis*)
Sumatran Rhinoceros
Cambodia (ex?); India (ex?); Indonesia: Kalimantan, Sumatra; Laos (ex?); Malaysia: Peninsular Malaysia, Sabah, Sarawak; Myanmar; Thailand; Viet Nam

E **Diceros bicornis**
Black Rhinoceros
Angola; Botswana; Cameroon; Central African Republic (ex?); Chad (ex?); Congo (ex?); Ethiopia (ex?); Kenya; Malawi (ex?); Mozambique; Namibia; Nigeria (ex?); Rwanda; South Africa; Sudan (ex?); Swaziland; Tanzania; Zambia; Zimbabwe

E **Rhinoceros sondaicus**
Javan Rhinoceros
Cambodia; Indonesia: Java; Laos; Myanmar (ex?); Thailand (ex?); Viet Nam

E **Rhinoceros unicornis**
Great Indian Rhinoceros
Bhutan; India; Nepal

Order HYRACOIDEA

Family PROCAVIIDAE

I **Dendrohyrax validus**
Eastern Tree Hyrax
Kenya; Tanzania: including Pemba Island, Zanzibar

Order ARTIODACTYLA

Family SUIDAE

V **Babyrousa babyrussa**
Babirusa
Indonesia: Buru, Sula Islands, Sulawesi, Togian Islands

E **Sus cebifrons**
(*Sus barbatus cebifrons*)
Visayan Warty Pig
Philippines: Cebu and Negros Islands

E **Sus salvanius**
Pygmy Hog
Bhutan (ex?); India; Nepal (ex?)

V **Sus verrucosus**
Javan Warty Pig
Indonesia: Bawean Island, Java

Family TAYASSUIDAE

E **Catagonus wagneri**
Chacoan Peccary
Argentina; Bolivia; Paraguay

Family HIPPOPOTAMIDAE

V **Hexaprotodon liberiensis**
(*Choeropsis liberiensis*)
Pygmy Hippopotamus
Côte d'Ivoire; Guinea; Guinea-Bissau?; Liberia; Sierra Leone

Family CAMELIDAE

V **Camelus bactrianus**
(*C. ferus*)
Wild Bactrian Camel
China; Mongolia

V **Vicugna vicugna**
Vicuña
Argentina; Bolivia; Chile; Peru,

Family MOSCHIDAE

E **Moschus moschiferus**
(*M. sibiricus*, includes *M. anhueiensis*)
Siberian Musk Deer
China; Korea D.P.R; Korea Republic; Mongolia; Russia

Family CERVIDAE

E **Axis calamianensis**
(*Axis porcinus calamianensis*, sometimes included in *Cervus*)
Calamian Hog Deer
Philippines: Calamian Islands

E **Axis kuhlii**
(*Axis porcinus kuhli*, sometimes included in *Cervus*)
Kuhl's Hog Deer, Bawean Deer
Indonesia: Bawean Island

V **Blastocerus dichotomus**
Marsh Deer
Argentina; Bolivia; Brazil; Paraguay; Peru

V **Cervus albirostris**
Thorold's Deer
China

E **Cervus alfredi**
(*C. unicolor alfredi*)
Visayan Spotted Deer
Philippines: Visayan Islands

E **Cervus duvauceli**
Swamp Deer
India; Nepal

V **Cervus eldii**
Thamin
Cambodia; China (ex?); India; Laos;
Myanmar; Thailand; Viet Nam

R **Cervus mariannus**
Philippine Brown Deer
Philippines

E **Dama mesopotamica**
(*Dama dama mesopotamica*, sometimes included
in *Cervus*)
Persian Fallow Deer
Iran; Iraq (ex?)

E **Elaphurus davidianus**
Père David's Deer
[Captive populations only, reintroduction in
progress in China]

V **Hippocamelus antisensis**
North Andean Huemul
Argentina; Bolivia; Chile; Peru

E **Hippocamelus bisulcus**
South Andean Huemul
Argentina; Chile

V **Hydropotes inermis**
Chinese Water Deer
China; Korea D.P.R; Korea Republic
[France; United Kingdom]

I **Mazama chunyi**
Chunyi
Bolivia; Peru

V **Muntiacus crinifrons**
Black Muntjac
China

E **Muntiacus feae**
Fea's Muntjac
China; Myanmar; Thailand

I **Muntiacus gongshanensis**
Gongshan Muntjac
China; Myanmar?

K **Ozotoceros bezoarticus**
Pampas Deer
Argentina; Bolivia; Brazil; Paraguay; Uruguay

I **Pudu mephistophiles**
Northern Pudu
Colombia; Ecuador; Peru

K **Pudu puda**
Southern Pudu
Argentina; Chile

Family BOVIDAE

E **Addax nasomaculatus**
Addax
Algeria (ex?); Chad; Egypt (ex?); Libya (ex?);
Mali; Mauritania; Niger; Sudan (ex?)

V **Ammodorcas clarkei**
Dibatag
Ethiopia; Somalia

I **Ammotragus lervia**
Aoudad
Algeria; Chad; Libya; Mali; Mauritania (ex?);
Morocco (ex?); Niger; Sudan; Tunisia (ex?)
[USA]

V **Antilope cervicapra**
Blackbuck
India, Nepal, Pakistan
[Argentina; USA]

V **Bison bonasus**
(*B. bison bonasus*)
European Bison
[Reintroduced in: Belarus; Lithuania; Moldova;
Poland; Romania; Russia; Ukraine]

V **Bos gaurus**
(alternatively given the same name as the
domestic Gayal or Mithan *B. frontalis*)
Gaur
Bangladesh; Bhutan; Cambodia; China; India;
Laos; Malaysia: Peninsular Malaysia;
Myanmar; Nepal; Thailand; Viet Nam

V **Bos javanicus**
(*B. banteng*)
Banteng
Bangladesh (ex?); Cambodia?; Indonesia: Bali,
Java, Kalimantan; Laos; Malaysia: Peninsular
Malaysia (ex?), Sabah; Myanmar; Thailand;
Viet Nam

E **Bos mutus**
(alternatively given the same name as the
domestic Yak *B. grunniens*)
Wild Yak
Afghanistan?; Bhutan?; China; India; Nepal

E ***Bos sauveli***
(*Novibos sauveli*)
Kouprey
   Cambodia; Laos; Thailand (ex?); Viet Nam

E ***Bubalus arnee***
(alternatively given the same name as the domestic buffalo *B. bubalus*)
Wild Water Buffalo
   Bhutan; India; Nepal; Thailand
   (Free-living animals of uncertain pedigree occur in adjacent countries)

E ***Bubalus depressicornis***
(*Anoa depressicornis*)
Lowland Anoa
   Indonesia: Sulawesi

E ***Bubalus mindorensis***
(*Anoa mindorensis*)
Tamaraw
   Philippines: Mindoro

E ***Bubalus quarlesi***
(*Anoa quarlesi*)
Mountain Anoa
   Indonesia: Sulawesi, Buton

R ***Capra caucasica***
(*C. ibex caucasica*)
Kuban, West Caucasian Tur
   Georgia; Russia

R ***Capra cylindricornis***
Daghestan Tur, East Caucasian Tur
   Azerbaijan?; Georgia; Russia

E ***Capra falconeri***
Markhor
   Afghanistan; India; Pakistan; Tajikistan; Turkmenistan; Uzbekistan

I ***Capra nubiana***
(*C. ibex nubiana*)
Nubian Ibex
   Egypt; Ethiopia; Israel; Jordan; Oman; Saudi Arabia; Sudan; Yemen

E ***Capra walia***
(*C. ibex walia*)
Walia Ibex
   Ethiopia

I ***Capricornis sumatraensis***
(*Naemorhedus sumatraensis*)
Mainland Serow
   Bangladesh; Bhutan; Cambodia; China; India; Indonesia: Sumatra; Laos; Malaysia; Myanmar; Nepal; Thailand; Viet Nam

V ***Capricornis swinhoei***
(*Naemorhedus swinhoei*)
Formosan Serow
   Taiwan

V ***Cephalophus adersi***
Aders' Duiker
   Kenya; Tanzania: Zanzibar

E ***Cephalophus jentinki***
Jentink's Duiker
   Côte d'Ivoire; Liberia; Sierra Leone

V ***Cepahlophus ogilbyi***
Ogilby's Duiker
   Cameroon; Congo?; Côte d'Ivoire; Equatorial Guinea: Bioko; Gabon; Ghana; Guinea?; Liberia; Nigeria; Sierra Leone

V ***Cephalophus spadix***
Abbott's Duiker
   Tanzania

V ***Cephalophus zebra***
Zebra Duiker
   Côte d'Ivoire; Liberia; Sierra Leone

V ***Connochaetes gnou***
Black Wildebeest
   Lesotho; South Africa; Swaziland

E ***Damaliscus hunteri***
Hirola
   Kenya; Somalia

K ***Dorcatragus megalotis***
Beira Antelope
   Djibouti?; Ethiopia; Somalia

V ***Gazella bennetti***
Chinkara
   Afghanistan?; India; Iran; Pakistan

E ***Gazella cuvieri***
Cuvier's Gazelle
   Algeria; Morocco; Tunisia

E ***Gazella dama***
Dama Gazelle
   Algeria (ex?); Burkina Faso; Chad; Mali; Niger; Sudan

V ***Gazella dorcas***
Dorcas Gazelle
   Algeria; Burkina Faso; Chad; Djibouti; Egypt; Eritrea; Ethiopia; Israel; Jordan?; Libya; Mali; Mauritania; Morocco; Niger; Nigeria; Saudi Arabia?; Senegal; Somalia; Sudan; Tunisia; Western Sahara

V **Gazella gazella**
Mountain Gazelle
Israel; Jordan; Lebanon?; Oman; Saudi Arabia;
Syria?; Yemen

E **Gazella leptoceros**
Slender-horned Gazelle
Algeria; Chad; Egypt; Libya; Mali;
Mauritania?; Niger; Sudan; Tunisia; Western
Sahara?

V **Gazella rufifrons**
Red-fronted Gazelle
Burkina Faso; Cameroon; Central African
Republic; Chad; Eritrea; Ethiopia; Gambia?;
Ghana?; Mali; Mauritania; Niger; Nigeria;
Senegal; Sudan; Togo

V **Gazella soemmerringii**
Soemmerring's Gazelle
Djibouti; Eritrea; Ethiopia; Kenya; Somalia;
Sudan

V **Gazella spekei**
Speke's Gazelle
Ethiopia; Somalia

K **Hemitragus jemlahicus**
Himalayan Tahr
China; India; Nepal

V **Hemitragus hylocrius**
Nilgiri Tahr
India

V **Hemitragus jayakari**
Arabian Tahr
Oman; United Arab Emirates?: Abu Dhabi

V **Kobus leche**
Lechwe
Angola; Botswana; Namibia; Zaire; Zambia
[South Africa]

V **Kobus megaceros**
Nile Lechwe
Ethiopia; Sudan

K **Madoqua piacentinii**
Silver Dikdik
Somalia

I **Naemorhedus caudatus**
Long-tailed Goral
China; Korea D.P.R; Korea Republic; Laos;
Russia; Thailand

E **Oryx dammah**
(*O. tao*)
Scimitar-horned Oryx
Chad

E **Oryx leucoryx**
Arabian Oryx
[Reintroduced in Oman]

K **Procapra przewalskii**
Przewalski's Gazelle
China

E **Pseudois schaeferi**
(*P. nayaur schaeferi*)
Dwarf Blue Sheep
China

E **Pseudoryx nghetinhensis**
Vu Quang Ox
Laos?; Viet Nam

V **Tetracerus quadricornis**
Four-horned Antelope
India; Nepal

E **Tragelaphus buxtoni**
Mountain Nyala
Ethiopia

V **Tragelaphus derbianus**
(*Taurotragus derbianus*)
Giant Eland
Cameroon; Central African Republic; Chad?;
Guinea?; Guinea Bissau; Mali?; Nigeria?;
Senegal; Sudan; Uganda?; Zaire

Order RODENTIA

Family SCIURIDAE

E **Cynomys mexicanus**
Mexican Prairie Dog
Mexico

V **Cynomys parvidens**
Utah Prairie Dog
USA

K **Epixerus ebii**
Côte d'Ivoire; Ghana; Liberia; Sierra Leone

V **Funisciurus carruthersi**
Carruther's Mountain Squirrel
Burundi; Rwanda; Uganda; Zaire?

V **Marmota menzbieri**
Menzbier's Marmot
Kazakhstan; Tajikistan; Turkmenistan;
Uzbekistan

E **Marmota vancouverensis**
Vancouver Island Marmot
Canada: Vancouver Island

V **Myosciurus pumilio**
African Pygmy Squirrel
Cameroon; Equatorial Guinea: Bioko; Gabon;
Nigeria

R   *Paraxerus vexillarius*
     Tanzania

R   *Pteromys momonga*
     Small Japanese Flying-squirrel
     Japan

K   *Syntheosciurus brochus*
     Mountain Squirrel
      Costa Rica; Panama

Family GEOMYIDAE

I   *Zygogeomys trichopus*
     Michoacan Pocket Gopher
     Mexico

Family HETEROMYIDAE

R   *Dipodomys elator*
     Texas Kangaroo-rat
     USA

E   *Dipodomys gravipes*
     San Quintin Kangaroo Rat
     Mexico

I   *Dipodomys ingens*
     Giant Kangaroo Rat
     USA

E   *Dipodomys stephensi*
     Stephens' Kangaroo Rat
     USA

V   *Perognathus alticola*
     (*Perognathus parvus alticola*)
     White-eared Pocket Mouse
     USA

Family DIPODIDAE

V   *Allactaga tetradactyla*
     Egypt; Libya

Family MURIDAE

I   *Abrawayaomys ruschi*
     Brazil

R   *Aethomys silindensis*
     Selinda Veld Rat
      Mozambique?; Zimbabwe

K   *Ammodillus imbellis*
      Ethiopia; Somalia

K   *Anonymomys mindorensis*
     Mindoro Climbing Rat
      Philippines: Mindoro

R   *Archboldomys luzonensis*
     Mt Isarog Shrew-mouse
      Philippines: Luzon

I   *Batomys granti*
     Luzon Forest Rat
      Philippines: Luzon

V   *Beamys hindei*
     Lesser Hamster-rat
      Kenya; Tanzania

V   *Beamys major*
     (*B. hindei major*)
     Greater Hamster-rat
      Malawi; Tanzania; Zambia

R   *Chrotomys gonzalesi*
     Mt Isarog Striped Rat
      Philippines: Luzon

K   *Crateromys australis*
     Dinagat Island Cloud Rat
      Philippines: Dinagat Island

R   *Crateromys schadenbergi*
     Giant Bushy-tailed Cloud Rat
      Philippines: Luzon

K   *Crateromys* sp.
     Panay Bushy-tailed Cloud Rat
      Philippines: Panay

R   *Delanymys brooksi*
     Delany's Mouse
      Rwanda; Uganda; Zaire

R   *Dendromus kahuziensis*
     Zaire

R   *Dendroprionomys rousseloti*
     Congo

V   *Diplothrix legatus*
     Ryukyu Long-tailed Giant Rat
      Japan: Nasei-shoto

K   *Eliurus minor*
     Madagascar

K   *Gerbillus acticola*
     Somalia

K   *Gerbillus maghrebi*
     (*Dipodillus maghrebi*)
     Morocco

K   *Gerbillus mauritaniae*
     Mauritania

K   *Gerbillus muriculus*
     (*G. nanus muriculus*)
     Sudan

K   *Gerbillus nancillus*
     Sudan

K   *Gerbillus rosalinda*
     Sudan

R   *Gymnuromys roberti*
      Madagascar

R   *Hylomyscus baeri*
      Côte d'Ivoire; Ghana

K   *Hylomyscus fumosus*
      Cameroon; Central African Republic; Gabon

K   *Hylomyscus parvus*
      Cameroon; Congo; Gabon

K   *Hypogeomys antimena*
      Madagascar

E   *Juscelinomys candango*
      Brazil

I   *Kunsia tomentosus*
      Bolivia; Brazil

K   *Leggadina lakedownensis*
      Lakeland Downs Mouse
      Australia

R   *Lemniscomys mittendorfi*
      (*L. striatus mittendorfi*)
      Cameroon

R   *Leporillus conditor*
      Greater Stick-nest Rat
      Australia: Franklin Island

K   *Lophuromys cinereus*
      Zaire

R   *Lophuromys medicaudatus*
      Rwanda; Zaire

R   *Lophuromys melanonyx*
      Ethiopia

R   *Lophuromys rahmi*
      Rwanda; Zaire

K   *Macrotarsomys ingens*
      Madagascar

K   *Macruromys elegans*
      Western Small-toothed Rat
      Indonesia: Irian Jaya

K   *Malacomys verschureni*
      Zaire

K   *Mastomys pernanus*
      Kenya; Rwanda; Tanzania

R   *Megadendromus nikolausi*
      Ethiopia

K   *Melomys albidens*
      White-toothed Melomys
      Indonesia: Irian Jaya

K   *Microdillus peeli*
      Somalia

R   *Microtus breweri*
      (*M. pennsylvanicus breweri*)
      Beach Vole
      USA: Muskeget Island

V   *Muriculus imberbis*
      Ethiopia

K   *Myomys ruppi*
      (*Praomys ruppi*)
      Ethiopia

E   *Neotoma anthonyi*
      Anthony's Woodrat
      Mexico: Todos Santos Island

E   *Neotoma bunkeri*
      (*N. lepida bunkeri*)
      Bunker's Woodrat
      Mexico

E   *Neotoma martinensis*
      San Martin Island Woodrat
      Mexico: San Martin Island

K   *Notomys aquilo*
      (includes *N. carpentarius*)
      Northern Hopping-mouse
      Australia

V   *Notomys fuscus*
      Dusky Hopping-mouse
      Australia

V   *Pelomys hopkinsi*
      Kenya; Rwanda; Uganda

V   *Pelomys isseli*
      Uganda: Bugala, Bunyama, Kome Islands
      (Lake Victoria)

E   *Phaenomys ferrugineus*
      Brazil

R   *Phaulomys andersoni*
      (*P. imaizumii*, *P. niigatae*, sometimes referred to
      Eothenomys or *Clethrionomys*)
      Wakayama Red-backed Vole
      Japan: Honshu

R   *Phloeomys cumingi*
      Southern Giant Slender-tailed Cloud Rat
      Philippines

R   *Praomys hartwigi*
      Cameroon; Nigeria

R   *Prionomys batesi*
      Dollman's Tree Mouse
      Cameroon; Central African Republic

R **Pseudomys fumeus**
Smoky Mouse
Australia

R **Pseudomys occidentalis**
Western Mouse
Australia

R **Pseudomys oralis**
Hastings River Mouse
Australia

I **Pseudomys pilligaensis**
Pilliga Mouse
Australia

R **Pseudomys praeconis**
Shark Bay Mouse
Australia

V **Pseudomys shortridgei**
Heath Rat
Australia

R **Rattus giluwensis**
Giluwe Rat
Papua New Guinea

K **Rattus tawitawiensis**
Tawitawi Island Rat
Philippines: Tawitawi Island

E **Reithrodontomys raviventris**
Saltmarsh Harvest Mouse
USA

E **Rhagomys rufescens**
Brazil

R **Rhynchomys isarogensis**
Mt Isarog Shrew-rat
Philippines: Luzon

E **Solomys ponceleti**
Poncelet's Giant Rat
Papua New Guinea: Bougainville

R **Steatomys jacksoni**
Ghana; Nigeria

K **Thamnomys venustus**
Rwanda; Uganda; Zaire

V **Tokudaia muenninki**
(*T. osimensis muenninki*)
Japan: Nansei-shoto (Okinawa)

V **Tokudaia osimensis**
Japan: Nansei-shoto (Amami-oshima)

I **Wilfredomys oenax**
Brazil; Uruguay

R **Xenuromys barbatus**
Rock-dwelling Rat
Indonesia: Irian Jaya; Papua New Guinea

R **Xeromys myoides**
False Water-rat
Australia

R **Zelotomys woosnami**
Botswana; Namibia; South Africa

E **Zyzomys pedunculatus**
Central Rock-rat
Australia

Family ANOMALURIDAE

K **Zenkerella insignis**
Flightless Scaly-tailed Squirrel
Cameroon; Central African Republic; Equatorial Guinea; Gabon

Family CTENODACTYLIDAE

K **Felovia vae**
Felou Gundi
Mali; Mauritania; Senegal

Family MYOXIDAE

R **Glirulus japonicus**
Japanese Dormouse
Japan

Family BATHYERGIDAE

V **Bathyergus janetta**
Namibia; South Africa

K **Cryptomys zechi**
Ghana; Togo

Family ERETHIZONTIDAE

V **Chaetomys subspinosus**
Thin-spined Porcupine
Brazil

Family CHINCHILLIDAE

I **Chinchilla brevicaudata**
Short-tailed Chinchilla
Argentina; Bolivia; Chile; Peru (ex?)

I **Chinchilla lanigera**
Long-tailed Chinchilla
Argentina?; Chile

Family DINOMYIDAE

E **Dinomys branickii**
Pacarana
Bolivia; Brazil; Colombia; Ecuador; Peru; Venezuela

Family OCTODONTIDAE

V   *Octomys barrerae*
    (*Tympanoctomys barrerae*)
    Red Vizcacha Rat
        Argentina

Family CAPROMYIDAE

E   *Capromys angelcabrerai*
    (*Mesocapromys angelcabrerai*)
    Cabrera's Hutia
        Cuba: Cay Ana Maria

E   *Capromys auritus*
    (*Mesocapromys auritus*)
    Large-eared Hutia
        Cuba: Cay Fragoso

E   *Capromys garridoi*
    (*Mysateles garridoi*)
    Garrido's Hutia
        Cuba: Canarreos Archipelago

I   *Capromys gundlachi*
    (*Mysateles gundlachi*)
    Chapman's Prehensile-tailed Hutia
        Cuba: Isle de Juventud

R   *Capromys melanurus*
    (*Mysateles melanurus*)
    Bushy-tailed Hutia
        Cuba

I   *Capromys meridionalis*
    (*Mysateles meridionalis*)
    Isla de la Juventud Tree Hutia
        Cuba: Isle de Juventud

E   *Capromys nanus*
    (*Mesocapromys nanus*)
    Dwarf Hutia
        Cuba

E   *Capromys sanfelipensis*
    (*Mesocapromys sanfelipensis*)
    Little Earth Hutia
        Cuba

I   *Geocapromys brownii*
    (includes *G. thoracatus*, sometimes included in
    Capromys)
    Jamaican Hutia
        Jamaica

R   *Geocapromys ingrahami*
    (*Capromys ingrahami*)
    Bahamian Hutia
        Bahamas: Plana Keys

R   *Plagiodontia aedium*
    (includes *P. hylaeum*)
    Hispaniolan Hutia
        Dominican Republic; Haiti

Order LAGOMORPHA

Family OCHOTONIDAE

K   *Ochotona forresti*
    Forrest's Pika
        Bhutan, China, India, Myanmar

I   *Ochotona gaoligongensis*
    Gaoligong Pika
        China

I   *Ochotona iliensis*
    Ili Pika
        China

V   *Ochotona koslowi*
    Kozlov's Pika
        China

I   *Ochotona muliensis*
    Muli Pika
        China

I   *Ochotona nubrica*
    Nubra Pika
        China, India, Nepal

V   *Ochotona pusilla*
    Steppe Pika, Little Pika
        Russia

I   *Ochotona thomasi*
    Thomas' Pika
        China

Family LEPORIDAE

V   *Brachylagus idahoensis*
    Pygmy Rabbit
        USA

E   *Bunolagus monticularis*
    Riverine Rabbit
        South Africa

E   *Caprolagus hispidus*
    Hispid Hare
        Bangladesh; India; Nepal

I   *Lepus callotis*
    White-sided Jackrabbit
        Mexico, USA

E   *Lepus flavigularis*
    Tehuantepec Jackrabbit
        Mexico

K   ***Lepus hainanus***
    (*L. pequensis hainanus*)
    Hainan Hare
        China

R   ***Lepus insularis***
    Black Jackrabbit
        Mexico

K   ***Lepus othus***
    (*Lepus timidus othus*)
    Alaskan Hare
        USA: Alaska

E   ***Nesolagus netscheri***
    Sumatran Rabbit
        Indonesia: Sumatra

E   ***Pentalagus furnessi***
    Amami Rabbit
        Japan

E   ***Romerolagus diazi***
    Volcano Rabbit
        Mexico

K   ***Sylvilagus dicei***
    (*S. brasiliensis dicei*)
    Dice's Cottontail
        Costa Rica; Panama

E   ***Sylvilagus graysoni***
    Tres Marias Rabbit
        Mexico: Tres Marias Islands

E   ***Sylvilagus insonus***
    Omilteme Rabbit
        Mexico

I   ***Sylvilagus mansuetus***
    (*Sylvilagus bachmani mansuetus*)
    San Jose Brush Rabbit
        Mexico

Order MACROSCELIDEA

Family MACROSCELIDIDAE

V   ***Rhynchocyon chrysopygus***
    Golden-rumped Elephant-shrew
        Kenya

R   ***Rhynchocyon petersi***
    Black-and-rufous Elephant-shrew
        Kenya; Tanzania: including Pemba Island,
        Zanzibar

Class AVES

Order APTERYGIFORMES

Family APTERYGIDAE

V   *Apteryx owenii*
    Little Spotted Kiwi
    New Zealand

Order TINAMIFORMES

Family TINAMIDAE

I   *Crypturellus kerriae*
    Choco Tinamou
    Colombia; Panama

E/Ex *Nothoprocta kalinowskii*
    Kalinowski's Tinamou
    Peru

V   *Nothoprocta taczanowskii*
    Taczanowski's Tinamou
    Peru

I   *Nothura minor*
    Lesser Nothura
    Brazil

I   *Taoniscus nanus*
    Dwarf Tinamou
    Argentina (ex?); Brazil

K   *Tinamus osgoodi*
    Black Tinamou
    Colombia; Peru

Order SPHENISCIFORMES

Family SPHENISCIDAE

V   *Megadyptes antipodes*
    Yellow-eyed Penguin
    New Zealand: Auckland Islands, Campbell
    Island, South Island, Stewart Island

K   *Spheniscus demersus*
    Jackass Penguin
    Namibia; South Africa. * Angola;
    Mozambique

Order PODICIPEDIFORMES

Family PODICIPEDIDAE

E/Ex *Podiceps andinus*
    Colombian Grebe
    Colombia

E   *Podiceps taczanowskii*
    Puna Grebe
    Peru

K   *Tachybaptus pelzelnii*
    Madagascar Grebe
    Madagascar

E   *Tachybaptus rufolavatus*
    Alaotra Grebe
    Madagascar

Order PROCELLARIIFORMES

Family DIOMEDEIDAE

E   *Diomedea albatrus*
    Short-tailed Albatross
    Japan: Izu Islands. * North Pacific inc. China;
    USA: Hawaiian Islands; Russia; Taiwan

E   *Diomedea amsterdamensis*
    Amsterdam Island Albatross
    French Southern and Antarctic Territories:
    Amsterdam Island

Family PROCELLARIIDAE

E   *Procellaria parkinsoni*
    Black Petrel
    New Zealand. * South Pacific north to Costa
    Rica; Ecuador; Peru

V   *Procellaria westlandica*
    Westland Petrel
    New Zealand. * Australia

E   *Pterodroma aterrima*
    (*Pseudobulweria aterrima*)
    Mascarene Petrel
    Réunion

E   *Pterodroma axillaris*
    Chatham Islands Petrel
    New Zealand: Chatham Islands

I   *Pterodroma becki*
    (*Pterodroma rostrata becki*)
    Beck's Petrel
    Papua New Guinea (ex?)?; Solomon Islands
    (ex?)?

E   *Pterodroma cahow*
    Bermuda Petrel
    Bermuda

R   *Pterodroma cookii*
    Cook's Petrel
    New Zealand. * seas off South America;
    Chile; Peru

V   *Pterodroma defilippiana*
    Defilippe's Petrel
    Chile: Desventuradas Islands; Juan Fernández
    Islands

R **Pterodroma feae**
Cape Verde Petrel
Cape Verde; Portugal: Madeira. * Tropical and subtropical Atlantic

I **Pterodroma hasitata**
Black-capped Petrel
Cuba; Dominican Republic; Haiti. * Caribbean and western North Atlantic

E **Pterodroma madeira**
Madeira Petrel
Portugal: Madeira

E **Pterodroma magentae**
Magenta Petrel
New Zealand: Chatham Islands. * South Pacific

I **Pterodroma macgillivrayi**
(*Pseudobulweria macgillivrayi*)
MacGillivray's Petrel
Fiji: Gau Island

E **Pterodroma phaeopygia**
(*P. p. phaeopygia*)
Galapagos Petrel
Ecuador: Galapagos Islands. * Chile; Colombia: Malpelo Island; Costa Rica; Ecuador; French Polynesia: Clipperton Island; Mexico; Panama; Peru

V **Pterodroma pycrofti**
Pycroft's Petrel
New Zealand

E **Pterodroma sandwichensis**
(*P. phaeopygia sandwichensis*)
Hawaiian Petrel
USA: Hawaiian Islands (Hawaii, Kauai?, Lanai, Maui, Molokai). * French Polynesia?: Marquesas Islands; Kiribati: Line Islands

I **Puffinus auricularis**
Townsend's Shearwater
Mexico: Revillagigedos Islands

V/R **Puffinus creatopus**
Pink-footed Shearwater
Chile: Isla Mocha, Juan Fernández Islands. * Cocos (Keeling) Islands; Costa Rica; Ecuador; Peru; USA

I **Puffinus heinrothi**
Heinroth's Shearwater
Papua New Guinea: Bougainville, New Britain

Family HYDROBATIDAE

E/Ex **Oceanodroma macrodactyla**
Guadalupe Storm-Petrel
Mexico: Guadalupe Island

K **Oceanodroma tristrami**
Tristram's Storm-Petrel
USA: Hawaiian Islands; Japan: Izu Islands, Kazan-retto (Volcano Islands)

Family PELECANOIDIDAE

V **Pelecanoides garnotii**
Peruvian Diving-Petrel
Chile; Peru

Order PELECANIFORMES

Family PELECANIDAE

V **Pelecanus crispus**
Dalmatian Pelican
Albania; Armenia; Azerbaijan; Bulgaria; China; Greece; Iran; Kazakhstan; Mongolia; Romania; Russia; Turkey; Turkmenistan; Ukraine; Uzbekistan; Yugoslavia. * Afghanistan; Bangladesh; Egypt; Hong Kong; India; Iraq; Lebanon; Pakistan; Syria

I **Pelecanus philippensis**
Spot-billed Pelican
India; Sri Lanka. * Bangladesh; Cambodia; China; Indonesia: Java, Sumatra; Laos; Malaysia: Peninsular Malaysia; Myanmar; Nepal; Thailand; Viet Nam

Family SULIDAE

E **Papasula abbotti**
(*Sula abbotti*)
Abbott's Booby
Christmas Island; Costa Rica?: Cocos (Keeling) Islands. * Indonesia: Java

Family PHALACROCORACIDAE

R **Phalacrocorax carunculatus**
Rough-faced Shag
New Zealand: Cook Strait

R **Phalacrocorax chalconotus**
Bronze Shag
(*P. carunculatus chalconotus*)
New Zealand: South Island, Stewart Island

R **Phalacrocorax harrisi**
(*Nannopterum harrisi*)
Flightless Cormorant
Ecuador: Galapagos Islands: Fernandina, Isabela

R **Phalacrocorax onslowi**
(*P. carunculatus onslowi*)
Chatham Islands Shag
New Zealand: Chatham Islands

K   *Phalacrocorax pygmeus*
    (*Halietor pygmeus*)
    Pygmy Cormorant
        Albania; Azerbaijan; Bulgaria; Greece;
        Hungary; Iran; Iraq; Italy; Kazakhstan;
        Moldova; Romania; Russia; Tajikistan;
        Turkey; Turkmenistan; Uzbekistan;
        Yugoslavia. * Afghanistan; Austria; Georgia;
        Israel

Family FREGATIDAE

V   *Fregata andrewsi*
    Christmas Island Frigatebird
        Christmas Island. * Indonesia: Bali, Java,
        Sumatra; Malaysia: Peninsular Malaysia,
        Sabah, Sarawak; Singapore; Thailand; Viet
        Nam

R   *Fregata aquila*
    Ascension Frigatebird
        Ascension: Saint Helena. * tropical Atlantic

Order CICONIIFORMES

Family ARDEIDAE

K   *Ardea humbloti*
    Madagascar Heron
        Comoros?; Madagascar. * Comoros; Mayotte

E   *Ardea insignis*
    (*Ardea imperialis*)
    White-bellied Heron
        Bangladesh; Bhutan; India; Myanmar

V   *Egretta eulophotes*
    Chinese Egret
        China; Hong Kong?; Korea D.P.R.; Korea
        Republic. * Brunei; Japan; Malaysia:
        Peninsular Malaysia, Sabah, Sarawak;
        Philippines: Basilan, Batan, Bohol, Cebu,
        Luzon, Mindoro, Palawan, Panay, Samar;
        Russia; Singapore; Taiwan

I   *Egretta vinaceigula*
    Slaty Egret
        Botswana; Namibia; Zambia?

V   *Gorsachius goisagi*
    Japanese Night-Heron
        Japan. * China; Philippines; Taiwan

E   *Gorsachius magnificus*
    White-eared Night-Heron
        China: Hainan

Family BALAENICIPITIDAE

K   *Balaeniceps rex*
    Shoebill
        Burundi?; Central African Republic; Ethiopia;
        Rwanda; Sudan; Tanzania; Uganda; Zaire;
        Zambia

Family CICONIIDAE

E   *Ciconia boyciana*
    Oriental Stork
        China; Russia. * Japan; Korea D.P.R.; Korea
        Republic

I   *Ciconia stormi*
    Storm's Stork
        Indonesia: Kalimantan, Sumatra?; Malaysia:
        Sabah, Sarawak; Thailand. * Brunei; Malaysia:
        Peninsular Malaysia

E   *Leptoptilos dubius*
    Greater Adjutant
        Cambodia (ex?); India; Laos (ex?); Myanmar
        (ex?); Viet Nam (ex?). * Nepal; Thailand

V   *Leptoptilos javanicus*
    Lesser Adjutant
        Bangladesh; Cambodia?; China; India;
        Indonesia: Bali, Kalimantan, Sumatra;
        Malaysia: Peninsular Malaysia, Sabah,
        Sarawak; Laos?; Myanmar; Nepal; Sri Lanka;
        Thailand; Viet Nam. * Bhutan; Brunei;
        Singapore

V   *Mycteria cinerea*
    Milky Stork
        Cambodia; Indonesia: Java, Sumatra, Sulawesi;
        Malaysia: Peninsular Malaysia; Viet Nam

Family THRESKIORNITHIDAE

R   *Geronticus calvus*
    Bald Ibis
        Lesotho; South Africa; Swaziland

E   *Geronticus eremita*
    Waldrapp
        Morocco. * Ethiopia; Syria; Yemen

E   *Nipponia nippon*
    Crested Ibis
        China

E   *Platalea minor*
    Black-faced Spoonbill
        China; Korea D.P.R. * Cambodia; China;
        Hong Kong; Japan; Taiwan; Viet Nam

I   *Pseudibis davisoni*
White-shouldered Ibis
Cambodia?; China; Indonesia: Kalimantan;
Laos?; Myanmar?; Viet Nam. * Malaysia:
Peninsular Malaysia, Sarawak

R   *Pseudibis gigantea*
Giant Ibis
Cambodia (ex?); Laos

Order ANSERIFORMES

Family ANATIDAE

K   *Aix galericulata*
Mandarin Duck
China; Japan; Korea D.P.R.; Korea Republic;
Russia. * Taiwan
[Austria; Belgium; Netherlands; United
Kingdom]

V   *Anas aucklandica*
Brown Teal
New Zealand

V   *Anas bernieri*
Bernier's Teal
Madagascar

V   *Anas formosa*
Baikal Teal
Russia. * China; Japan; Korea D.P.R.; Korea
Republic

R   *Anas wyvilliana*
Hawaiian Duck
USA: Hawaiian Islands (Kauai)
[Hawaiian Islands: Hawaii, Oahu]

R   *Anser erythropus*
Lesser White-fronted Goose
Finland; Norway; Sweden; Russia. * Albania;
Bulgaria; China; Greece; Hungary; India; Iran;
Iraq; Japan; Latvia; Pakistan; Romania;
Turkey; Turkmenistan; Yugoslavia

V   *Aythya baeri*
Baer's Pochard
China; Korea D.P.R.?; Russia. * Bangladesh;
Hong Kong; India; Japan; Myanmar; Nepal;
Korea Republic; Thailand; Viet Nam

E   *Aythya innotata*
Madagascar Pochard
Madagascar

K   *Branta ruficollis*
Red-breasted Goose
Russia. * Bulgaria; Greece; Hungary; Iran;
Iraq; Kazakhstan; Romania; Turkey;
Turkmenistan

V   *Branta sandvicensis*
Nene
USA: Hawaiian Islands (Hawaii, Maui)

V   *Cairina scutulata*
White-winged Duck
Bangladesh; Cambodia?; India; Indonesia:
Sumatra; Laos; Myanmar; Thailand; Viet Nam

V   *Dendrocygna arborea*
West Indian Whistling-Duck
Antigua and Barbuda; Bahamas; British Virgin
Islands; Cayman Islands; Cuba; Dominican
Republic; Haiti; Jamaica; Puerto Rico; Turks
and Caicos Islands; Virgin Islands of the
United States

V   *Marmaronetta angustirostris*
Marbled Teal
Afghanistan; Algeria; Armenia; Azerbaijan;
China?; Egypt?; Georgia; Iran; Iraq; Israel;
Kazakhstan; Morocco; Pakistan?; Russia;
Senegal; Spain; Tajikistan; Tunisia (ex?);
Turkey; Turkmenistan; Uzbekistan. * Chad;
Egypt; India; Mali; Morocco; Pakistan; Turkey

E   *Mergus octosetaceus*
Brazilian Merganser
Argentina; Brazil; Paraguay

I   *Mergus squamatus*
Scaly-sided Merganser
China; Korea D.P.R.; Russia

V   *Oxyura leucocephala*
White-headed Duck
Afghanistan; Algeria; France: Corsica (ex?);
Iran; Kazakhstan; Romania; Russia; Spain;
Tunisia; Turkey; Turkmenistan; Uzbekistan. *
Albania; Bulgaria; China; Cyprus; Egypt;
Greece; India; Iraq; Italy; Morocco; Pakistan;
Syria; Tajikistan

K   *Stictonetta naevosa*
Freckled Duck
Australia

E   *Tadorna cristata*
Crested Shelduck
China?; Korea D.P.R.?; Russia. * China?;
Korea Republic

Order FALCONIFORMES

Family CATHARTIDAE

E   *Gymnogyps californianus*
California Condor
[Reintroduced to USA]

Family ACCIPITRIDAE

R   *Accipiter brachyurus*
New Britain Sparrowhawk
   Papua New Guinea: New Britain

V/R   *Accipiter gundlachi*
Gundlach's Hawk
   Cuba

R   *Accipiter imitator*
Imitator Sparrowhawk
   Papua New Guinea: Bougainville; Solomon
   Islands: Choiseul, Santa Isabel

R   *Accipiter nanus*
Small Sparrowhawk
   Indonesia: Sulawesi

V   *Aegypius monachus*
Cinereous Vulture
   Afghanistan; Albania (ex?); Armenia;
   Azerbaijan; Bulgaria?; China; Cyprus?;
   Georgia; Greece; Iran; Kazakhstan;
   Kyrgyzstan; Mongolia; Pakistan; Portugal;
   Russia; Spain: including Balearic Islands:
   Mallorca; Syria?; Tajikistan; Turkey;
   Turkmenistan; Uzbekistan; Yugoslavia. *
   Bangladesh?; Bhutan?; Egypt; Hong Kong;
   India; Italy; Korea D.P.R.; Korea Republic;
   Morocco; Myanmar; Nepal; Oman; Saudi
   Arabia; Thailand

E   *Aquila adalberti*
Adalbert's Eagle
   Portugal; Spain

R   *Aquila heliaca*
Imperial Eagle
   Albania?; Azerbaijan; Bulgaria; China; Cyprus;
   Czechoslovakia; Georgia; Greece; Hungary;
   Iran; Kazakhstan; Moldova; Romania; Russia;
   Turkey; Turkmenistan; Ukraine; Uzbekistan;
   Yugoslavia. * Afghanistan; Bangladesh;
   Djibouti; Egypt; Ethiopia; Hong Kong; India;
   Iraq; Israel; Jordan; Kuwait; Laos; Lebanon;
   Nepal; Oman; Pakistan; Saudi Arabia; Sudan;
   United Arab Emirates; Viet Nam; Yemen

R   *Buteo galapagoensis*
Galapagos Hawk
   Ecuador: Galapagos Islands

I   *Buteo ridgwayi*
Ridgway's Hawk
   Dominican Republic; Haiti

R   *Buteo solitarius*
Hawaiian Hawk
   USA: Hawaiian Islands (Hawaii)

K   *Erythrotriorchis radiatus*
   (*Accipiter radiatus*)
Red Goshawk
   Australia

E   *Eutriorchis astur*
Madagascar Serpent-Eagle
   Madagascar

R   *Gyps coprotheres*
Cape Griffon
   Botswana; Lesotho; Mozambique; Namibia;
   South Africa. * Swaziland

V   *Haliaeetus albicilla*
White-tailed Eagle
   Albania (ex?); Armenia; Austria; Azerbaijan;
   Belarus; Bulgaria; China; Czechoslovakia;
   Denmark; Estonia; Finland; Georgia; Germany;
   Greece; Greenland; Hungary; Iceland; Iran;
   Israel; Japan; Kazakhstan; Latvia; Lithuania;
   Moldova; Mongolia; Nepal; Norway; Poland;
   Romania; Russia; Sweden; Turkey;
   Turkmenistan; Ukraine; Yugoslavia. *
   Afghanistan; France; Faeroe Islands; India;
   Israel; Japan; Korea D.P.R.; Korea Republic;
   Nepal; Pakistan; Taiwan; Tajikistan; USA;
   Uzbekistan
   [Reintroduced to United Kingdom]

R   *Haliaeetus leucoryphus*
Pallas's Sea-Eagle
   Bangladesh; Bhutan; China; India; Kazakhstan;
   Mongolia; Myanmar; Nepal; Pakistan; Russia?;
   Tajikistan; Uzbekistan. * Afghanistan

R   *Haliaeetus pelagicus*
Steller's Sea-Eagle
   Russia. * Japan; Korea D.P.R.?; Korea
   Republic

E   *Haliaeetus vociferoides*
Madagascar Fish-Eagle
   Madagascar

V   *Harpyhaliaetus coronatus*
Crowned Eagle
   Argentina; Bolivia; Brazil; Paraguay; Uruguay

V   *Harpyopsis novaeguineae*
New Guinea Eagle
   Indonesia: Irian Jaya; Papua New Guinea

I   *Henicopernis infuscatus*
Black Honey-buzzard
   Papua New Guinea: New Britain

V/R   *Leucopternis lacernulata*
White-necked Hawk
   Brazil

E   *Leucopternis occidentalis*
     Grey-backed Hawk
        Ecuador; Peru

K   *Milvus milvus*
     Red Kite
        Algeria (ex?); Armenia?; Austria; Belarus;
        Belgium; Cape Verde; Czechoslovakia;
        Denmark; France; Georgia; Germany;
        Hungary; Iran; Italy; Latvia?; Lithuania;
        Luxembourg; Moldova; Morocco; Netherlands;
        Poland; Portugal; Romania; Russia; Spain;
        Sweden; Switzerland; Tunisia (ex?); Ukraine;
        United Kingdom; Yugoslavia. * Austria;
        Bulgaria; Gibraltar; Greece; Liechtenstein;
        Turkey

E   *Pithecophaga jefferyi*
     Great Philippine Eagle
        Philippines: Leyte, Luzon, Mindanao, Samar

R   *Spilornis elgini*
     Andaman Serpent-Eagle
        India: Andaman Islands

R   *Spilornis kinabaluensis*
     Mountain Serpent-Eagle
        Brunei; Indonesia: Kalimantan; Malaysia:
        Sabah, Sarawak

V   *Spizaetus bartelsi*
     Javan Hawk-Eagle
        Indonesia: Java

R   *Spizaetus nanus*
     Wallace's Hawk-Eagle
        Brunei; Indonesia: Kalimantan, Sumatra;
        Malaysia: Peninsular Malaysia, Sabah,
        Sarawak; Myanmar; Thailand

Family FALCONIDAE

K   *Falco hypoleucos*
     Grey Falcon
        Australia

R   *Falco naumanni*
     Lesser Kestrel
        Afghanistan; Albania?; Algeria; Armenia;
        Austria; Azerbaijan; Bulgaria; China;
        Czechoslovakia?; France; Georgia; Gibraltar;
        Greece; Hungary; Iran; Iraq?; Israel; Italy;
        Jordan; Kazakhstan; Kyrgyzstan; Lebanon?;
        Libya; Moldova; Mongolia; Morocco; Poland?;
        Portugal; Romania; Russia; Saudi Arabia;
        Spain; Switzerland?; Syria; Tajikistan; Tunisia;
        Turkey; Turkmenistan; Ukraine; Uzbekistan;
        Yugoslavia. * Angola; Bahrain; Bangladesh;
        Benin; Botswana; Burkina Faso;
        Burundi; Central African Republic; Chad;
        Congo; Côte d'Ivoire; Cyprus; Djibouti; Egypt;
        Ethiopia; Ghana; Guinea-Bissau?; India; Iraq;
        Kenya; Kuwait; Laos; Lebanon; Lesotho;
        Malawi; Maldives; Mali; Malta; Mauritania;
        Mozambique; Myanmar; Namibia; Nepal;
        Niger; Nigeria; Oman; Pakistan; Poland; Qatar;
        Rwanda; Senegal; Sierra Leone?; South Africa;
        Sudan; Tanzania; Togo?; Turkey; Uganda;
        United Arab Emirates; Western Sahara?;
        Yemen; Zaire; Zambia; Zimbabwe

E   *Falco punctatus*
     Mauritius Kestrel
        Mauritius

K   *Micrastur buckleyi*
     Buckley's Forest-Falcon
        Brazil; Colombia?; Ecuador; Peru

V   *Micrastur plumbeus*
     Plumbeous Forest-Falcon
        Colombia; Ecuador

Order GALLIFORMES

Family MEGAPODIIDAE

R   *Aepypodius bruijnii*
     Bruijn's Brush-turkey
        Indonesia: Waigeo Island

K   *Leipoa ocellata*
     Malleefowl
        Australia

V   *Macrocephalon maleo*
     Maleo
        Indonesia: Lembeh, Sulawesi

V   *Megapodius bernsteinii*
     Sula Scrubfowl
        Indonesia: Banggai (ex?), Sula

R   *Megapodius laperouse*
     Micronesian Scrubfowl
        Northern Marianas; Palau

R   *Megapodius nicobariensis*
     Nicobar Scrubfowl
        India: North Nicobar Islands

V   *Megapodius pritchardii*
     Niuafo'ou Scrubfowl
        Tonga: Niuafo'ou

R   *Megapodius wallacei*
     Moluccan Scrubfowl
        Indonesia: Ambon, Bacan, Buru, Halmahera,
        Haruku, Misool, Seram, Ternate

Family CRACIDAE

E   *Crax alberti*
     Blue-knobbed Curassow
       Colombia

R   *Crax blumenbachii*
     Red-billed Curassow
       Brazil

I   *Crax globulosa*
     Wattled Curassow
       Bolivia; Brazil; Colombia; Ecuador; Peru

E   *Mitu mitu*
     Alagoas Curassow
       Brazil

V/R   *Oreophasis derbianus*
     Horned Guan
       Guatemala; Mexico

E   *Pauxi pauxi*
     Helmeted Curassow
       Colombia; Venezuela

V/R   *Pauxi unicornis*
     Horned Curassow
       Peru; Bolivia

E   *Penelope albipennis*
     White-winged Guan
       Peru

V/R   *Penelope barbata*
     Bearded Guan
       Ecuador; Peru

V/R   *Penelope ochrogaster*
     Chestnut-bellied Guan
       Brazil

R   *Penelope perspicax*
     Cauca Guan
       Colombia

V/R   *Pipile jacutinga*
     Black-fronted Piping-Guan
       Argentina; Brazil; Paraguay

E   *Pipile pipile*
     Trinidad Piping-Guan
       Trinidad and Tobago: Trinidad

Family PHASIANIDAE

K   *Afropavo congensis*
     Congo Peafowl
       Zaire

E   *Agelastes meleagrides*
     White-breasted Guineafowl
       Côte d'Ivoire; Ghana (ex?); Liberia; Sierra
       Leone

E   *Arborophila ardens*
     Hainan Partridge
       China

R   *Arborophila cambodiana*
     Chestnut-headed Partridge
       Cambodia; Thailand

R   *Arborophila charltonii*
     Chestnut-necklaced Partridge
       Indonesia: Sumatra; Malaysia: Peninsular
       Malaysia, Sabah; Thailand; Viet Nam

I   *Arborophila davidi*
     Orange-necked Partridge
       Viet Nam

R   *Arborophila gingica*
     White-necklaced Partridge
       China

E   *Arborophila rufipectus*
     Sichuan Partridge
       China

E   *Catreus wallichii*
     Cheer Pheasant
       India; Nepal; Pakistan

V   *Crossoptilon crossoptilon*
     White Eared-Pheasant
       China

E   *Crossoptilon mantchuricum*
     Brown Eared-Pheasant
       China

E   *Dendrortyx barbatus*
     Bearded Wood-Partridge
       Mexico

R   *Francolinus camerunensis*
     Cameroon Francolin
       Cameroon

V   *Francolinus gularis*
     Swamp Francolin
       Bangladesh; India; Nepal

R   *Francolinus nahani*
     Nahan's Francolin
       Uganda; Zaire

E   *Francolinus ochropectus*
     Ochre-breasted Francolin
       Djibouti

I   *Francolinus swierstrai*
     Swierstra's Francolin
       Angola

E   *Lophophorus lhuysii*
     Chinese Monal
       China

R   *Lophophorus sclateri*
Sclater's Monal
China; India; Myanmar

V   *Lophura bulweri*
Bulwer's Pheasant
Brunei; Indonesia: Kalimantan; Malaysia:
Sabah, Sarawak

R   *Lophura diardi*
Siamese Fireback
Cambodia; Laos; Thailand; Viet Nam

V   *Lophura edwardsi*
Edwards's Pheasant
Viet Nam

I   *Lophura hatinhensis*
Vietnamese Pheasant
Viet Nam

V   *Lophura ignita*
Crested Fireback
Brunei; Indonesia: Kalimantan, Sumatra;
Malaysia: Peninsular Malaysia, Sabah,
Sarawak; Myanmar; Thailand

V   *Lophura imperialis*
Imperial Pheasant
Laos?; Viet Nam

V   *Lophura inornata*
Salvadori's Pheasant
Indonesia: Sumatra

V   *Lophura swinhoii*
Swinhoe's Pheasant
Taiwan

V/R   *Odontophorus strophium*
Gorgeted Wood-Quail
Colombia

V   *Pavo muticus*
Green Peafowl
Bangladesh (ex?); Cambodia; China; India;
Indonesia: Java; Laos; Malaysia: Peninsular
Malaysia; Myanmar; Thailand; Viet Nam

R   *Perdicula manipurensis*
Manipur Bush-Quail
Bangladesh; India

V   *Polyplectron emphanum*
Palawan Peacock-Pheasant
Philippines: Palawan

R   *Polyplectron germaini*
Germain's Peacock-Pheasant
Laos?; Viet Nam

R   *Polyplectron malacense*
Malayan Peacock-Pheasant
Malaysia: Peninsular Malaysia; Myanmar;
Thailand

R   *Polyplectron schleiermacheri*
(*P. malacense schleiermacheri*)
Bornean Peacock-Pheasant
Indonesia: Kalimantan; Malaysia: Sabah,
Sarawak

R   *Rheinardia ocellata*
(includes *R. nigrescens*)
Crested Argus
Laos; Malaysia: Peninsular Malaysia; Viet
Nam

E   *Syrmaticus ellioti*
Elliot's Pheasant
China

R   *Syrmaticus humiae*
Hume's Pheasant
China; India; Myanmar; Thailand

V   *Syrmaticus mikado*
Mikado Pheasant
Taiwan

R   *Syrmaticus reevesii*
Reeves's Pheasant
China
[Czechoslovakia]

K   *Tetrao mlokosiewiczi*
Caucasian Grouse
Armenia; Azerbaijan; Georgia; Iran; Russia;
Turkey

R   *Tragopan blythii*
Blyth's Tragopan
Bhutan; China; India; Myanmar

E   *Tragopan caboti*
Cabot's Tragopan
China

E   *Tragopan melanocephalus*
Western Tragopan
China; India; Nepal?; Pakistan

Order GRUIFORMES

Family MESITORNITHIDAE

K   *Mesitornis unicolor*
Brown Roatelo
Madagascar

R   *Mesitornis variegata*
White-breasted Roatelo
Madagascar

R   *Monias benschi*
Monias
　Madagascar

Family TURNICIDAE

I   *Turnix everetti*
Sumba Buttonquail
　Indonesia: Sumba

K   *Turnix melanogaster*
Black-breasted Buttonquail
　Australia

K   *Turnix olivii*
Buff-breasted Buttonquail
　Australia

I   *Turnix worcesteri*
Worcester's Buttonquail
　Philippines: Luzon

Family PEDIONOMIDAE

K   *Pedionomus torquatus*
Plains-wanderer
　Australia

Family GRUIDAE

E   *Grus americana*
Whooping Crane
　Canada. * USA

K   *Grus carunculatus*
(*Bugeranus carunculatus*)
Wattled Crane
　Angola;　Botswana;　Ethiopia;　Malawi;
　Mozambique;　Namibia;　South　Africa;
　Tanzania; Zaire; Zambia; Zimbabwe

V   *Grus japonensis*
Red-crowned Crane
　China;　Japan;　Russia;　Mongolia. * Korea
　D.P.R.; Korea Republic

V   *Grus leucogeranus*
Siberian Crane
　China;　Mongolia?;　Russia. * Afghanistan;
　India; Iran; Pakistan

V   *Grus monacha*
Hooded Crane
　Russia. * Japan;　Korea　D.P.R.;　Korea
　Republic; Taiwan

V   *Grus nigricollis*
Black-necked Crane
　China; India. * Bhutan; Myanmar; Viet Nam

V   *Grus vipio*
White-naped Crane
　China;　Mongolia;　Russia. * Japan;　Korea
　D.P.R.; Korea Republic

Family RALLIDAE

K   *Amaurornis olivieri*
Sakalava Rail
　Madagascar

I   *Aramidopsis plateni*
Snoring Rail
　Indonesia: Sulawesi

R   *Atlantisia rogersi*
Inaccessible Rail
　Saint Helena: Inaccessible Island

R   *Coturnicops exquisitus*
Swinhoe's Rail
　China; Russia. * Japan; Korea D.P.R.; Korea
　Republic

I   *Coturnicops notatus*
Speckled Rail
　Argentina;　Brazil;　Colombia;　Guyana;
　Paraguay; Uruguay; Venezuela

R   *Crex crex*
Corn Crake
　Afghanistan;　Albania;　Armenia?;　Austria;
　Azerbaijan (ex?); Belarus; Belgium; Bulgaria;
　China; Czechoslovakia; Denmark; Estonia;
　Finland; France; Georgia; Germany; Greece;
　Hungary; Iran; Ireland; Italy; Kazakhstan;
　Kyrgyzstan; Latvia; Liechtenstein; Lithuania;
　Luxembourg; Moldova; Netherlands; Norway;
　Poland; Romania; Russia; Spain; Sweden;
　Switzerland; Tajikistan; Turkey?; Ukraine;
　United Kingdom; Yugoslavia. * Afghanistan;
　Algeria;　Azerbaijan;　Botswana;　Egypt;
　Ethiopia; Ghana; Iraq; Israel; Kenya; Malawi;
　Mali; Mauritania; Morocco; Mozambique;
　Namibia; Nigeria; Portugal; Saudi Arabia;
　South Africa; Sudan; Swaziland; Tanzania;
　Tunisia;　Turkmenistan;　Uganda;　United
　Kingdom: Channel Islands (Guernsey, Jersey);
　Uzbekistan; Zaire; Zambia; Zimbabwe

I   *Cyanolimnas cerverai*
Zapata Rail
　Cuba

K   *Fulica cornuta*
Horned Coot
　Argentina; Bolivia; Chile

I   *Gallinula nesiotis*
Tristan Moorhen
　Saint Helena: Tristan da Cunha, Gough Island

I   *Gallinula silvestris*
San Cristobal Moorhen
　Solomon Islands: San Cristobal

I   *Gallirallus lafresnayanus*
    (*Tricholimnas lafresnayanus*)
    New Caledonian Rail
        New Caledonia (ex?)

V   *Gallirallus okinawae*
    (*Rallus okinawae*)
    Okinawa Rail
        Japan: Okinawa

V   *Gallirallus owstoni*
    (*Rallus owstoni*)
    Guam Rail
        Guam

E   *Gallirallus sylvestris*
    (*Tricholimnas sylvestris*)
    Lord Howe Rail
        Australia: Lord Howe Island

I   *Gymnocrex rosenbergii*
    Bald-faced Rail
        Indonesia: Peleng, Sulawesi

I   *Habroptila wallacii*
    Invisible Rail
        Indonesia: Halmahera

V   *Laterallus levraudi*
    Rusty-flanked Crake
        Venezuela

E   *Laterallus tuerosi*
    (*L. jamaicensis tuerosi*)
    Junin Rail
        Peru

V/R *Laterallus xenopterus*
    Rufous-faced Crake
        Brazil; Paraguay

I   *Lewinia mirificus*
    (*Dryolimnas mirificus, Rallus mirificus*)
    Brown-banded Rail
        Philippines: Luzon

E   *Nesoclopeus poecilopterus*
    Bar-winged Rail
        Fiji: Viti Levu, Ovalau

E   *Porphyrio mantelli*
    (*Notornis mantelli*)
    Takahe
        New Zealand: South Island

R   *Porzana atra*
    (*Nesophylax ater*)
    Henderson Island Crake
        Pitcairn Islands: Henderson Island

I   *Porzana spiloptera*
    Dot-winged Crake
        Argentina; Uruguay

E/Ex *Rallus antarcticus*
    Austral Rail
        Argentina; Chile

V/R *Rallus semiplumbeus*
    Bogotá Rail
        Colombia; Ecuador?

E   *Rallus wetmorei*
    Plain-flanked Rail
        Venezuela

I   *Sarothrura ayresi*
    White-winged Flufftail
        Ethiopia (ex?); South Africa

I   *Sarothrura watersi*
    Waters's Flufftail
        Madagascar

Family HELIORNITHIDAE

V   *Heliopais personata*
    Masked Finfoot
        Bangladesh; Cambodia?; India; Myanmar;
        Thailand?; Viet Nam. * Cambodia?; Indonesia:
        Java, Sumatra; Malaysia: Peninsular Malaysia;
        Thailand; Viet Nam

Family RHYNOCHETIDAE

E   *Rhynochetos jubatus*
    Kagu
        New Caledonia

Family OTIDIDAE

V   *Ardeotis nigriceps*
    Indian Bustard
        India; Pakistan. * Pakistan?

V   *Chlamydotis undulata*
    Houbara Bustard
        Afghanistan?; Algeria; China; Egypt; Iran;
        Iraq; Israel; Jordan; Kazakhstan; Kyrgyzstan;
        Libya; Mauritania; Mongolia; Morocco; Oman;
        Pakistan; Russia; Saudi Arabia; Spain: Canary
        Islands; Sudan; Syria; Tajikistan; Tunisia;
        Turkmenistan; Uzbekistan; Western Sahara;
        Yemen. * Afghanistan; Bahrain; India; Kuwait;
        Qatar; United Arab Emirates

E   *Eupodotis bengalensis*
    (*Houbaropsis bengalensis*)
    Bengal Florican
        Bhutan?; Cambodia?; India; Nepal; Viet Nam

E   *Eupodotis indica*
    (*Sypheotides indica*)
    Lesser Florican
        India; Nepal. * Bangladesh?; Nepal; Pakistan

R   *Otis tarda*
Great Bustard
   Austria; China; Czechoslovakia; Germany;
   Hungary; Iran; Kazakhstan; Kyrgyzstan;
   Moldova; Mongolia; Morocco; Portugal;
   Romania; Russia; Spain; Syria?; Tajikistan;
   Turkey; Ukraine; Uzbekistan; Yugoslavia. *
   Afghanistan?; Azerbaijan; Bulgaria; Iraq;
   Syria; Turkmenistan; Yugoslavia

R   *Tetrax tetrax*
Little Bustard
   Albania?; Algeria; China; France; Iran; Iraq?;
   Italy; Kazakhstan; Kyrgyzstan; Morocco;
   Portugal; Russia; Spain; Turkey; Ukraine;
   Uzbekistan. * Azerbaijan?; Egypt; Georgia;
   Israel; Libya; Pakistan; Romania; Tajikistan;
   Tunisia; Turkmenistan; Yugoslavia

Order CHARADRIIFORMES

Family RECURVIROSTRIDAE

E   *Himantopus novaezelandiae*
Black Stilt
   New Zealand: South Island. * New Zealand:
   North Island

Family GLAREOLIDAE

I   *Rhinoptilus bitorquatus*
(*Cursorius bitorquatus*)
Jerdon's Courser
   India

Family CHARADRIIDAE

V/R   *Charadrius melodus*
Piping Plover
   Canada; USA. * Bahamas; Barbados;
   Bermuda; British Virgin Islands; Cuba;
   Dominican Republic; Haiti; Mexico; Puerto
   Rico; Virgin Islands of the United States

E   *Charadrius novaeseelandiae*
(*Thinornis novaeseelandiae*)
Shore Plover
   New Zealand: Chatham Islands (Rangatira
   Island)

K   *Charadrius rubricollis*
Hooded Plover
   Australia

R   *Charadrius sanctaehelenae*
Saint Helena Plover
   Saint Helena

R   *Charadrius thoracicus*
Black-banded Plover
   Madagascar

R   *Vanellus gregarius*
(*Chettusia gregaria*)
Sociable Lapwing
   Kazakhstan; Russia. * Ethiopia; India; Iran;
   Iraq; Israel; Kyrgyzstan; Oman; Pakistan;
   Saudi Arabia; Sudan; Tajikistan; Turkey;
   Turkmenistan; Uzbekistan; Yemen

I   *Vanellus macropterus*
Javanese Lapwing
   Indonesia: Java (ex?)

Family SCOLOPACIDAE

K   *Calidris paramelanotos*
Cox's Sandpiper
   not known, possibly Russia

R   *Coenocorypha aucklandica*
(includes *C. pusilla*)
Subantarctic Snipe
   New Zealand: Antipodes Island, Auckland
   Islands, Chatham Islands, Snares Island

I   *Eurynorhynchus pygmeus*
Spoonbill Sandpiper
   Russia. * Bangladesh; China; Hong Kong;
   India; Japan; Korea D.P.R.; Korea Republic;
   Singapore

I   *Gallinago nemoricola*
Wood Snipe
   Bhutan; China; India; Nepal. * Pakistan

R   *Limnodromus semipalmatus*
Asian Dowitcher
   China; Mongolia; Russia. * Australia;
   Bangladesh; Brunei; Cambodia; Hong Kong;
   India; Indonesia: Java, Kalimantan, Sumatra;
   Malaysia: Peninsular Malaysia, Sabah,
   Sarawak; Myanmar; Philippines: Cebu, Luzon,
   Olango, Simunul; Singapore; Thailand; Viet
   Nam

E/Ex   *Numenius borealis*
Eskimo Curlew
   Canada; USA?: Alaska. * Brazil; French
   Guiana; Guyana; Paraguay; Suriname

V/R   *Numenius tahitiensis*
Bristle-thighed Curlew
   USA: Alaska. * American Samoa; Fiji; French
   Polynesia: Marquesas Islands, Tuamotu
   Archipelago; Tonga; USA: Hawaiian Islands;
   Marshall Islands; Western Samoa

K   *Numenius tenuirostris*
Slender-billed Curlew
   Russia. * Greece; Hungary; Italy; Morocco;
   Romania; Tunisia; Turkey; Yugoslavia

V   *Prosobonia cancellatus*
Tuamotu Sandpiper
   French Polynesia: Tuamoto Archipelago

I   *Scolopax celebensis*
Sulawesi Woodcock
   Indonesia: Sulawesi

I   *Scolopax rochussenii*
Moluccan Woodcock
   Indonesia: Bacan, Halmahera?, Obi, Ternate?

I   *Tringa guttifer*
Nordmann's Greenshank
   Russia. * Bangladesh; Cambodia?; China;
Japan; Korea D.P.R.; Korea Republic; Laos?;
Malaysia: Peninsular Malaysia; Myanmar;
Philippines: Cebu, Luzon; Thailand

Family LARIDAE

V   *Chlidonias albostriatus*
(*Sterna albostriata*)
Black-fronted Tern
   New Zealand: South Island

K   *Larus atlanticus*
Olrog's Gull
   Argentina. * Brazil; Uruguay

R   *Larus audouinii*
Audouin's Gull
   Algeria; Cyprus; France: Corsica; Greece;
Italy: Sardinia: Morocco; Spain; Tunisia;
Turkey. * Gibraltar; Libya; Western Sahara

K   *Larus leucophthalmus*
White-eyed Gull
   Egypt; Ethiopia; Saudi Arabia; Somalia;
Sudan; Yemen

R   *Larus relictus*
Relict Gull
   China; Kazakhstan; Mongolia; Russia. * Korea
Republic

R   *Larus saundersi*
Saunders's Gull
   China. * Hong Kong; Japan; Korea D.P.R.?;
Korea Republic?; Taiwan; Viet Nam

R   *Sterna balaenarum*
Damara Tern
   Angola?; Namibia; South Africa. * Angola;
Cameroon; Gabon; Ghana; Nigeria; Zaire?

I   *Sterna bernsteini*
Chinese Crested Tern
   China?

V   *Sterna virgata*
Kerguelen Tern
   French Southern and Antarctic Territories:
Crozet Islands, Kerguelen Islands; South
Africa: Prince Edward Island

Family ALCIDAE

V   *Synthliboramphus wumizusume*
Japanese Murrelet
   Japan: including Izu Islands. * Korea D.P.R.;
Korea Republic; Russia

Order COLUMBIFORMES

Family COLUMBIDAE

R   *Caloenas nicobarica*
Nicobar Pigeon
   Cambodia; India: Andaman and Nicobar
Islands: South Sentinal; Indonesia; Malaysia:
Peninsular Malaysia, Sabah, Sarawak;
Myanmar; Palau; Papua New Guinea;
Philippines; Solomon Islands; Thailand; Viet
Nam

E/Ex   *Claravis godefrida*
Purple-winged Ground-Dove
   Argentina; Brazil; Paraguay

V   *Columba argentina*
Silvery Wood-Pigeon
   Indonesia: Anamba Islands (ex?), Kalimantan
(ex?), Karimata Islands (ex?), Lingga
Archipelago (ex?), Mentawai Islands (ex?),
Natuna Islands (ex?), Riau Archipelago (ex?),
Simeulue (ex?), Sumatra

R   *Columba bollii*
Bolle's Pigeon
   Spain: Canary Islands

V   *Columba caribaea*
Ring-tailed Pigeon
   Jamaica

V   *Columba elphinstonii*
Nilgiri Wood-Pigeon
   India

I   *Columba inornata*
Plain Pigeon
   Cuba; Dominican Republic; Haiti; Jamaica;
Puerto Rico

R   *Columba junoniae*
Laurel Pigeon
   Spain: Canary Islands

E   *Columba mayeri*
(*Nesoenas mayeri*)
Pink Pigeon
   Mauritius

V   *Columba oenops*
Peruvian Pigeon
  Peru

R   *Columba oliviae*
Somali Pigeon
  Somalia

I   *Columba pallidiceps*
Yellow-legged Pigeon
  Papua New Guinea: Bismarck Archipelago;
  Solomon Islands (ex?)

R   *Columba punicea*
Pale-capped Pigeon
  China; India; Laos; Myanmar; Thailand; Viet
  Nam

V   *Columba thomensis*
Maroon Pigeon
  São Tomé and Príncipe: São Tomé

V   *Columba torringtoni*
Ceylon Wood-Pigeon
  Sri Lanka

R   *Columba trocaz*
Trocaz Pigeon
  Portugal: Madeira

E   *Columbina cyanopis*
Blue-eyed Ground-Dove
  Brazil

V   *Didunculus strigirostris*
Tooth-billed Pigeon
  Western Samoa: Savaii, Upolu

V   *Drepanoptila holosericea*
Cloven-feathered Dove
  New Caledonia

V   *Ducula aurorae*
Polynesian Imperial-Pigeon
  French Polynesia: Tahiti, Makatea

E   *Ducula galeata*
Marquesan Imperial-Pigeon
  French Polynesia: Nukuhiva

V   *Ducula goliath*
New Caledonian Imperial-Pigeon
  New Caledonia

R   *Ducula mindorensis*
Mindoro Imperial-Pigeon
  Philippines: Mindoro

R   *Ducula pickeringii*
Grey Imperial-Pigeon
  Indonesia: Miangas, Talaud; Malaysia: Sabah;
  Philippines

V   *Ducula whartoni*
Christmas Island Imperial-Pigeon
  Christmas Island

I   *Gallicolumba erythroptera*
Polynesian Ground-Dove
  French Polynesia: Tuamoto Archipelago

I   *Gallicolumba hoedtii*
Wetar Ground-Dove
  Indonesia: Timor, Wetar

I   *Gallicolumba keayi*
Negros Bleeding-heart
  Philippines: Negros

I   *Gallicolumba menagei*
Sulu Bleeding-heart
  Philippines: Sulu Archipelago, Tawitawi

I   *Gallicolumba platenae*
Mindoro Bleeding-heart
  Philippines: Mindoro

I   *Gallicolumba rubescens*
Marquesan Ground-Dove
  French Polynesia: Hatutu, Fatuhuku

I   *Gallicolumba salamonis*
Thick-billed Ground-Dove
  Solomon Islands: Malaita, San Cristobal

R   *Gallicolumba santaecrucis*
Santa Cruz Ground-Dove
  Solomon Islands: Tinakula, Utupua; Vanuatu:
  Espiritu Santo

R   *Goura cristata*
Western Crowned-Pigeon
  Indonesia: Batanta, Irian Jaya, Misool,
  Salawati, Waigeo

R   *Goura scheepmakeri*
Southern Crowned-Pigeon
  Indonesia: Irian Jaya; Papua New Guinea

R   *Goura victoria*
Victoria Crowned-Pigeon
  Indonesia: Biak, Irian Jaya, Yapen; Papua New
  Guinea

V/R *Leptotila conoveri*
Tolima Dove
  Colombia

E   *Leptotila ochraceiventris*
Ochre-bellied Dove
  Ecuador; Peru

E   *Leptotila wellsi*
Grenada Dove
  Grenada

I *Ptilinopus arcanus*
Negros Fruit-Dove
 Philippines: Negros

R *Ptilinopus dohertyi*
Red-naped Fruit-Dove
 Indonesia: Sumba

I *Ptilinopus granulifrons*
Carunculated Fruit-Dove
 Indonesia: Obi

R *Ptilinopus huttoni*
Rapa Fruit-Dove
 French Polynesia: Tubuai Islands (Rapa)

V *Ptilinopus roseicapilla*
Marianas Fruit-Dove
 Guam; Northern Marianas

I *Starnoenas cyanocephala*
Blue-headed Quail-Dove
 Cuba

V *Treron capellei*
Large Green-Pigeon
 Brunei; Indonesia: Java, Kalimantan, Sumatra;
 Malaysia: Peninsular, Sabah, Sarawak;
 Myanmar; Thailand

V *Treron psittacea*
Timor Green-Pigeon
 Indonesia: Roti, Semau, Timor

V *Treron teysmannii*
Sumba Green-Pigeon
 Indonesia: Sumba

E *Zenaida graysoni*
Socorro Dove
 Mexico: Revillagigedos Islands

Order PSITTACIFORMES

Family LORIIDAE

I *Charmosyna diadema*
New Caledonian Lorikeet
 New Caledonia (ex?)

I *Charmosyna toxopei*
Blue-fronted Lorikeet
 Indonesia: Buru

R *Eos cyanogenia*
Black-winged Lory
 Indonesia: Biak, Manim, Meos Num, Numfor

R *Eos histrio*
Red-and-blue Lory
 Indonesia: Miangas, Ruang, Sangihe, Siau,
 Talaud

R *Eos reticulata*
Blue-streaked Lory
 Indonesia: Babar, Tanimbar
 [Indonesia: Damar, Kai Islands]

R *Lorius domicella*
Purple-naped Lory
 Indonesia: Ambon, Seram
 [Indonesia: Buru]

R *Vini kuhlii*
Kuhl's Lorikeet
 French Polynesia: Rimitara, Tubuai?
 [Kiribati: Kiritimati, Tabuaeran, Teraina]

R *Vini peruviana*
Tahitian Lorikeet
 Cook Islands: [Aitutaki]?; French Polynesia:
 Society Islands, Tuamotu Archipelago

R *Vini stepheni*
Stephen's Lorikeet
 Pitcairn Islands: Henderson Island

R *Vini ultramarina*
Ultramarine Lorikeet
 French Polynesia: Nukuhiva, Uapou
 [French Polynesia: Uahuka]

Family CACATUIDAE

E *Cacatua alba*
White Cockatoo
 Indonesia: Bacan, Halmahera, Obi, Ternate,
 Tidore

E *Cacatua goffini*
Tanimbar Cockatoo
 Indonesia: Tanimbar Islands
 [Indonesia: Kai Islands (Tual)]

E *Cacatua haematuropygia*
Philippine Cockatoo
 Philippines

E *Cacatua moluccensis*
Salmon-crested Cockatoo
 Indonesia: Haruku, Seram, Saparua
 [Indonesia: Ambon; Singapore]

V *Cacatua sulphurea*
Yellow-crested Cockatoo
 Indonesia: Alor, Besar, Butung, Flores, Kalao,
 Kalaotoa, Kayunadi, Komodo, Lombok, Madu,
 Muna, Sulawesi, Sumbawa, Padar, Pantar,
 Penida, Rinca, Salembu, Seman, Sumba,
 Tanahjampea, Timor, Tukanbesi
 [Hong Kong; Singapore]

Family PSITTACIDAE

R   *Agapornis nigrigenis*
    Black-cheeked Lovebird
        Botswana; Namibia?; Zambia; Zimbabwe (ex?)

R   *Amazona arausiaca*
    Red-necked Parrot
        Dominica

K   *Amazona barbadensis*
    Yellow-shouldered Parrot
        Aruba (ex?); Netherlands Antilles: Bonaire;
        Venezuela

E   *Amazona brasiliensis*
    Red-tailed Parrot
        Brazil

R   *Amazona guildingii*
    Saint Vincent Parrot
        Saint Vincent

E   *Amazona imperialis*
    Imperial Parrot
        Dominica

V   *Amazona oratrix*
    Yellow-headed Parrot
        Belize; Guatemala?; Mexico
        [Puerto Rico]

V/R *Amazona pretrei*
    Red-spectacled Parrot
        Argentina; Brazil; Paraguay?; Uruguay

V/R *Amazona rhodocorytha*
    Red-browed Parrot
        Brazil

R   *Amazona versicolor*
    Saint Lucia Parrot
        Saint Lucia

V/R *Amazona vinacea*
    Vinaceous Parrot
        Argentina; Brazil; Paraguay

V   *Amazona viridigenalis*
    Red-crowned Parrot
        Mexico
        [Puerto Rico; USA]

E   *Amazona vittata*
    Puerto Rican Parrot
        Puerto Rico

E/Ex *Anodorhynchus glaucus*
    Glaucous Macaw
        Argentina; Brazil; Paraguay

V/R *Anodorhynchus hyacinthinus*
    Hyacinth Macaw
        Bolivia; Brazil; Paraguay

E   *Anodorhynchus leari*
    Indigo Macaw
        Brazil

E   *Ara glaucogularis*
    (*A. caninde* misapplied)
    Blue-throated Macaw
        Argentina?; Bolivia; Paraguay?

V   *Ara rubrogenys*
    Red-fronted Macaw
        Bolivia

V   *Aratinga auricapilla*
    Golden-capped Parakeet
        Brazil

V   *Aratinga euops*
    Cuban Parakeet
        Cuba

V   *Aratinga guarouba*
    (*Guaruba guarouba*)
    Golden Parakeet
        Brazil

V/R *Bolborhynchus ferrugineifrons*
    Rufous-fronted Parakeet
        Colombia

E   *Cyanopsitta spixii*
    Little Blue Macaw
        Brazil

R   *Cyanoramphus unicolor*
    Antipodes Parakeet
        New Zealand: Antipodes Islands

V   *Forpus xanthops*
    Yellow-faced Parrotlet
        Peru

V/R *Hapalopsittaca amazonina*
    Rusty-faced Parrot
        Colombia; Venezuela

E   *Hapalopsittaca fuertesi*
    (*H. amazonina fuertesi*)
    Indigo-winged Parrot
        Colombia

E   *Hapalopsittaca pyrrhops*
    (*H. amazonina pyrrhops*)
    Red-faced Parrot
        Ecuador; Peru

V/R *Leptosittaca branickii*
    Golden-plumed Parakeet
        Colombia; Ecuador; Peru

V   *Loriculus catamene*
    Sangihe Hanging-Parrot
        Indonesia: Sangihe

R   *Neophema chrysogaster*
Orange-bellied Parrot
  Australia: Tasmania. * Australia

R   *Neophema splendida*
Scarlet-chested Parrot
Australia

E   *Ognorhynchus icterotis*
Yellow-eared Parrot
  Colombia; Ecuador

I   *Pezoporus occidentalis*
(*Geopsittacus occidentalis*)
Night Parrot
  Australia (ex?)

E   *Pezoporus wallicus*
Ground Parrot
Australia

K   *Polytelis alexandrae*
Alexandra's Parrot
Australia

R   *Prioniturus luconensis*
Green Racquet-tail
  Philippines: Luzon, Marinduque

I   *Prioniturus mada*
Buru Racquet-tail
  Indonesia: Buru

R   *Psephotus chrysopterygius*
Golden-shouldered Parrot
Australia

K   *Psephotus dissimilis*
Hooded Parrot
Australia

E   *Psephotus pulcherrimus*
Paradise Parrot
  Australia (ex?)

I   *Psittacula caniceps*
Nicobar Parakeet
  India: Nicobar Islands

E   *Psittacula echo*
Mauritius Parakeet
Mauritius

I   *Psittacula intermedia*
Intermediate Parakeet
  India?

R   *Psittaculirostris salvadorii*
Salvadori's Fig-Parrot
  Indonesia: Irian Jaya

K   *Pyrrhura albipectus*
White-necked Parakeet
Ecuador

V/R   *Pyrrhura calliptera*
Brown-breasted Parakeet
Colombia

R   *Pyrrhura cruentata*
Blue-throated Parakeet
Brazil

V/R   *Pyrrhura orcesi*
El Oro Parakeet
Ecuador

V   *Rhynchopsitta pachyrhyncha*
Thick-billed Parrot
Mexico
[USA]

V   *Rhynchopsitta terrisi*
Maroon-fronted Parrot
Mexico

E   *Strigops habroptilus*
Kakapo
  New Zealand: South Island, Stewart Island

V/R   *Touit melanonotus*
Brown-backed Parrotlet
Brazil

K   *Touit stictoptera*
Spot-winged Parrotlet
  Colombia; Ecuador; Peru

V/R   *Touit surda*
Golden-tailed Parrotlet
Brazil

V/R   *Triclaria malachitacea*
Blue-bellied Parrot
  Argentina; Brazil

Order CUCULIFORMES

Family MUSOPHAGIDAE

E   *Tauraco bannermani*
Bannerman's Turaco
Cameroon

R   *Tauraco ruspolii*
Ruspoli's Turaco
Ethiopia

Family CUCULIDAE

K   *Carpococcyx radiceus*
Sunda Ground-Cuckoo
  Brunei; Indonesia: Kalimantan, Sumatra;
  Malaysia: Sabah, Sarawak

E   *Centropus chlororhynchus*
Green-billed Coucal
  Sri Lanka

V   *Centropus nigrorufus*
Sunda Coucal
Indonesia: Java, Sumatra?

R   *Centropus rectunguis*
Short-toed Coucal
Brunei; Indonesia: Kalimantan, Sumatra; Malaysia: Peninsular Malaysia, Sabah, Sarawak

I   *Centropus steerii*
Black-hooded Coucal
Philippines: Mindoro

I   *Chrysococcyx rufomerus*
Green-cheeked Bronze-Cuckoo
Indonesia: Damar, Romang

I   *Hyetornis rufigularis*
Rufous-breasted Cuckoo
Dominican Republic; Haiti

V   *Neomorphus radiolosus*
Banded Ground-Cuckoo
Colombia; Ecuador

V   *Phaenicophaeus pyrrhocephalus*
Red-faced Malkoha
Sri Lanka

Order STRIGIFORMES

Family TYTONIDAE

I   *Phodilus prigoginei*
Congo Bay-Owl
Burundi?; Zaire

K   *Tyto aurantia*
Bismarck Masked-Owl
Papua New Guinea: New Britain

I   *Tyto inexspectata*
Minahassa Masked-Owl
Indonesia: Sulawesi

I   *Tyto nigrobrunnea*
Taliabu Masked-Owl
Indonesia: Taliabu

I   *Tyto sororcula*
Lesser Masked-Owl
Indonesia: Buru, Tanimbar Islands

I   *Tyto soumagnei*
Madagascar Red Owl
Madagascar (ex?)

Family STRIGIDAE

I   *Athene blewitti*
Forest Owlet
India (ex?)

R   *Glaucidium albertinum*
Albertine Owlet
Rwanda; Zaire

R   *Ketupa blakistoni*
(*Bubo blakistoni*)
Blakiston's Fish-Owl
China; Japan: Hokkaido; Russia

R   *Otus angelinae*
Javan Scops-Owl
Indonesia: Java

R   *Otus hartlaubi*
São Tomé Scops-Owl
São Tomé and Príncipe: São Tomé, Príncipe?

E   *Otus ireneae*
Sokoke Scops-Owl
Kenya; Tanzania?

R   *Otus mindorensis*
Mindoro Scops-Owl
Philippines: Mindoro

R   *Otus pauliani*
Comoro Scops-Owl
Comoros: Grand Comoro

I   *Otus sagittatus*
White-fronted Scops-Owl
Indonesia: Sumatra?; Malaysia: Peninsular Malaysia; Myanmar; Thailand

R   *Scotopelia ussheri*
Rufous Fishing-Owl
Côte d'Ivoire; Ghana; Guinea; Liberia; Sierra Leone

K   *Xenoglaux loweryi*
Long-whiskered Owlet
Peru

Order CAPRIMULGIFORMES

Family PODARGIDAE

K   *Batrachostomus harterti*
Dulit Frogmouth
Indonesia: Kalimantan; Malaysia: Sarawak

Family CAPRIMULGIDAE

E   *Caprimulgus candicans*
White-winged Nightjar
Brazil; Paraguay?

I   *Caprimulgus centralasicus*
Vaurie's Nightjar
China

I   *Caprimulgus maculosus*
Cayenne Nightjar
French Guiana

R   *Caprimulgus noctitherus*
     Puerto Rican Nightjar
        Puerto Rico

I   *Caprimulgus pulchellus*
     Salvadori's Nightjar
        Indonesia: Java, Sumatra

K   *Eleothreptus anomalus*
     Sickle-winged Nightjar
        Argentina; Brazil; Paraguay

I   *Eurostopodus diabolicus*
     Satanic Eared-Nightjar
        Indonesia: Sulawesi

E/Ex *Siphonorhis americanus*
     Jamaican Poorwill
        Jamaica

Order APODIFORMES

Family APODIDAE

I   *Apus acuticauda*
     Dark-rumped Swift
        India

R   *Collocalia elaphra*
     Seychelles Swiftlet
        Seychelles

V   *Collocalia leucophaeus*
     (*Aerodramus leucophaeus*)
     Tahiti Swiftlet
        French Polynesia: Tahiti

R   *Collocalia sawtelli*
     (*Aerodramus sawtelli*)
     Atiu Swiftlet
        Cook Islands: Atiu

I   *Cypseloides lemosi*
     White-chested Swift
        Colombia; Ecuador?

I   *Hydrochous gigas*
     Waterfall Swift
        Indonesia: Java, Kalimantan?, Sumatra;
        Malaysia: Peninsular Malaysia, Sabah?,
        Sarawak?

I   *Schoutedenapus schoutedeni*
     Schouteden's Swift
        Zaire

Family TROCHILIDAE

E   *Acestrura berlepschi*
     Esmeraldas Woodstar
        Ecuador

E   *Acestrura bombus*
     Little Woodstar
        Ecuador; Peru

I   *Aglaeactis aliciae*
     Purple-backed Sunbeam
        Peru

V   *Amazilia boucardi*
     Mangrove Hummingbird
        Costa Rica

V   *Amazilia castaneiventris*
     Chestnut-bellied Hummingbird
        Colombia

V   *Amazilia distans*
     Tachira Emerald
        Venezuela

E   *Amazilia luciae*
     Honduran Emerald
        Honduras

V/R *Campylopterus ensipennis*
     White-tailed Sabrewing
        Trinidad and Tobago: Tobago; Venezuela

V/R *Coeligena prunellei*
     Black Inca
        Colombia

E/Ex *Eriocnemis godini*
     Turquoise-throated Puffleg
        Colombia; Ecuador

R   *Eriocnemis mirabilis*
     Colourful Puffleg
        Colombia

E   *Eriocnemis nigrivestis*
     Black-breasted Puffleg
        Ecuador

K   *Eulidia yarrellii*
     Chilean Woodstar
        Chile; Peru

V   *Eupherusa cyanophrys*
     Blue-capped Hummingbird
        Mexico

V   *Eupherusa poliocerca*
     White-tailed Hummingbird
        Mexico

V/R *Haplophaedia lugens*
     Hoary Puffleg
        Colombia; Ecuador

K   *Heliangelus regalis*
     Royal Sunangel
        Peru

V/R **Hylonympha macrocerca**
Scissor-tailed Hummingbird
Venezuela

I **Lepidopyga lilliae**
Sapphire-bellied Hummingbird
Colombia

V **Loddigesia mirabilis**
Marvelous Spatuletail
Peru

E **Lophornis brachylopha**
Short-crested Coquette
Mexico

R **Metallura baroni**
Violet-throated Metaltail
Ecuador

R **Metallura odomae**
Neblina Metaltail
Peru

I **Popelairia letitiae**
Coppery Thorntail
Bolivia?

V/R **Ramphodon dohrnii**
(*Glaucis dohrnii*)
Hook-billed Hermit
Brazil

V **Selasphorus ardens**
Glow-throated Hummingbird
Panama

V/R **Sephanoides fernandensis**
Juan Fernandez Firecrown
Chile: Juan Fernandez Islands

V **Taphrolesbia griseiventris**
Grey-bellied Comet
Peru

I **Thalurania ridgwayi**
Mexican Woodnymph
Mexico

Order TROGONIFORMES

Family TROGONIDAE

I **Euptilotis neoxenus**
Eared Trogon
Mexico; USA

Order CORACIIFORMES

Family ALCEDINIDAE

I **Actenoides bougainvillei**
(*Halcyon bougainvillei*)
Moustached Kingfisher
Papua New Guinea: Bougainville; Solomon
Islands: Guadalcanal (ex?)

V **Actenoides hombroni**
(*Halcyon hombroni*)
Blue-capped Kingfisher
Philippines: Mindanao

I **Alcedo hercules**
Blyth's Kingfisher
Bangladesh; Bhutan; China; Laos; India;
Myanmar; Nepal?; Viet Nam

V **Tanysiptera riedelii**
Biak Paradise-Kingfisher
Indonesia

V **Todirhamphus australasia**
(*Halcyon australasia*)
Cinnamon-banded Kingfisher
Indonesia: Lombok, Sumba, Timor, Wetar and
small islands east to Tanimbar

R **Todirhamphus gambieri**
(*Halcyon gambieri*)
Tuamotu Kingfisher
French Polynesia: Tuamotu Archipelago (Niau)

V **Todirhamphus godeffroyi**
(*Halcyon godeffroyi*)
Marquesan Kingfisher
French Polynesia: Marquesas Islands (Hivaoa,
Tahuata)

R **Todirhamphus ruficollaris**
(*Halcyon ruficollaris, H. mangaia*)
Mangaia Kingfisher
Cook Islands: Mangaia

Family MOMOTIDAE

K **Electron carinatum**
Keel-billed Motmot
Belize; Costa Rica; Guatemala; Honduras;
Mexico; Nicaragua

Family BRACHYPTERACIIDAE

R **Atelornis crossleyi**
Rufous-headed Ground-Roller
Madagascar

R   *Brachypteracias leptosomus*
Short-legged Ground-Roller
Madagascar

R   *Brachypteracias squamigera*
Scaly Ground-Roller
Madagascar

R   *Uratelornis chimaera*
Long-tailed Ground-Roller
Madagascar

Family BUCEROTIDAE

R   *Aceros corrugatus*
Wrinkled Hornbill
Brunei; Indonesia: Batu Islands, Kalimantan,
Sumatra; Malaysia: Peninsular Malaysia,
Sabah, Sarawak; Thailand

V   *Aceros everetti*
(*Rhyticeros everetti*)
Sumba Hornbill
Indonesia: Sumba

R   *Aceros narcondami*
Narcondam Hornbill
India: Narcondam

R   *Aceros nipalensis*
Rufous-necked Hornbill
Bangladesh; Bhutan; China; Laos; India;
Myanmar; Nepal (ex?); Thailand; Viet Nam

I   *Aceros subruficollis*
Plain-pouched Hornbill
India; Indonesia: Sumatra; Myanmar; Thailand

R   *Anthracoceros montani*
Sulu Hornbill
Philippines: Jolo, Tawitawi

I   *Buceros vigil*
(*Rhinoplax vigil*)
Helmeted Hornbill
Brunei; Indonesia: Kalimantan, Sumatra;
Malaysia: Peninsular Malaysia, Sabah,
Sarawak; Myanmar; Thailand

Order PICIFORMES

Family GALBULIDAE

K   *Galbula pastazae*
Coppery-chested Jacamar
Brazil?; Colombia; Ecuador

E   *Jacamaralcyon tridactyla*
Three-toed Jacamar
Brazil

Family CAPITONIDAE

V/R *Capito hypoleucus*
White-mantled Barbet
Colombia

R   *Megalaima javensis*
Black-banded Barbet
Indonesia: Java

I   *Pogoniulus makawai*
White-chested Tinkerbird
Zambia

Family INDICATORIDAE

K   *Melignomon eisentrauti*
Yellow-footed Honeyguide
Cameroon; Côte d'Ivoire?; Ghana; Guinea?;
Liberia

Family RAMPHASTIDAE

K   *Aulacorhynchus huallagae*
Yellow-browed Toucanet
Peru

Family PICIDAE

E/Ex *Campephilus imperialis*
Imperial Woodpecker
Mexico

E/Ex *Campephilus principalis*
Ivory-billed Woodpecker
Cuba; USA

I   *Colaptes fernandinae*
Fernandina's Flicker
Cuba

V/R *Dryocopus galeatus*
Helmeted Woodpecker
Argentina; Brazil; Paraguay

E   *Picoides borealis*
Red-cockaded Woodpecker
USA

I   *Picus rabieri*
Red-collared Woodpecker
China; Laos; Viet Nam

E   *Sapheopipo noguchii*
Okinawa Woodpecker
Japan: Okinawa

Order PASSERIFORMES

Family EURYLAIMIDAE

R   *Pseudocalyptomena graueri*
Grauer's Broadbill
Uganda; Zaire

Family DENDROCOLAPTIDAE

V   *Xiphocolaptes falcirostris*
    (includes *X. franciscanus*)
    Moustached Woodcreeper
    Brazil

Family FURNARIIDAE

K   *Aphrastura masafuerae*
    Mas Afuera Rayadito
        Chile: Juan Fernandez Islands

K   *Asthenes anthoides*
    Austral Canastero
        Argentina; Chile

I   *Asthenes berlepschi*
    Berlepsch's Canastero
    Bolivia

I   *Asthenes luizae*
    Cipó Canastero
    Brazil

E   *Automolus ruficollis*
    Rufous-necked Foliage-gleaner
    Ecuador; Peru

V   *Cinclodes palliatus*
    White-bellied Cinclodes
    Peru

I   *Hylocryptus erythrocephalus*
    (*Automolus erythrocephalus*)
    Henna-hooded Foliage-gleaner
    Ecuador; Peru

E   *Leptasthenura xenothorax*
    White-browed Tit-Spinetail
    Peru

K   *Megaxenops parnaguae*
    Great Xenops
    Brazil

E   *Philydor novaesi*
    Alagoas Foliage-gleaner
    Brazil

V/R *Premnoplex tatei*
    (*Margarornis tatei*)
    White-throated Barbtail
    Venezuela

E   *Simoxenops striatus*
    Bolivian Recurvebill
    Bolivia

K   *Synallaxis cherriei*
    Chestnut-throated Spinetail
    Brazil; Colombia; Ecuador; Peru

I   *Synallaxis courseni*
    Apurimac Spinetail
    Peru

V/R *Synallaxis infuscata*
    Pinto's Spinetail
    Brazil

V   *Synallaxis kollari*
    Hoary-throated Spinetail
    Brazil

E   *Synallaxis tithys*
    Blackish-headed Spinetail
    Ecuador; Peru

V   *Synallaxis zimmeri*
    Russet-bellied Spinetail
    Peru

V/R *Thripophaga berlepschi*
    Russet-mantled Softtail
    Peru

V   *Thripophaga cherriei*
    Orinoco Softtail
    Venezuela

V/R *Thripophaga macroura*
    Striated Softtail
    Brazil

Family FORMICARIIDAE

V/R *Biatas nigropectus*
    White-bearded Antshrike
    Argentina; Brazil

V   *Cercomacra carbonaria*
    Rio Branco Antbird
    Brazil

E   *Clytoctantes alixii*
    Recurve-billed Bushbird
    Colombia; Venezuela

I   *Clytoctantes atrogularis*
    Rondônia Bushbird
    Brazil

V/R *Dysithamnus occidentalis*
    Bicolored Antvireo
    Colombia; Ecuador

V/R *Dysithamnus plumbeus*
    (*Thamnomanes plumbeus*)
    Plumbeous Antvireo
    Brazil

V   *Formicarius rufifrons*
    Rufous-fronted Antthrush
    Peru

E   **Formicivora erythronotos**
Black-hooded Antwren
   Brazil

V   **Formicivora iheringi**
Narrow-billed Antwren
   Brazil

E   **Formicivora littoralis**
Restinga Antwren
   Brazil

E/Ex **Grallaria alleni**
Moustached Antpitta
   Colombia

E   **Grallaria chthonia**
Tachira Antpitta
   Venezuela

K   **Grallaria gigantea**
Giant Antpitta
   Colombia; Ecuador

E/Ex **Grallaria milleri**
Brown-banded Antpitta
   Colombia

I   **Grallaria rufocinerea**
Bicolored Antpitta
   Colombia

V/R **Grallaricula cucullata**
Hooded Antpitta
   Colombia; Venezuela

E   **Herpsilochmus parkeri**
Ash-throated Antwren
   Peru

V   **Herpsilochmus pectoralis**
Pectoral Antwren
   Brazil

E   **Myrmeciza griseiceps**
Grey-headed Antbird
   Ecuador; Peru

V/R **Myrmeciza ruficauda**
Scalloped Antbird
   Brazil

I   **Myrmotherula fluminensis**
Rio de Janeiro Antwren
   Brazil

V/R **Myrmotherula grisea**
Ashy Antwren
   Bolivia

E   **Myrmotherula snowi**
Alagoas Antwren
   Brazil

I   **Pithys castanea**
White-masked Antbird
   Peru

E   **Pyriglena atra**
Fringe-backed Fire-eye
   Brazil

V   **Rhopornis ardesiaca**
Slender Antbird
   Brazil

V   **Terenura sharpei**
Yellow-rumped Antwren
   Bolivia; Peru

E   **Terenura sicki**
Alagoas Antwren
   Brazil

K   **Xenornis setifrons**
Speckled Antshrike
   Colombia; Panama

Family RHINOCRYPTIDAE

I   **Merulaxis stresemanni**
Stresemann's Bristlefront
   Brazil

R   **Scytalopus novacapitalis**
Brasilia Tapaculo
   Brazil

E   **Scytalopus psychopompus**
Chestnut-sided Tapaculo
   Brazil

Family COTINGIDAE

E/Ex **Calyptura cristata**
Kinglet Calyptura
   Brazil

V   **Carpodectes antoniae**
Yellow-billed Cotinga
   Costa Rica; Panama

V/R **Carpornis melanocephalus**
Black-headed Berryeater
   Brazil

V/R **Cephalopterus glabricollis**
Bare-necked Umbrellabird
   Costa Rica; Panama

R   **Cotinga maculata**
Banded Cotinga
   Brazil

V/R **Iodopleura pipra**
Buff-throated Purpletuft
   Brazil

V/R   *Lipaugus lanioides*
Cinnamon-vented Piha
Brazil

E   *Pachyramphus spodiurus*
Slaty Becard
Ecuador; Peru

R   *Tijuca condita*
Grey-winged Cotinga
Brazil

R   *Xipholena atropurpurea*
White-winged Cotinga
Brazil

K   *Zaratornis stresemanni*
(*Ampelion stresemanni*)
White-cheeked Cotinga
Peru

Family PIPRIDAE

I   *Pipra vilasboasi*
Golden-crowned Manakin
Brazil

V/R   *Piprites pileatus*
Black-capped Piprites
Argentina; Brazil

Family TYRANNIDAE

V/R   *Agriornis andicola*
(*A. albicauda*)
White-tailed Shrike-Tyrant
Argentina; Bolivia; Chile; Ecuador; Peru

V   *Alectrurus risora*
(*Yetapa risora*)
Strange-tailed Tyrant
Argentina; Brazil (ex?); Paraguay; Uruguay
(ex?)

E   *Anairetes alpinus*
Ash-breasted Tit-Tyrant
Bolivia; Peru

E   *Attila torridus*
Ochraceous Attila
Colombia; Ecuador; Peru

V/R   *Lathrotriccus griseipectus*
(*Empidonax griseipectus*)
Grey-breasted Flycatcher
Ecuador; Peru

I   *Euscarthmus rufomarginatus*
Rufous-sided Pygmy-Tyrant
Bolivia; Brazil; Suriname

V   *Hemitriccus cinnamomeipectus*
Cinnamon-breasted Tody-Tyrant
Peru

R   *Hemitriccus furcatus*
(*Ceratotriccus furcatus*)
Fork-tailed Tody-Tyrant
Brazil

I   *Hemitriccus kaempferi*
(*Idioptilon kaempferi*)
Kaempfer's Tody-Tyrant
Brazil

V/R   *Hemitriccus mirandae*
Buff-breasted Tody-Tyrant
Brazil

E   *Phylloscartes ceciliae*
Alagoas Tyrannulet
Brazil

I   *Phylloscartes lanyoni*
Antioquia Bristle-Tyrant
Colombia

V/R   *Phylloscartes paulistus*
São Paulo Tyrannulet
Argentina?; Brazil; Paraguay

V   *Phylloscartes roquettei*
Minas Gerais Tyrannulet
Brazil

V/R   *Platyrinchus leucoryphus*
Russet-winged Spadebill
Argentina?; Brazil; Paraguay

V/R   *Pseudocolopteryx dinellianus*
Dinelli's Doradito
Argentina; Bolivia; Paraguay

I   *Todirostrum senex*
Buff-cheeked Tody-Flycatcher
Brazil

I   *Tyrannus cubensis*
Giant Kingbird
Cuba; Turks and Caicos Islands

Family PHYTOTOMIDAE

E   *Phytotoma raimondii*
Peruvian Plantcutter
Peru

Family PITTIDAE

I   *Pitta anerythra*
Black-faced Pitta
Papua New Guinea: Bougainville (ex?);
Solomon Islands: Santa Isabel (ex?)

R   *Pitta elliotii*
Bar-bellied Pitta
Cambodia; Laos; Thailand; Viet Nam

E   *Pitta gurneyi*
    Gurney's Pitta
        Myanmar (ex?); Thailand

I   *Pitta kochi*
    Whiskered Pitta
        Philippines: Luzon

R   *Pitta nympha*
    Fairy Pitta
        China; Japan; Korea Republic: Cheju Do and
        nearby islands; Taiwan. * Indonesia:
        Kalimantan; Malaysia: Sarawak; Viet Nam

E   *Pitta schneideri*
    Schneider's Pitta
        Indonesia: Sumatra

R   *Pitta steerii*
    Azure-breasted Pitta
        Philippines: Bohol, Leyte, Mindanao, Samar

I   *Pitta superba*
    Superb Pitta
        Papua New Guinea: Manus

Family XENICIDAE

E   *Xenicus longipes*
    Bush Wren
        New Zealand (ex?)

Family PHILEPITTIDAE

I   *Neodrepanis hypoxanthus*
    Yellow bellied Asity
        Madagascar

Family ATRICHORNITHIDAE

E   *Atrichornis clamosus*
    Noisy Scrub-bird
        Australia

R   *Atrichornis rufescens*
    Rufous Scrub-bird
        Australia

Family ALAUDIDAE

I   *Spizocorys fringillaris*
    Botha's Lark
        South Africa

E   *Alauda razae*
    Raso Lark
        Cape Verde: Raso Island

I   *Heteromirafra archeri*
    Archer's Lark
        Somalia

I   *Heteromirafra ruddi*
    Rudd's Lark
        Lesotho; South Africa; Swaziland

I   *Heteromirafra sidamoensis*
    Sidamo Lark
        Ethiopia

K   *Mirafra ashi*
    Ash's Lark
        Somalia

K   *Mirafra degodiensis*
    Degodi Lark
        Ethiopia

Family HIRUNDINIDAE

R   *Hirundo megaensis*
    White-tailed Swallow
        Ethiopia

K   *Hirundo perdita*
    Red Sea Swallow
        Sudan?

I   *Pseudochelidon sirintarae*
    White-eyed River-Martin
        Thailand

Family MOTACILLIDAE

K   *Anthus chloris*
    Yellow-breasted Pipit
        Lesotho; South Africa

I   *Anthus nattereri*
    Ochre-breasted Pipit
        Argentina; Brazil; Paraguay

V   *Anthus sokokensis*
    Sokoke Pipit
        Kenya; Tanzania (ex?)

Family CAMPEPHAGIDAE

V   *Campephaga lobata*
    Ghana Cuckooshrike
        Côte d'Ivoire; Ghana; Liberia; Sierra Leone

R   *Coracina coerulescens*
    Blackish Cuckooshrike
        Philippines: Luzon

R   *Coracina sula*
    Sula Cicadabird
        Indonesia: Sula Islands

V   *Coracina newtoni*
    Réunion Cuckooshrike
        Réunion

R   *Coracina ostenta*
    White-winged Cuckooshrike
        Philippines: Guimaras, Negros, Panay

R   *Coracina schistacea*
    Slaty Cuckooshrike
        Indonesia: Banggai, Peleng, Sula

V   **Coracina typica**
Mauritius Cuckooshrike
Mauritius

Family PYCNONOTIDAE

V   **Chlorocichla prigoginei**
Prigogine's Greenbul
Zaire

V   **Criniger olivaceus**
Yellow-bearded Bulbul
Côte d'Ivoire; Ghana; Guinea; Liberia; Senegal; Sierra Leone

I   **Ixos siquijorensis**
(*Hypsipetes siquijorensis*)
Streak-breasted Bulbul
Philippines: Romblon, Siquijor, Tablas

R   **Phyllastrephus apperti**
Appert's Greenbul
Madagascar

R   **Phyllastrephus cinereiceps**
Grey-crowned Greenbul
Madagascar

K   **Phyllastrephus leucolepis**
Liberian Greenbul
Liberia

R   **Phyllastrephus tenebrosus**
Dusky Greenbul
Madagascar

I   **Pycnonotus nieuwenhuisii**
Blue-wattled Bulbul
Indonesia: Kalimantan, Sumatra

Family LANIIDAE

K   **Laniarius liberatus**
Bulo Burti Boubou
Somalia

I   **Lanius newtoni**
Newton's Fiscal Shrike
São Tomé and Príncipe: São Tomé (ex?)

R   **Malaconotus alius**
Uluguru Bushshrike
Tanzania

I   **Malaconotus monteiri**
Monteiro's Bushshrike
Angola; Cameroon (ex?); Kenya

R   **Malaconotus gladiator**
Green-breasted Bushshrike
Cameroon; Nigeria?

I   **Prionops gabela**
Angola Helmetshrike
Angola

I   **Telophorus kupeensis**
(*Malaconotus kupeensis*)
Serle's Bushshrike
Cameroon

Family VANGIDAE

R   **Xenopirostris damii**
Van Dam's Vanga
Madagascar

R   **Xenopirostris polleni**
Pollen's Vanga
Madagascar

Family CINCLIDAE

K   **Cinclus schulzi**
Rufous-throated Dipper
Argentina; Bolivia

Family TROGLODYTIDAE

V/R   **Hylorchilus sumichrasti**
(*Catherpes sumichrasti*)
Slender-billed Wren
Mexico

R   **Cistothorus apolinari**
Apolinar's Wren
Colombia

V/R   **Ferminia cerverai**
Zapata Wren
Cuba

I   **Thryothorus nicefori**
Niceforo's Wren
Colombia

Family MIMIDAE

E   **Mimodes graysoni**
Socorro Mockingbird
Mexico: Socorro

E   **Nesomimus trifasciatus**
Charles Mockingbird
Ecuador: Galapagos Islands: Champion, Gardner

E   **Ramphocinclus brachyurus**
White-breasted Thrasher
Martinique; Saint Lucia

Family MUSCICAPIDAE

V   **Acrocephalus familiaris**
(includes *A. kingi*)
Millerbird
USA: Hawaiian Islands (Nihoa)

K **Acrocephalus paludicola**
Aquatic Warbler
Austria; Belarus; Germany; Hungary; Latvia;
Lithuania; Moldova; Poland; Russia; Ukraine.
* France; Iran; Italy; Latvia; Mali; Morocco;
Netherlands; Portugal; Senegal; Spain;
Switzerland; United Kingdom

E **Acrocephalus rehsei**
Nauru Reed-Warbler
Nauru

R **Acrocephalus sorghophilus**
Streaked Reed-Warbler
China. * Philippines

V **Alcippe variegaticeps**
Gold-fronted Fulvetta
China

E **Alethe choloensis**
Cholo Alethe
Malawi; Mozambique

I **Amaurocichla bocagii**
Bocage's Longbill
São Tomé and Príncipe: São Tomé

K **Amytornis barbatus**
Grey Grasswren
Australia

K **Amytornis dorotheae**
Carpentarian Grasswren
Australia

I **Amytornis goyderi**
Eyrean Grasswren
Australia

K **Amytornis textilis**
Thick-billed Grasswren
Australia

R **Apalis argentea**
Kungwe Apalis
Burundi; Rwanda; Tanzania; Zaire

K **Apalis chariessa**
White-winged Apalis
Kenya (ex?); Malawi; Mozambique; Tanzania

R **Apalis kaboboensis**
Kabobo Apalis
Zaire

K **Apalis karamojae**
Karamoja Apalis
Tanzania; Uganda

K **Aphelocephala pectoralis**
Chestnut-breasted Whiteface
Australia

R **Arcanator orostruthus**
(*Modulatrix orostruthus*)
Dapple-throat
Mozambique; Tanzania

K **Batis minima**
Verreaux's Batis
Cameroon; Gabon

E **Bebrornis rodericanus**
(*Acrocephalus rodericanus*)
Rodriguesz Brush-Warbler
Mauritius: Rodrigues

R **Bebrornis sechellensis**
(*Acrocephalus sechellensis*)
Seychelles Brush-Warbler
Seychelles: Cousin

I **Brachypteryx hyperythra**
Rusty-bellied Shortwing
China; India

K **Bradypterus grandis**
Ja River Scrub-Warbler
Cameroon; Gabon

V **Bradypterus graueri**
Grauer's Scrub-Warbler
Burundi; Rwanda; Uganda; Zaire

R **Bradypterus major**
Long-billed Bush-Warbler
China; India; Pakistan

K **Chaetornis striatus**
Bristled Grassbird
Bangladesh; India; Nepal; Pakistan

R **Chloropeta gracilirostris**
Thin-billed Flycatcher-Warbler
Burundi; Kenya; Rwanda; Uganda; Zaire;
Zambia

V **Chrysomma altirostre**
(*Moupinia altirostris*)
Jerdon's Babbler
India; Myanmar (ex?); Nepal; Pakistan

I **Cisticola haesitatus**
Island Cisticola
Yemen: Socotra

K **Cisticola restrictus**
Tana River Cisticola
Kenya; Somalia?

R **Clytorhynchus hamlini**
Rennell Shrikebill
Solomon Islands: Rennell

R *Cochoa azurea*
Javan Cochoa
    Indonesia: Java

I *Cochoa beccarii*
Sumatran Cochoa
    Indonesia: Sumatra

E *Copsychus cebuensis*
Black Shama
    Philippines: Cebu

E *Copsychus sechellarum*
Seychelles Magpie-Robin
    Seychelles: Aride, Fregate

I *Cossypha heinrichi*
White-headed Robin-Chat
    Angola; Zaire

I *Crocias langbianis*
Grey-crowned Crocias
    Viet Nam

I *Crossleyia xanthophrys*
Yellow-browed Oxylabes
    Madagascar

R *Cyornis herioti*
Blue-breasted Flycatcher
    Philippines: Catanduanes, Luzon

I *Cyornis ruckii*
Rueck's Blue-Flycatcher
    Indonesia: Sumatra (ex?);   Malaysia?:
    Peninsular Malaysia

R *Cyornis sanfordi*
Matinan Flycatcher
    Indonesia: Sulawesi

V *Dasyornis brachypterus*
Eastern Bristlebird
    Australia

R *Dasyornis longirostris*
Western Bristlebird
    Australia

R *Eremomela turneri*
Turner's Eremomela
    Kenya; Uganda; Zaire

K *Ficedula bonthaina*
Lompobattang Flycatcher
    Indonesia: Sulawesi

V *Ficedula harterti*
Sumba Flycatcher
    Indonesia: Sumba

I *Ficedula henrici*
Damar Flycatcher
    Indonesia: Damar

R *Ficedula timorensis*
Black-banded Flycatcher
    Indonesia: Timor

I *Garrulax bieti*
White-speckled Laughingthrush
    China

V *Garrulax cinereifrons*
Ashy-headed Laughingthrush
    Sri Lanka

I *Garrulax milleti*
Black-hooded Laughingthrush
    Viet Nam

K *Garrulax sukatschewi*
Snowy-cheeked Laughingthrush
    China

I *Garrulax yersini*
Collared Laughingthrush
    Viet Nam

R *Humblotia flavirostris*
Humblot's Flycatcher
    Comoros: Grand Comoro

K *Hypothymis coelestis*
Celestial Monarch
    Philippines: Basilan,   Dinagat,   Luzon,
    Mindanao, Negros, Samar, Sibuyan

R *Hypothymis helenae*
Short-crested Monarch
    Philippines: Dinagat, Luzon, Mindanao, North
    Camiguin, Polillo Islands, Samar

I *Jabouilleia danjoui*
Short-tailed Scimitar-Babbler
    Viet Nam

R *Kupeornis gilberti*
(*Lioptilus gilberti*)
White-throated Mountain-Babbler
    Cameroon; Nigeria

R *Liocichla omeiensis*
Omei Shan Liocichla
    China

I *Luscinia obscura*
(*Erithacus obscurus*)
Black-throated Blue Robin
    China

I *Luscinia ruficeps*
(*Erithacus ruficeps*)
Rufous-headed Robin
    China

I   *Macrosphenus pulitzeri*
Pulitzer's Longbill
Angola

I   *Malacocincla perspicillata*
(*Trichastoma perspicillatum*)
Black-browed Babbler
Indonesia: Kalimantan

I   *Malacocincla vanderbilti*
(*Trichastoma vanderbilti*)
Vanderbilt's Babbler
Indonesia: Sumatra

K   *Malurus coronatus*
Purple-crowned Fairy-wren
Australia

R   *Megalurus albolimbatus*
Marsh Grassbird
China; Japan; Mongolia?

K   *Megalurus pryeri*
Marsh Grassbird, Japanese Marsh Warbler
China; Japan; Mongolia?

I   *Melaenornis annamarulae*
West African Black-Flycatcher
Côte d'Ivoire; Liberia

R   *Metabolus rugensis*
Chuuk Monarch
Federated States of Micronesia: Chuuk

I   *Monarcha boanensis*
Black-chinned Monarch
Indonesia: Boano

R   *Monarcha brehmii*
Biak Monarch
Indonesia: Biak

I   *Monarcha everetti*
White-tipped Monarch
Indonesia: Tanahjampea

R   *Muscicapa lendu*
Chapin's Alseonax
Kenya; Uganda; Zaire

E   *Myadestes lanaiensis*
Olomao
USA: Hawaiian Islands (Molokai)

E   *Myadestes myadestinus*
Kamao
USA: Hawaiian Islands (Kauai)

E   *Myadestes palmeri*
Puaiohi
USA: Hawaiian Islands (Kauai)

R   *Myiagra atra*
Biak Flycatcher
Indonesia: Biak, Numfor

E   *Myiagra freycineti*
Guam Flycatcher
Guam

V   *Myiophonus blighi*
Ceylon Whistling-Thrush
Sri Lanka

K   *Napothera rabori*
Rabor's Wren-Babbler
Philippines: Luzon

E   *Nesillas aldabrana*
Aldabra Bush-warbler
Seychelles: Aldabra (ex?)

I   *Newtonia fanovanae*
Red-tailed Newtonia
Madagascar

R   *Orthotomus moreaui*
(*Apalis moreaui*)
Long-billed Tailorbird
Mozambique; Tanzania

R   *Pachycephala meyeri*
Vogelkop Whistler
Indonesia: Irian Jaya

K   *Pachycephala rufogularis*
Red-lored Whistler
Australia

R   *Paradoxornis davidianus*
Short-tailed Parrotbill
China; Laos; Myanmar; Thailand; Viet Nam.

I   *Paradoxornis flavirostris*
Black-breasted Parrotbill
Bangladesh; India; Myanmar; Nepal (ex?)

K   *Paradoxornis przewalskii*
Rusty-throated Parrotbill
China

R   *Paradoxornis ruficeps*
Rufous-headed Parrotbill
Bangladesh; Bhutan; China; India; Laos;
Myanmar; Viet Nam

R   *Paradoxornis zappeyi*
Grey-hooded Parrotbill
China

K   *Pellorneum palustre*
Marsh Babbler
Bangladesh; India

62

E   **Petroica traversi**
Chatham Robin
[Reintroduced to Mangere and Rangatira, Chatham Islands, New Zealand]

I   **Phylloscopus amoenus**
Sombre Leaf-Warbler
Solomon Islands: Kulambangra

V   **Picathartes gymnocephalus**
White-necked Rockfowl
Côte d'Ivoire; Ghana; Guinea; Liberia; Sierra Leone

R   **Picathartes oreas**
Grey-necked Rockfowl
Cameroon; Equatorial Guinea: Bioko, continental?; Gabon; Nigeria

E   **Platysteira laticincta**
Banded Wattle-eye
Cameroon

V   **Pomarea dimidiata**
Rarotonga Monarch
Cook Islands: Rarotonga

R   **Pomarea iphis**
Iphis Monarch
French Polynesia: Marquesas Islands (Uahuka)

V   **Pomarea mendozae**
Marquesan Monarch
French Polynesia: Marquesas Islands (Tahuata (ex?), Nukuhiva (ex?), Mohotani, Uapoa, Hivaoa)

E   **Pomarea nigra**
Tahiti Monarch
French Polynesia: Tahiti

R   **Pomarea whitneyi**
Fatuhiva Monarch
French Polynesia: Fatuhiva

R   **Prinia burnesii**
Rufous-vented Prinia
India; Pakistan

K   **Prinia fluviatilis**
River Prinia
Cameroon; Chad; Mali; Senegal

K   **Pseudocossyphus bensoni**
(*Monticola bensoni*)
Benson's Rock-Thrush
Madagascar

K   **Psophodes nigrogularis**
Western Whipbird
Australia

V   **Rhinomyias albigularis**
White-throated Jungle-Flycatcher
Philippines: Guimaras, Negros

V   **Rhinomyias brunneata**
Brown-chested Jungle-Flycatcher
China; India: Nicobar Islands. * Malaysia?: Peninsular Malaysia; Thailand

R   **Rhinomyias colonus**
Henna-tailed Jungle-Flycatcher
Indonesia: Mangole, Peleng, Sanana, Sulawesi

I   **Rhipidura malaitae**
Malaita Fantail
Solomon Islands: Malaita (ex?)

R   **Rhyacornis bicolor**
Luzon Water-Redstart
Philippines: Luzon

R   **Saxicola dacotiae**
Canary Islands Chat
Spain: Canary Islands (Fuerteventura, Alegranza?, Montaña Clara?)

R   **Saxicola gutturalis**
White-bellied Bushchat
Indonesia: Roti, Semau, Timor

K   **Saxicola insignis**
White-throated Bushchat
Kazakhstan; Mongolia; Russia. * China?; India; Nepal

V   **Saxicola macrorhyncha**
White-browed Bushchat
India; Pakistan

R   **Scepomycter winifredae**
(*Bathmocercus winifredae*)
Mrs Moreau's Warbler
Tanzania

I   **Sheppardia gabela**
(*Erithacus gabela*)
Gabela Akalat
Angola

R   **Sheppardia gunningi**
(*Erithacus gunningi*)
East Coast Akalat
Kenya; Malawi; Mozambique; Tanzania

R   **Sheppardia lowei**
(*Dryocichloides lowei*)
Iringa Akalat
Tanzania

R   **Sheppardia montana**
(*Dryocichloides montanus*)
Usambara Akalat
Tanzania

I **Spelaeornis badeigularis**
Rusty-throated Wren-Babbler
India

K **Spelaeornis caudatus**
Rufous-throated Wren-Babbler
Bhutan; India; Nepal

R **Spelaeornis longicaudatus**
Tawny-breasted Wren-Babbler
India

R **Sphenocichla humei**
Wedge-billed Wren-Babbler
China; India; Myanmar

V **Stachyris grammiceps**
White-breasted Babbler
Indonesia: Java

R **Stachyris herberti**
Sooty Babbler
Laos

V **Stachyris nigrorum**
Negros Striped-Babbler
Philippines: Negros, Panay

R **Stachyris oglei**
Snowy-throated Babbler
India

R **Stachyris rodolphei**
Deignan's Babbler
Thailand

V **Stachyris speciosa**
Flame-templed Babbler
Philippines: Negros, Panay

R **Swynnertonia swynnertoni**
Swynnerton's Robin
Mozambique; Tanzania; Zimbabwe

R **Terpsiphone corvina**
Seychelles Paradise-Flycatcher
Seychelles: Felicite?, La Digue, Praslin

I **Trichastoma woodi**
(*Leonardina woodi*)
Bagobo Babbler
Philippines: Mindanao

E **Trichocichla rufa**
Long-legged Thicketbird
Fiji: Viti Levu, Vanua Levu

V **Turdoides hindei**
Hinde's Pied-Babbler
Kenya

K **Turdus feae**
Grey-sided Thrush
China. * India; Myanmar; Thailand

K **Turdus haplochrous**
Unicolored Thrush
Bolivia

K **Turdus menachensis**
Yemen Thrush
Saudi Arabia; Yemen

R **Turdus swalesi**
La Selle Thrush
Dominican Republic; Haiti

R **Zoothera everetti**
Everett's Thrush
Malaysia: Sabah, Sarawak

R **Zoothera guttata**
Spotted Ground-Thrush
Malawi; Mozambique?; South Africa; Sudan;
Zaire. * Kenya; Tanzania

I **Zoothera kibalensis**
(*Turdus kibalensis*)
Kibale Ground-Thrush
Uganda

R **Zoothera machiki**
Fawn-breasted Thrush
Indonesia: Larat, Yamdena

R **Zoothera major**
Amami Thrush
Japan: Amami-o-shima

R **Zoothera oberlaenderi**
(*Turdus oberlaenderi*)
Oberlaender's Ground-Thrush
Uganda; Zaire

R **Zoothera peronii**
Orange-banded Thrush
Indonesia: Babar, Damar, Romang, Timor,
Wetar

R **Zoothera schistacea**
Slaty-backed Thrush
Indonesia: Tanimbar Islands

Family PARIDAE

V **Parus holsti**
Yellow Tit
Taiwan

V **Parus nuchalis**
White-naped Tit
India

Family SITTIDAE

R **Sitta formosa**
Beautiful Nuthatch
China; India; Laos; Myanmar; Thailand; Viet
Nam

R   *Sitta ledanti*
Algerian Nuthatch
    Algeria

R   *Sitta magna*
Giant Nuthatch
    China; Myanmar; Thailand

I   *Sitta solangiae*
Yellow-billed Nuthatch
    China; Viet Nam

I   *Sitta victoriae*
White-browed Nuthatch
    Myanmar

V   *Sitta yunnanensis*
Yunnan Nuthatch
    China

Family RHABDORNITHIDAE

R   *Rhabdornis grandis*
Long-billed Rhabdornis
    Philippines: Luzon

Family DICAEIDAE

R   *Dicaeum everetti*
Brown-backed Flowerpecker
    Indonesia: Kalimantan, Natuna Islands, Riau
    Archipelago; Malaysia: Peninsular Malaysia,
    Sabah, Sarawak

I   *Dicaeum quadricolor*
Four-coloured Flowerpecker
    Philippines: Cebu

K   *Pardalotus quadragintus*
Forty-spotted Pardalote
    Australia: Tasmania

Family NECTARINIIDAE

V   *Aethopyga duyvenbodei*
Elegant Sunbird
    Indonesia: Sangihe, Siau

R   *Anthreptes pallidigaster*
Amani Sunbird
    Kenya; Tanzania

R   *Anthreptes rubritorques*
Banded Sunbird
    Tanzania

V   *Nectarinia buettikoferi*
Apricot-breasted Sunbird
    Indonesia: Sumba

E   *Nectarinia prigoginei*
Prigogine's Double-collared Sunbird
    Zaire

R   *Nectarinia rockefelleri*
Rockefeller's Sunbird
    Zaire

R   *Nectarinia rufipennis*
Rufous-winged Sunbird
    Tanzania

R   *Nectarinia thomensis*
(*Dreptes thomensis*)
São Tomé Sunbird
    São Tomé and Príncipe: São Tomé

Family ZOSTEROPIDAE

R   *Heleia muelleri*
Spot-breasted White-eye
    Indonesia: Timor

I   *Madanga ruficollis*
Rufous-throated White-eye
    Indonesia: Buru

R   *Rukia longirostra*
Long-billed White-eye
    Federated States of Micronesia: Pohnpei

E   *Rukia ruki*
Truk White-eye
    Federated States of Micronesia: Chuuk (Tol
    Island, Polle?, Onei?, Pata?)

R   *Speirops brunneus*
Fernando Po Speirops
    Equatorial Guinea: Bioko

R   *Speirops leucophoeus*
Príncipe Speirops
    São Tomé and Príncipe: Príncipe

K   *Woodfordia lacertosa*
Sanford's White-eye
    Solomon Islands: Ndeni Island

E   *Zosterops albogularis*
White-chested White-eye
    Norfolk Island

R   *Zosterops anomalus*
Lemon-throated White-eye
    Indonesia: Sulawesi

V   *Zosterops chloronothos*
Mauritius Olive White-eye
    Mauritius

R   *Zosterops flavus*
Javan White-eye
    Indonesia: Java, Kalimantan; Malaysia:
    Sarawak

R   *Zosterops kuehni*
Ambon Yellow White-eye
    Indonesia: Ambon, Seram?

R   *Zosterops luteirostris*
Splendid White-eye
Solomon Islands: Gizo, Ranongga

K   *Zosterops meeki*
White-throated White-eye
Papua New Guinea: Tagula Island

E   *Zosterops modestus*
Seychelles Grey White-eye
Seychelles: Mahé

R   *Zosterops mouroniensis*
Comoro White-eye
Comoros: Grand Comoro

K   *Zosterops sanctaecrucis*
Santa Cruz White-eye, Nendo White-eye
Solomon Islands: Nendo

I   *Zosterops uropygialis*
Golden-bellied White-eye
Indonesia: Kai Islands

Family MELIPHAGIDAE

V   *Apalopteron familiare*
Bonin Honeyeater
Japan: Haha-jima and possibly offshore islands

I   *Lichmera notabilis*
Black-chested Honeyeater
Indonesia: Wetar

R   *Melidectes princeps*
Long-bearded Melidectes
Papua New Guinea

I   *Meliphaga vicina*
Tagula Honeyeater
Papua New Guinea: Tagula Island

E   *Moho bishopi*
Bishop's Oo
USA: Hawaiian Islands (Maui)

E   *Moho braccatus*
Kauai Oo
USA: Hawaiian Islands (Kauai)

I   *Myzomela kuehni*
Crimson-hooded Myzomela
Indonesia: Wetar (ex?)

V   *Notiomystis cincta*
Stitchbird
New Zealand: Little Barrier Island

I   *Philemon brassi*
Brass's Friarbird
Indonesia: Irian Jaya

R   *Philemon fuscicapillus*
Dusky Friarbird
Indonesia: Bacan, Halmahera, Morotai

K   *Xanthomyza phrygia*
Regent Honeyeater
Australia

Family EMBERIZIDAE

I   *Atlapetes flaviceps*
Olive-headed Brush-Finch
Colombia

E/Ex   *Atlapetes pallidiceps*
Pale-headed Brush-Finch
Ecuador

V   *Bangsia aureocincta*
(*Buthraupis aureocincta*)
Gold-ringed Tanager
Colombia

V/R   *Bangsia melanochlamys*
(*Buthraupis melanochlamys*)
Black-and-gold Tanager
Colombia

K   *Buthraupis aureodorsalis*
(*Bangsia aureodorsalis*)
Golden-backed Mountain-Tanager
Peru

V/R   *Buthraupis wetmorei*
Masked Mountain-Tanager
Colombia; Ecuador; Peru

V/R   *Calyptophilus frugivorus*
Chat Tanager
Dominican Republic; Haiti

I   *Camarhynchus heliobates*
Mangrove Finch
Ecuador: Galapagos Islands: Fernandina, Isabela

V/R   *Chlorochrysa nitidissima*
Multicolored Tanager
Colombia

K   *Chlorospingus flavovirens*
Yellow-green Bush-Tanager
Colombia; Ecuador

E/Ex   *Conothraupis mesoleuca*
Cone-billed Tanager
Brazil

I   *Dacnis berlepschi*
Scarlet-breasted Dacnis
Colombia; Ecuador

V/R **Dacnis nigripes**
Black-legged Dacnis
Brazil

I **Diglossa venezuelensis**
Venezuelan Flowerpiercer
Venezuela

R **Emberiza sulphurata**
Yellow Bunting
Japan. * China; Hong Kong; Korea D.P.R.;
Korea Republic; Philippines; Taiwan

V **Gubernatrix cristata**
Yellow Cardinal
Argentina; Brazil; Paraguay (ex?); Uruguay

V/R **Hemispingus goeringi**
Slaty-backed Hemispingus
Venezuela

V **Incaspiza ortizi**
Grey-winged Inca-Finch
Peru

E **Junco insularis**
(*J. hyemalis insularis*)
Guadalupe Junco
Mexico: Guadalupe Island

E/Ex **Nemosia rourei**
Cherry-throated Tanager
Brazil

R **Nesospiza acunhae**
Nightingale Finch
Saint Helena: Inaccessible Island, Nightingale
Island, Middle Island, Stoltenhoff Island,
Tristan da Cunha

R **Nesospiza wilkinsi**
Wilkins's Finch
Saint Helena: Tristan da Cunha, Inaccessible
Island, Nightingale Island

V/R **Oreothraupis arremonops**
Tanager Finch
Colombia; Ecuador

V/R **Poospiza alticola**
Plain-tailed Warbling-Finch
Peru

V/R **Poospiza baeri**
Tucuman Mountain-Finch
Argentina

I **Poospiza cinerea**
Cinereous Warbling-Finch
Brazil

E **Poospiza garleppi**
Cochabamba Mountain-Finch
Bolivia

E **Poospiza rubecula**
Rufous-breasted Warbling-Finch
Peru

V/R **Pseudodacnis hartlaubi**
(*Dacnis hartlaubi*)
Turquoise Dacnis-Tanager
Colombia

R **Rowettia goughensis**
Gough Finch
Saint Helena: Gough Island

V/R **Saltator rufiventris**
Rufous-bellied Saltator
Argentina; Bolivia

V/R **Sporophila falcirostris**
Temminck's Seedeater
Argentina; Brazil; Paraguay

V/R **Sporophila frontalis**
Buffy-fronted Seedeater
Argentina?; Brazil; Paraguay

K **Sporophila hypochroma**
Grey-and-chestnut Seedeater
Argentina; Bolivia; Brazil; Paraguay

E/Ex **Sporophila insulata**
Tumaco Seedeater
Colombia: Tumaco Island

E/Ex **Sporophila melanops**
Hooded Seedeater
Brazil

I **Sporophila nigrorufa**
Black-and-tawny Seedeater
Bolivia; Brazil

K **Sporophila palustris**
Marsh Seedeater
Argentina; Brazil; Paraguay; Uruguay

E **Sporophila zelichi**
Narosky's Seedeater
Argentina

V/R **Tangara cabanisi**
Azure-rumped Tanager
Guatemala; Mexico

V/R **Tangara fastuosa**
Seven-colored Tanager
Brazil

K **Tangara meyerdeschauenseei**
Green-capped Tanager
Peru

V/R **Tangara peruviana**
Black-backed Tanager
Brazil

K **Tangara phillipsi**
Sira Tanager
Peru

V/R **Torreornis inexpectata**
Zapata Sparrow
Cuba

V **Wetmorethraupis sterrhopteron**
Orange-throated Tanager
Ecuador; Peru

V **Xenospingus concolor**
Slender-billed Finch
Chile; Peru

V/R **Xenospiza baileyi**
(*Ammodramus baileyi*)
Sierra Madre Sparrow
Mexico

Family PARULIDAE

I **Basileuterus griseiceps**
Grey-headed Warbler
Venezuela

I **Conirostrum tamaragense**
Tamarugo Conebill
Chile; Peru

V/R **Dendroica chrysoparia**
Golden-cheeked Warbler
USA. * Guatemala; Honduras; Mexico;
Nicaragua

E **Dendroica kirtlandii**
Kirtland's Warbler
Canada?; USA. * Bahamas; Turks and Caicos
Islands

V **Geothlypis speciosa**
Black-polled Yellowthroat
Mexico

E/Ex **Leucopeza semperi**
Semper's Warbler
Saint Lucia

E **Myioborus pariae**
Yellow-faced Redstart
Venezuela

E/Ex **Vermivora bachmanii**
Bachman's Warbler
USA. * Cuba?

V/R **Xenoligea montana**
White-winged Warbler
Dominican Republic; Haiti

Family DREPANIDIDAE

E **Hemignathus lucidus**
Nukupuu
USA: Hawaiian Islands (Hawaii, Kauai (ex?),
Maui)

E **Hemignathus wilsoni**
(*H. munroi*)
Akiapolaau
USA: Hawaiian Islands (Hawaii)

E **Hemignathus obscurus**
Akialoa
USA: Hawaiian Islands (Kauai)

E **Loxioides bailleui**
Palila
USA: Hawaiian Islands (Hawaii)

R **Loxops coccineus**
Akepa
USA: Hawaiian Islands (Hawaii, Kauai, Maui,
Molokai)

R **Melamprosops phaeosoma**
Poo-uli
USA: Hawaiian Islands (Maui)

R **Oreomystis bairdi**
Kauai Creeper
USA: Hawaiian Islands (Kauai)

V **Palmeria dolei**
Akohekohe
USA: Hawaiian Islands (Maui)

E **Paroreomyza maculata**
Oahu Creeper
USA: Hawaiian Islands (Oahu)

V **Pseudonestor xanthophrys**
Maui Parrotbill
USA: Hawaiian Islands (Maui)

E **Psittirostra psittacea**
Ou
USA: Hawaiian Islands (Hawaii, Kauai)

R **Telespiza cantans**
Laysan Finch
USA: Hawaiian Islands (Laysan)
[USA: Hawaiian Islands (Hermes Reef, Pearl)]

R **Telespiza ultima**
Nihoa Finch
USA: Hawaiian Islands (Nihoa)
[USA: Hawaiian Islands (French Frigate
Shoals)]

Family VIREONIDAE

E **Vireo atricapillus**
Black-capped Vireo
Mexico; USA

I **Vireo caribaeus**
Saint Andrew Vireo
Colombia: San Andrés Island

Family ICTERIDAE

V **Agelaius flavus**
(*Xanthopsar flavus*)
Saffron-cowled Blackbird
Argentina; Brazil; Paraguay; Uruguay

E **Agelaius xanthomus**
Yellow-shouldered Blackbird
Puerto Rico

K **Cacicus koepckeae**
Selva Cacique
Peru

E **Curaeus forbesi**
Forbes's Blackbird
Brazil

I **Gymnostinops cassini**
(*Psarocolius cassini*)
Chestnut-mantled Oropendola
Colombia

I **Hypopyrrhus pyrohypogaster**
Red-bellied Grackle
Colombia

E **Icterus bonana**
Martinique Oriole
Martinique

I **Sturnella militaris**
(*S. defilippii*)
Pampas Meadowlark
Argentina; Brazil?; Uruguay. * Brazil?;
Uruguay

Family FRINGILLIDAE

E **Carduelis cucullata**
Red Siskin
Colombia; Venezuela
[Puerto Rico]

R **Carduelis johannis**
(*Acanthis johannis*)
Warsangli Linnet
Somalia

V **Carduelis siemiradzkii**
Saffron Siskin
Ecuador; Peru?

V/R **Carduelis yarrellii**
Yellow-faced Siskin
Brazil; Venezuela

R **Fringilla teydea**
Teydefinch
Spain: Canary Islands (Tenerife, Gran Canaria)

I **Neospiza concolor**
São Tomé Canary
São Tomé and Príncipe: São Tomé (ex?)

R **Serinus ankoberensis**
Ankober Serin
Ethiopia

I **Serinus flavigula**
Yellow-throated Seedeater
Ethiopia

Family ESTRILDIDAE

R **Amandava formosa**
(*Estrilda formosa*)
Green Avadavat
India

K **Chloebia gouldiae**
Gouldian Finch
Australia

R **Erythrura coloria**
Red-eared Parrotfinch
Philippines: Mindanao

R **Erythrura kleinschmidti**
Pink-billed Parrotfinch
Fiji: Viti Levu

R **Erythrura viridifacies**
Green-faced Parrotfinch
Philippines: Luzon

K **Estrilda nigriloris**
Black-faced Waxbill
Zaire

K **Estrilda poliopareia**
Fawn-breasted Waxbill
Nigeria

Family PLOCEIDAE

E **Foudia flavicans**
Yellow Fody
Mauritius: Rodrigues

E **Foudia rubra**
Mauritius Fody
Mauritius

R **Foudia sechellarum**
Seychelles Fody
Seychelles: Cousin, Cousine, Fregate

I   *Malimbus ballmanni*
Ballmann's Malimbe
Côte d'Ivoire?; Liberia; Sierra Leone

R   *Malimbus flavipes*
(*Ploceus flavipes*)
Yellow-legged Malimbe
Zaire

E   *Malimbus ibadanensis*
Ibadan Malimbe
Nigeria

R   *Ploceus aureonucha*
Golden-naped Weaver
Zaire

V   *Ploceus bannermani*
Bannerman's Weaver
Cameroon; Nigeria?

R   *Ploceus batesi*
Bates's Weaver
Cameroon

E   *Ploceus golandi*
Clarke's Weaver
Kenya

R   *Ploceus megarhynchus*
Yellow Weaver
India

R   *Ploceus nicolli*
Usambara Weaver
Tanzania

K   *Ploceus nigrimentum*
Black-chinned Weaver
Angola; Congo?

K   *Ploceus ruweti*
Ruwet's Masked-Weaver
Zaire

K   *Ploceus subpersonatus*
Loango Weaver
Angola; Gabon; Zaire

K   *Ploceus victoriae*
Victoria Masked-Weaver
Uganda

Family STURNIDAE

E   *Aplonis cinerascens*
Rarotonga Starling
Cook Islands: Rarotonga

R   *Aplonis santovestris*
Mountain Starling
Vanuatu: Espirito Santo

R   *Basilornis galeatus*
Helmeted Myna
Indonesia: Banggai Islands, Sula Islands

K   *Cinnyricinclus femoralis*
Abbott's Starling
Kenya; Tanzania

E   *Leucopsar rothschildi*
Bali Myna
Indonesia: Bali

R   *Streptocitta albertinae*
Bare-eyed Myna
Indonesia: Sula Islands

Family ORIOLIDAE

R   *Oriolus isabellae*
Isabela Oriole
Philippines: Mindanao, Luzon

I   *Oriolus mellianus*
Silver Oriole
China. * Thailand

Family DICRURIDAE

R   *Dicrurus fuscipennis*
Comoro Drongo
Comoros: Grand Comoro

R   *Dicrurus waldenii*
Mayotte Drongo
Mayotte

Family CALLAEIDAE

E   *Callaeas cinerea*
Kokako
New Zealand

R   *Philesturnus carunculatus*
(*Creadion carunculatus*)
Saddleback
New Zealand

Family PTILONORHYNCHIDAE

K   *Amblyornis flavifrons*
Golden-fronted Bowerbird
Indonesia: Irian Jaya

R   *Sericulus bakeri*
Fire-maned Bowerbird
Papua New Guinea

Family PARADISAEIDAE

V   *Astrapia mayeri*
Ribbon-tailed Astrapia
Papua New Guinea

R   *Epimachus fastuosus*
Black Sicklebill
    Indonesia: Irian Jaya; Papua New Guinea

R   *Paradigalla carunculata*
Long-tailed Paradigalla
    Indonesia: Irian Jaya

R   *Paradisaea decora*
Goldie's Bird-of-paradise
    Papua New Guinea: Fergusson, Normanby

R   *Parotia wahnesi*
Wahnes's Parotia
    Papua New Guinea

Family CORVIDAE

R   *Corvus florensis*
Flores Crow
    Indonesia: Flores

E   *Corvus hawaiiensis*
Hawaiian Crow
    USA: Hawaiian Islands (Hawaii)

E   *Corvus kubaryi*
Mariana Crow
    Guam; Northern Marianas: Rota

R   *Corvus unicolor*
Banggai Crow
    Indonesia: Banggai

V   *Crypsirina cucullata*
Hooded Treepie
    Myanmar

V   *Cyanolyca mirabilis*
White-throated Jay
    Mexico

E   *Cyanolyca nana*
Dwarf Jay
    Mexico

V   *Perisoreus internigrans*
Sichuan Jay
    China

V   *Urocissa ornata*
Ceylon Magpie
    Sri Lanka

R   *Zavattariornis stresemanni*
Stresemann's Bush-Crow
    Ethiopia

Class REPTILIA

Order TESTUDINES

Family KINOSTERNIDAE

R **Kinosternon angustipons**
Narrow-bridged Mud Turtle
Costa Rica; Nicaragua; Panama

V **Kinosternon creaseri**
Creaser's Mud Turtle
Mexico: Yucatan Peninsula

V **Kinosternon depressum**
(*Sternotherus depressus, Sternotherus minor depressus*)
Flattened Musk Turtle
USA: Black Warrior River system

R **Kinosternon dunni**
Dunn's Mud Turtle
Colombia

I **Kinosternon oaxacae**
Oaxaca Mud Turtle
Mexico

Family DERMATEMYDIDAE

V **Dermatemys mawii**
Central American River Turtle
Belize; Guatemala; Honduras; Mexico

Family CHELYDRIDAE

V **Macroclemys temminckii**
Alligator Snapping Turtle
USA

Family EMYDIDAE

K **Annamemys annamensis**
Annam Leaf Turtle
Viet Nam

E **Batagur baska**
Batagur
Bangladesh; Cambodia?; India; Indonesia: Sumatra; Malaysia; Myanmar; Singapore?; Thailand; Viet Nam?

E **Callagur borneoensis**
Painted Terrapin
Brunei?; Indonesia: Kalimantan, Sumatra; Malaysia: Peninsular Malaysia, Sarawak; Thailand

R **Clemmys muhlenbergii**
Bog Turtle
USA

K **Cuora galbinifrons**
(*Cistoclemmys galbinifrons*, includes *Cuora hainanensis*)
Indochinese Box Turtle
China: Hainan Island; Viet Nam

K **Cuora yunnanensis**
(*Cyclemys yunnanensis*)
Yunnan Box Turtle
China: Yunnan

I **Geoclemys hamiltonii**
(*Damonia hamiltonii*)
Black Pond Turtle
Bangladesh; India; Nepal?; Pakistan

V **Geoemyda silvatica**
(*Heosemys silvatica*)
Cochin Forest Cane Turtle
India

K **Graptemys barbouri**
Barbour's Map Turtle
USA: Apalachicola-Chipola River system

K **Graptemys caglei**
Cagle's Map Turtle
USA: Guadelupe-San Antonio River system

I **Graptemys flavimaculata**
Yellow-blotched Map Turtle
USA: Pascagoula River system

K **Graptemys oculifera**
Ringed Map Turtle
USA: Pearl River system

K **Heosemys depressa**
Arakan Forest Turtle
Myanmar: Arakan hills

I **Heosemys leytensis**
Leyte Pond Turtle
Philippines: Leyte, Palawan

K **Heosemys spinosa**
(*Geoemyda spinosa*)
Spiny Turtle
Brunei; Indonesia; Malaysia: Peninsular Malaysia, Sabah, Sarawak; Myanmar?; Thailand

I **Kachuga kachuga**
Red-crowned Roofed Turtle
Bangladesh; India; Nepal

I **Kachuga sylhetensis**
Assam Roofed Turtle
Bangladesh; India: Assam

K **Kachuga trivittata**
Burmese Roofed Turtle
Myanmar

I **Melanochelys tricarinata**
(*Geoemyda* or *Nicoria tricarinata*)
Three-keeled Land Tortoise
Bangladesh; India; Nepal?

K **Morenia ocellata**
Burmese Eyed Turtle
Myanmar

K **Orlitia borneensis**
Malaysian Giant Turtle
Indonesia: Kalimantan, Sumatra; Malaysia:
Peninsular Malaysia, Sarawak

R **Pseudemys alabamensis**
Alabama Red-bellied Turtle
USA: Mobile Bay area

K **Rhinoclemmys rubida**
Mexican Spotted Wood Turtle
Mexico

V **Terrapene coahuila**
Aquatic Box Turtle
Mexico: Cuatro Cienegas basin

K **Terrapene nelsoni**
Spotted Box Turtle
Mexico

K **Trachemys decorata**
(*Trachemys stejnegeri decorata*)
Hispaniolan Slider
Dominican Republic; Haiti

Family TESTUDINIDAE

V **Geochelone chilensis**
(*Chelonoides chilensis*, includes *Geochelone donosobarrosi, Geochelone petersi*)
Argentine Tortoise
Argentina; Paraguay

V **Geochelone elephantopus**
(*G. nigra*)
Galapagos Giant Tortoise
Ecuador: Galapagos Islands

R **Geochelone gigantea**
(*Aldabrachelys elephantina, Dipsochelys elephantina*)
Aldabra Giant Tortoise
Seychelles: Aldabra
[several introduced populations in region]

K **Geochelone platynota**
Burmese Starred Tortoise
Myanmar

V **Geochelone radiata**
Radiated Tortoise
Madagascar
[Mauritius; Réunion]

E **Geochelone yniphora**
Madagascar Tortoise
Madagascar: near Baly Bay

V **Gopherus agassizii**
(*Gopherus polyphemus agassizii, Scaptochelys* or *Xerobates agassizii*)
Desert Tortoise
Mexico; USA

I **Gopherus berlandieri**
(*Gopherus polyphemus berlandieri, Scaptochelys* or *Xerobates berlandieri*)
Texas Tortoise
Mexico; USA

E **Gopherus flavomarginatus**
Bolson Tortoise
Mexico

V **Gopherus polyphemus**
Gopher Tortoise
USA

K **Homopus bergeri**
Berger's Cape Tortoise
Namibia

K **Indotestudo elongata**
(*Geochelone elongata*)
Elongated Tortoise
Bangladesh; Cambodia; China: Guangxi; India;
Laos; Malaysia; Myanmar; Nepal; Thailand;
Viet Nam

R **Indotestudo forstenii**
(includes *Geochelone travancorica* and *Geochelone forstenii*)
Travancore Tortoise
India; Indonesia: Halmahera, Sulawesi

K **Malacochersus tornieri**
Pancake Tortoise
Kenya; Tanzania

V **Manouria emys**
(*Geochelone emys*, includes *Testudo nutapundi*)
Asian Giant Tortoise
Bangladesh; Cambodia?; China?; India;
Indonesia: Kalimantan, Sumatra; Laos?;
Malaysia: Peninsular Malaysia, Sabah?,
Sarawak; Myanmar; Thailand; Viet Nam?

K   *Manouria impressa*
(*Geochelone impressa*)
Impressed Tortoise
  Cambodia?; China?: Hainan; Laos?; Malaysia:
  Peninsular Malaysia; Myanmar; Thailand; Viet
  Nam

V   *Psammobates geometricus*
(*Testudo geometrica*)
Geometric Tortoise
  South Africa

I   *Pyxis arachnoides*
Spider Tortoise
  Madagascar

I   *Pyxis planicauda*
(*Acinixys planicauda, Testudo planicauda*)
Madagascar Flat-shelled Tortoise
  Madagascar: Andranomena forest

V   *Testudo hermanni*
  Albania; Bulgaria; France; Greece; Italy;
  Romania; Spain: Balearic Islands; Turkey;
  Yugoslavia
  [Malta; Spain: mainland]

V   *Testudo kleinmanni*
Egyptian Tortoise
  Egypt; Israel; Libya

R   *Testudo marginata*
Marginated Tortoise
  Albania; Greece
  [Italy]

Family CHELONIIDAE

V   *Caretta caretta*
Loggerhead
  (Nesting recorded on beaches of tropical,
  subtropical and temperate seas [Atlantic,
  Caribbean, Indian, Mediterranean, Pacific].
  Wandering individuals recorded in temperate
  and arctic waters.)
  Angola?; Australia; Bahamas; Bangladesh;
  Belize; Brazil; British Virgin Islands; Cape
  Verde?; Cayman Islands; Colombia; Costa
  Rica; Cuba; Cyprus; Dominican Republic;
  Egypt; Greece; Grenada; Guadeloupe;
  Guatemala; Haiti; Honduras; India?; Indonesia;
  Israel; Italy; Jamaica; Japan; Libya;
  Madagascar; Mexico; Montserrat; Morocco;
  Mozambique; Myanmar?; Namibia; New
  Caledonia; Nicaragua; Oman; Panama; Papua
  New Guinea?; Paracel Islands; Philippines;
  Puerto Rico; Senegal; South Africa; Sri Lanka;
  Saint Lucia; Turkey; Turks and Caicos Islands;
  USA; Venezuela

E   *Chelonia mydas*
(includes *C. agassizii*)
Green Turtle
  (Nesting recorded on beaches of tropical and
  subtropical seas [Atlantic, Caribbean, Indian,
  Mediterranean, Pacific]; wandering individuals
  recorded in temperate waters. Most numerous
  in Australia and Indonesia, large nesting
  populations also in Costa Rica and at several
  sites around the Indian Ocean.)
  American Samoa; Angola; Anguilla; Antigua
  and Barbuda; Ascension; Australia; Bahamas?;
  Bangladesh; Belize; Benin?; Brazil; British
  Indian Ocean Territory; British Virgin Islands;
  Cambodia?; Cameroon?; Cape Verde?; Chile?;
  China; Colombia; Comoros; Congo?; Cook
  Islands; Costa Rica; Côte d'Ivoire?; Cuba;
  Cyprus; Djibouti?; Dominica; Dominican
  Republic; Ecuador; Egypt; El Salvador;
  Equatorial Guinea: Bioko; Ethiopia; Federated
  States of Micronesia; Fiji; French Guiana;
  French Polynesia; Gabon?; Ecuador: Galapagos
  Islands; Ghana?; Grenada; Guadeloupe?;
  Guam; Guatemala; Guinea?; Guinea-Bissau?;
  Guyana; Haiti; Honduras?; India; Indonesia;
  Iran; Israel (ex?); Jamaica; Japan; Kenya;
  Kiribati; Kuwait; Liberia?; Line Islands: north;
  Madagascar; Malaysia: Peninsular Malaysia,
  Sabah, Sarawak; Maldives; Marshall Islands;
  Martinique; Mauritania; Mauritius: Saint
  Brandon; Mayotte; Mexico; Montserrat?;
  Mozambique; Myanmar; Netherlands Antilles;
  New Caledonia; Nicaragua; Nigeria?; Niue;
  Northern Marianas; Oman; Pakistan; Palau;
  Panama; Papua New Guinea; Peru; Philippines;
  Puerto Rico; Qatar?; Réunion: Europa,
  Glorieuses, Juan de Nova, Tromelin; São
  Tomé and Príncipe; Saudi Arabia; Senegal;
  Seychelles; Sierra Leone; Solomon Islands;
  Somalia; Sri Lanka; Saint Kitts-Nevis; Saint
  Lucia; Saint Vincent; Sudan?; Suriname;
  Taiwan?; Tanzania; Thailand; Togo?; Tokelau;
  Tonga; Trinidad and Tobago; Turkey; Turks
  and Caicos Islands; Tuvalu; United Arab
  Emirates; USA: including Hawaiian Islands;
  Virgin Islands of the United States; Vanuatu;
  Venezuela; Viet Nam; Western Sahara?;
  Western Samoa?; Yemen; Zaire?

E   *Eretmochelys imbricata*
Hawksbill Turtle
(Nesting recorded on beaches of tropical and subtropical seas [Atlantic, Caribbean, Indian, Pacific]. Wandering individuals occasionally recorded in temperate waters.)
American Samoa; Anguilla; Antigua and Barbuda; Aruba; Australia; Bahamas; Bangladesh; Barbados; Belize; Brazil; British Indian Ocean Territory; British Virgin Islands; Cambodia; Cameroon?; Cape Verde?; China?; Colombia; Comoros; Cook Islands; Costa Rica; Côte d'Ivoire?; Cuba; Djibouti?; Dominica; Dominican Republic; Ecuador; Egypt; El Salvador?; Equatorial Guinea: Bioko; Ethiopia; Federated States of Micronesia; Fiji; French Guiana; French Polynesia?; Gabon?; Ghana?; Grenada; Guadeloupe; Guam; Guatemala; Guinea?; Guinea-Bissau?; Guyana; Haiti; Honduras; India; Indonesia; Iran; Jamaica; Japan; Kenya; Kiribati?; Kuwait?; Madagascar; Malaysia: Peninsular Malaysia, Sabah, Sarawak; Maldives; Marshall Islands; Martinique; Mauritania?; Mayotte; Mexico; Montserrat; Mozambique; Myanmar; Netherlands Antilles; New Caledonia?; Nicaragua; Nigeria?; Northern Marianas?; Oman; Palau; Panama; Papua New Guinea; Philippines; Puerto Rico; Qatar; Réunion: Iles Glorieuses; São Tomé and Príncipe?; Saudi Arabia; Senegal?; Seychelles; Sierra Leone; Solomon Islands; Somalia; Sri Lanka; Saint Kitts-Nevis; Saint Lucia; Saint Vincent; Sudan; Suriname; Taiwan?; Tanzania; Thailand; Tokelau; Tonga?; Trinidad and Tobago; Turks and Caicos Islands; Tuvalu?; United Arab Emirates?; USA: including Hawaiian Islands; US Pacific Islands?; Virgin Islands of the United States; Vanuatu; Venezuela; Viet Nam?; Western Sahara?; Western Samoa; Yemen

E   *Lepidochelys kempii*
Kemp's Ridley
(Virtually all nesting occurs at Rancho Nuevo on the Gulf coast of Mexico [Tamaulipas State]. Single or sparse nesting elsewhere in Mexico, Colombia and USA. At sea, most frequently recorded in the Gulf of Mexico, also regular in Atlantic waters, particularly along the coast of North America, and very occasionally in the Mediterranean.)
[USA: attempts are being made to establish a nesting colony at Padre Island].
Mexico; USA

E   *Lepidochelys olivacea*
Olive Ridley
(Nesting recorded on beaches of tropical and subtropical seas [Atlantic, Indian, Pacific]. Major mass nesting occurs in India, Costa Rica and Mexico.)
Angola; Australia; Bangladesh; Brazil; Costa Rica; El Salvador; French Guiana; Guatemala; Guyana; Honduras; India; Indonesia; Kenya; Madagascar; Malaysia: Peninsular Malaysia, Sarawak; Mexico; Mozambique; Myanmar; Nicaragua; Oman; Pakistan; Panama; Papua New Guinea; Peru; Senegal; South Africa; Sri Lanka; Suriname; Tanzania; Thailand; Trinidad and Tobago; Venezuela

V   *Natator depressus*
Flatback
(Nests in Australia; recorded at sea in Indonesia and Papua New Guinea)
Australia; Indonesia; Papua New Guinea

Family DERMOCHELYIDAE

E   *Dermochelys coriacea*
Leatherback
(Nesting recorded on beaches of tropical and subtropical seas [Atlantic, Indian, Pacific]. Notable nesting in Mexico, Irian Jaya, Malaysia and French Guiana. Foraging populations regularly occur in cool temperate waters.)
Angola; Anguilla; Antigua and Barbuda; Australia; Brazil; British Virgin Islands; Colombia?; Costa Rica; Côte d'Ivoire; Cuba; Dominica; Dominican Republic; Ecuador; El Salvador; Fiji; French Guiana; Ghana; Grenada; Guadeloupe; Guatemala; Guyana; Honduras; India; Indonesia; Israel (ex?); Liberia; Malaysia: Peninsular Malaysia; Martinique; Mexico; Montserrat; Mozambique; Myanmar; Netherlands Antilles; Nicaragua; Panama; Papua New Guinea; Peru?; Puerto Rico; Senegal; Solomon Islands; South Africa; Sri Lanka; Saint Kitts-Nevis; Saint Lucia; Saint Vincent; Suriname; Thailand; Togo; Trinidad and Tobago; USA; Virgin Islands of the United States; Venezuela?; Zaire

Family CARETTOCHELYIDAE

K   *Carettochelys insculpta*
Pig-nosed Turtle
Australia; Indonesia: Irian Jaya; Papua New Guinea

Family TRIONYCHIDAE

R   ***Aspideretes nigricans***
(*Trionyx nigricans*)
Black Soft-shell Turtle
Bangladesh: Nasirabad near Chittagong

Family PELOMEDUSIDAE

I   ***Erymnochelys madagascariensis***
(*Podocnemis madagascariensis, Dumerilia madagascariensis*)
Madagascar Sideneck Turtle
Madagascar

K   ***Pelusios seychellensis***
Seychelles Mud Turtle
Seychelles

K   ***Podocnemis erythrocephala***
(*Podocnemis cayennensis*)
Red-headed Sideneck
Brazil; Colombia; Venezuela

E   ***Podocnemis expansa***
South American River Turtle
Bolivia; Brazil; Colombia; Ecuador; Guyana; Peru; Trinidad and Tobago; Venezuela

I   ***Podocnemis lewyana***
Magdalena River Turtle
Colombia: Rio Magdalena basin

K   ***Podocnemis sextuberculata***
Six-tubercled Amazon River Turtle
Brazil; Colombia; Peru

V   ***Podocnemis unifilis***
Yellow-headed Sideneck
Bolivia; Brazil; Colombia; Ecuador; French Guiana; Guyana; Peru; Suriname; Venezuela

Family CHELIDAE

K   ***Acanthochelys macrocephala***
(*Platemys macrocephala*)
Big-headed Pantanal Swamp Turtle
Argentina; Bolivia; Brazil; Paraguay

R   ***Acanthochelys pallidipectoris***
(*Platemys pallidipectoris*)
Chaco Sideneck Turtle
Argentina; Bolivia?; Paraguay

K   ***Acanthochelys spixii***
(*Platemys spixii*)
Spix's Sideneck Turtle
Argentina; Brazil; Paraguay?; Uruguay

V   ***Elseya sp.***
Namoi River Elseya
Australia

V   ***Emydura signata***
Bellinger River Emydura
Australia

I   ***Phrynops dahli***
Dahl's Toad-headed Turtle
Colombia: Sincelejo

I   ***Phrynops hogei***
Hoge's Sideneck Turtle
Brazil

K   ***Phrynops rufipes***
Red-footed Sideneck Turtle
Brazil; Colombia; Peru?

K   ***Phrynops zuliae***
(*Batrachemys zuliae*)
Zulia Toad-headed Turtle
Venezuela

E   ***Pseudemydura umbrina***
Western Swamp Turtle
Australia: near Perth

V   ***Rheodytes leukops***
Fitzroy Turtle
Australia

Order CROCODYLIA

Family ALLIGATORIDAE

E   ***Alligator sinensis***
Chinese Alligator
China: Yangtze River system

V   ***Melanosuchus niger***
Black Caiman
Bolivia; Brazil; Colombia; Ecuador; French Guiana; Guyana; Paraguay; Peru; Venezuela

Family CROCODYLIDAE

V   ***Crocodylus acutus***
American Crocodile
Belize?; Colombia; Costa Rica; Cuba; Dominican Republic; Ecuador; El Salvador; Guatemala; Haiti; Honduras; Jamaica; Mexico; Nicaragua; Panama; Peru; USA: Florida; Venezuela

V   ***Crocodylus cataphractus***
African Slender-snouted Crocodile
Angola: Cabinda; Benin; Burkina Faso; Cameroon; Central African Republic; Chad; Congo; Côte d'Ivoire; Equatorial Guinea; Gabon; Gambia (ex?); Ghana; Guinea; Guinea-Bissau (ex?); Liberia; Mali; Mauritania; Nigeria; Senegal (ex?); Sierra Leone; Tanzania; Togo; Zaire; Zambia

E   *Crocodylus intermedius*
Orinoco Crocodile
Colombia; Venezuela

E   *Crocodylus mindorensis*
Mindoro or Philippines Crocodile
Philippines

V   *Crocodylus palustris*
Mugger
Bangladesh (ex?); India; Iran; Nepal; Pakistan;
Sri Lanka

V   *Crocodylus porosus*
Estuarine Crocodile
Australia; Bangladesh; Brunei; Cambodia;
India; Indonesia; Malaysia: Peninsular
Malaysia, Sabah, Sarawak; Myanmar:
Irrawaddy Delta; Palau; Papua New Guinea;
Philippines; Solomon Islands; Sri Lanka;
Thailand (ex?); Vanuatu; Viet Nam

E   *Crocodylus rhombifer*
Cuban Crocodile
Cuba

E   *Crocodylus siamensis*
Siamese Crocodile
Brunei?; Cambodia; Indonesia: Kalimantan,
Sulawesi, Sumatra; Laos?; Malaysia:
Peninsular Malaysia, Sabah?, Sarawak?;
Myanmar?; Thailand (ex?); Viet Nam

E   *Tomistoma schlegelii*
False Gharial
Indonesia: Kalimantan, Sumatra; Malaysia:
Peninsular Malaysia, Sarawak; Myanmar?;
Thailand (ex?)

Family GAVIALIDAE

E   *Gavialis gangeticus*
Gharial
Bangladesh; Bhutan?; India; Nepal; Pakistan

Order RHYNCHOCEPHALIA

Family SPHENODONTIDAE

E   *Sphenodon guntheri*
Brother's Island Tuatara
New Zealand: North Brother Island

R   *Sphenodon punctatus*
Cook Strait Tuatara
New Zealand: offshore islands

Order SAURIA

Family GEKKONIDAE

R   *Afroedura hawequensis*
Hawequa Flat Gecko
South Africa

V   *Christinus guentheri*
Australia: Lord Howe Island, Norfolk Island

R   *Goniosaurus kuroiwae*
(*Eublepharis kuroiwae*)
Kuroiwa's Ground Gecko
Japan: Nansei-shoto

K   *Heteropholis rudis*
Rough Gecko
New Zealand

K   *Homonota peñai*
(*Garthia peñai*)
Chile

R   *Homopholis mulleri*
Muller's Velvet Gecko
South Africa

K   *Hoplodactylus chrysosireticus*
Gold-striped Gecko
New Zealand

K   *Hoplodactylus duvauceli*
Duvaucel's Gecko
New Zealand

I   *Hoplodactylus kabutarae*
Black-eyed Gecko
New Zealand

I   *Hoplodactylus rakiurae*
Harlequin Gecko
New Zealand

V   *Hoplodactylus stephensi*
Stephen's Island Gecko
New Zealand

V   *Lepidodactylus listeri*
Christmas Island

V   *Lygodactylus methueni*
Methuen's Dwarf Gecko
South Africa

R   *Nactus coindemerensis*
Mauritius: Gunner's Quoin

R   *Nactus serpensinsula*
(*Cyrtodactylus serpensinsula*)
Serpent Island Gecko
Mauritius: Round Island, Serpent Island

V   *Nephrurus deteani*
Australia

E   *Phelsuma guentheri*
Round Island Day Gecko
Mauritius: Round Island

R **Phelsuma ocellata**
Namaqua Day Gecko
Namibia; South Africa

I **Phelsuma standingi**
Standing's Day Gecko
Madagascar

V **Phyllodactylus europaeus**
European Leaf-toed Gekko
France; Italy; Tunisia

K **Phyllodactylus heterurus**
Chile

K **Phyllodactylus melanostictus**
Scarce Ground Gecko
Thailand

R **Phyllodactylus microlepidotus**
Small-scaled Leaf-toed Gecko
South Africa

I **Phyllodactylus peringueyi**
Peringueyi's Leaf-toed Gecko
South Africa?

E **Sphaerodactylus micropithecus**
Monito Gecko
Puerto Rico: Monito Island

V **Underwoodisaurus sphyurus**
Australia

Family PYGOPODIDAE

E **Aprasia aurita**
Australia

V **Aprasia pseudopulchella**
Flinders Ranges Worm-lizard
Australia

V **Delma impar**
Striped Legless Lizard
Australia

V **Delma labialis**
Striped Tailed Delma
Australia

V **Delma torquata**
Collared Delma
Australia

V **Ophidiocephalus taeniatus**
Bronzeback Snake-lizard
Australia

V **Paradelma orientalis**
Brigalow Scaly-foot
Australia

Family XANTUSIIDAE

R **Xantusia riversiana**
(*Klauberina riversiana*)
Island Night Lizard
USA

Family AGAMIDAE

V **Ceratophora tennentii**
Tennent's Leaf-nosed Lizard
Sri Lanka

V **Ctenophorus yinnietharra**
Yinnietharra Rock Dragon
Australia

K **Gonocephalus abbotti**
Abbott's Crested Lizard
Thailand

V **Hydrosaurus pustulatus**
Sail-fin Lizard
Philippines

Family CHAMAELEONIDAE

R **Bradypodion nemorale**
Zululand Dwarf Chamaeleon
South Africa

R **Bradypodion setaroi**
Setaro's Dwarf Chamaeleon
South Africa

E **Bradypodion taeniabronchum**
Smith's Dwarf Chamaeleon
South Africa

R **Bradypodion thamnobates**
Natal Midland Dwarf Chamaeleon
South Africa

Family IGUANIDAE

R **Amblyrhynchus cristatus**
Galapagos Marine Iguana
Ecuador: Galapagos Islands

E **Anolis roosevelti**
Culebra Island Giant Anole
Puerto Rico: Isla Culebra (ex?)

V **Brachylophus fasciatus**
Fiji Banded Iguana
Fiji; Tonga
[Vanuatu]

V **Brachylophus vitiensis**
Fiji Crested Iguana
Fiji

R **Conolophus pallidus**
Barrington Land Iguana
Ecuador: Galapagos Islands

V   **Conolophus subcristatus**
Galapagos Land Iguana
  Ecuador: Galapagos Islands

R   **Cyclura carinata**
Turks and Caicos Ground Iguana
  Bahamas: Booby Cay; Turks and Caicos Islands

E   **Cyclura collei**
(*Cyclura lophoma*)
Jamaica Ground Iguana
  Jamaica

I   **Cyclura cornuta**
(includes *Cyclura stejnegeri*)
Rhinoceros Iguana
  Dominican Republic; Haiti; Puerto Rico: Isla Mona; USA: Navassa Island (ex?)

R   **Cyclura cyclura**
(includes *Cyclura baelopha, Cyclura figginsi, Cyclura inornata*)
Andros Ground or Rock Iguana
  Bahamas

V   **Cyclura nubila**
(includes *Cyclura caymanensis, Cyclura macleayi*)
Cuban Ground Iguana
  Cayman Islands; Cuba
  [Puerto Rico: Isla Magueyes]

E   **Cyclura pinguis**
Anegada Ground Iguana
  British Virgin Islands: Anegada Island

I   **Cyclura ricordi**
Hispaniolan Ground Iguana
  Dominican Republic; Haiti

I   **Cyclura rileyi**
Acklin's Ground Iguana
  Bahamas

E   **Gambelia silus**
(*Crotaphytus silus, Crotaphytus wislizenii silus*)
Blunt-nosed or San Joaquin Leopard Lizard
  USA

V   **Iguana delicatissima**
Lesser Antillean Iguana, West Indian Iguana
  Anguilla; Antigua and Barbuda; Dominica; Guadeloupe; Netherlands Antilles: Saint Eustatius, Saint Maarten; Saint Kitts-Nevis; Martinique

R   **Liolaemus constanzae**
Chile

R   **Liolaemus curis**
Chile

R   **Liolaemus donosi**
Chile

V   **Liolaemus fuscus**
Argentina; Chile

E   **Liolaemus gravenhorstii**
Chile

R   **Liolaemus hellmichi**
Chile

R   **Liolaemus huacahuasicus**
Argentina: Cumbres Calchaquies mountains

V   **Liolaemus kuhlmanni**
Chile

V   **Liolaemus lemniscatus**
Argentina; Chile

V   **Liolaemus leopardinus**
Chile

R   **Liolaemus lorenzmuelleri**
Chile

K   **Liolaemus lutzae**
Brazil

V   **Liolaemus nitidus**
Chile

R   **Liolaemus paulinae**
Chile

I   **Liolaemus rabinoi**
Argentina: Lago Nihuil

K   **Liolaemus walkeri**
Chile

V   **Liolaemus zapallarensis**
Chile

R   **Pristidactylus alvaroi**
Chile

R   **Pristidactylus valeriae**
Chile

K   **Tropidurus tarapacensis**
Chile

V   **Uma inornata**
Coachella Valley Fringe-toed Lizard
  USA

Family LACERTIDAE

K   **Archaeolacerta monticola**
Iberian Rock Lizard
  Portugal; Spain

E   **Gallotia simonyi**
Hierro Giant Lizard
  Spain: Canary Islands (Hierro)

R   *Lacerta australis*
Southern Rock Lizard
South Africa

R   *Lacerta clarkorum*
Georgia; Turkey

R   *Lacerta rupicola*
Soutpansberg Rock Lizard
South Africa

K   *Lacerta schreiberi*
Portugal; Spain

V   *Podarcis lilfordi*
Lilford's Wall Lizard
Spain: Mallorca, Menorca

R   *Podarcis pityusensis*
Ibiza Wall Lizard
Spain: Formentera, Ibiza
[Spain: Mallorca]

Family CORDYLIDAE

V   *Cordylus cataphractus*
Armadillo Girdled Lizard
South Africa

V   *Cordylus giganteus*
Giant Girdled Lizard
South Africa

R   *Cordylus lawrencei*
Lawrence's Girdled Lizard
South Africa

R   *Cordylus mclachlani*
McLachlan's Girdled Lizard
South Africa

R   *Gerrhosaurus typicus*
Namaqua Plated Lizard
South Africa

R   *Platysaurus relictus*
Soutpansberg Flat Lizard
South Africa

R   *Pseudocordylus langi*
Lang's Crag Lizard
Lesotho; South Africa

R   *Pseudocordylus spinosus*
Spiny Crag Lizard
South Africa

R   *Tetradactylus breyeri*
Breyer's Long-tailed Seps
South Africa

Family TEIIDAE

E   *Ameiva polops*
Saint Croix Ground Lizard
Virgin Islands of the United States: Green
Cay, Protestant Key, [Buck Island]

V   *Callopistes maculatus*
Chile

V   *Cnemidophorus hyperythrus*
Orange-throated Whiptail
Mexico; USA

V   *Cnemidophorus vanzoi*
Saint Lucia: Maria Islands

Family SCINCIDAE

R   *Acanthiops lineatus*
Woodbush Legless Skink
South Africa

V   *Anomalopus mackayi*
Long-legged Worm-skink
Australia

R   *Barkudia insularis*
Legless Skink
India

V   *Coeranoscincus reticulatus*
Three-toed Snake-tooth Skink
Australia

E   *Ctenotus lancelini*
Lancelin Island Skink
Australia: Lancelin Island

V   *Ctenotus zastictus*
Hamelin Ctenotus
Australia

V   *Cyclodina alani*
Robust Skink
New Zealand

V   *Cyclodina macgregori*
MacGregor's Skink
New Zealand

K   *Cyclodina oliveri*
Marbled Skink
New Zealand

V   *Cyclodina whitakeri*
Whitaker's Skink
New Zealand

V   *Egernia kintorei*
Great Desert Skink
Australia

E **Eulamprus leuraensis**
Blue Mountain Water Skink
Australia

R **Eumeces kishinouyei**
Kishinoue's Giant Skink
Japan: Nansei-shoto

K **Isopachys gyldenstolpei**
Gyldenstolpe's Worm Skink
Thailand

E **Leiolopisma bomalonotum**
Chevron Skink
New Zealand

V **Leiolopisma grande**
Grand Skink
New Zealand

I **Leiolopisma microlepis**
Small-scaled Skink
New Zealand

I **Leiolopisma notosaurus**
Southern Skink
New Zealand

K **Leiolopisma otagense**
Otago Skink
New Zealand

K **Leiolopisma striatum**
Striped Skink
New Zealand

R **Leiolopisma telfairii**
Round Island Skink
Mauritius: Round Island

E **Lerista allanae**
Allan's Lerista
Australia

V **Lerista vittata**
Mount Cooper Striped Lerista
Australia

K **Lygosoma haroldyoungi**
Banded Supple Skink
Thailand

K **Lygosoma koratense**
Korat Supple Skink
Thailand

V **Neoseps reynoldsi**
Sand Skink
USA

V **Niveoscincus palfreymani**
Pedra Branca Skink
Australia: Pedra Branca Island

I **Phoboscincus bocourti**
New Caledonia

V **Pseudemoia lichenigera**
Lord Howe Island Skink
Australia: Lord Howe Island, Norfolk Island

R **Scelotes guentheri**
Günther's Dwarf Burrowing Skink
South Africa

R **Scelotes kasneri**
Kasner's Dwarf Burrowing Skink
South Africa

R **Scelotes gronovii**
Gronovi's Dwarf Burrowing Skink
South Africa

E **Tiliqua adelaidensis**
Pygmy Bluetongue
Australia

I **Tribolonotus ponceleti**
Solomon Islands: Shortland Island

R **Typhlosaurus lomii**
Lomi's Blind Legless Skink
South Africa

Family ANGUIDAE

E **Abronia montecristoi**
El Salvador

I **Celestus duquesneyi**
Jamaica

I **Celestus fowleri**
Jamaica

I **Celestus microblepharis**
Jamaica

E **Diploglossus anelpistus**
Dominican Republic

K **Diploglossus carruai**
Dominican Republic

I **Diploglossus montisserrati**
Montserrat

K **Diploglossus warreni**
Dominican Republic

K **Gerrhonotus panamintus**
Panamint Alligator Lizard
USA

Family HELODERMATIDAE

I **Heloderma horridum**
Beaded Lizard
Guatemala; Mexico

V **Heloderma suspectum**
Gila Monster
Mexico; USA

Family VARANIDAE

I **Varanus flavescens**
Yellow Monitor
Bangladesh; India; Nepal; Pakistan

R **Varanus komodoensis**
Komodo Dragon
Indonesia: Komodo and adjacent islands

R **Varanus olivaceus**
(*Varanus grayi*)
Gray's Monitor
Philippines: Luzon

Order SERPENTES

Family TYPHLOPIDAE

V **Ramphotyphlops exocoeti**
Christmas Island Blind Snake
Christmas Island

R **Typhlops monensis**
Mona Blind Snake
Puerto Rico: Isla Mona

Family ANILIIDAE

K **Anomochilus leonardi**
Leonard's Pipe Snake
Malaysia: Peninsular Malaysia

Family BOIDAE

K **Acrantophis dumerili**
Dumeril's Boa
Madagascar
[Réunion]?

K **Acrantophis madagascariensis**
Madagascar Boa
Madagascar

E **Aspidites ramsayi**
Woma
Australia

E **Casarea dussumieri**
Round Island Keel-scaled Boa
Mauritius: Round Island

I **Epicrates angulifer**
Cuban Tree Boa
Cuba

K **Epicrates inornatus**
Puerto Rican Boa
Puerto Rico

V **Epicrates subflavus**
Jamaican Boa
Jamaica

V **Python molurus**
Indian Python
Bangladesh; Cambodia; China; Hong Kong;
India; Indonesia; Laos; Myanmar; Nepal;
Pakistan; Sri Lanka; Thailand; Viet Nam

K **Sanzinia madagascariensis**
Madagascar Tree Boa
Madagascar

Family COLUBRIDAE

R **Achalinus werneri**
Amami Takachiho Snake
Japan: Nansei-shoto

I **Adelphicos daryi**
Guatemala

E **Alsophis antiguae**
Antiguan Racer
Antigua and Barbuda: Great Bird Island

E **Alsophis ater**
Black Racer
Jamaica

V **Alsophis rijersmai**
Leeward Island Racer
Anguilla; Guadeloupe: including Saint Martin;
Netherlands Antilles: Sint Maarten (ex?)

V **Alsophis rufiventris**
Red-bellied Racer
Netherlands Antilles: Saba, Saint Eustatius;
Saint Kitts-Nevis

R **Calamaria pfefferi**
(synonym of the widespread *C. pavimentata*?)
Pfeffer's Reed Snake
Japan

R **Chironius vincenti**
Saint Vincent

V **Coluber cypriensis**
Cyprus

R **Elachistodon westermanni**
Indian Egg-eating Snake
Bangladesh; India; Nepal

K **Elaphe situla**
Leopard Snake
Albania; Bulgaria; Greece; Italy; Malta;
Turkey; Ukraine; Yugoslavia

R **Homoroselaps dorsalis**
Striped Harlequin Snake
South Africa; Swaziland

I *Iguanognathus werneri*
Indonesia: Sumatra

R *Lamprophis fiskii*
Fisk's House Snake
South Africa

R *Lamprophis fuscus*
Yellow-bellied House Snake
South Africa

R *Lamprophis swazicus*
Swazi Rock Snake
South Africa; Swaziland

E *Liophis cursor*
Martinique: Rocher de Diamant

E *Liophis ornatus*
Saint Lucia: Maria Major Island

I *Liophis perfuscus*
Barbados

I *Natrix megalocephala*
Large-headed Water Snake
Azerbaijan; Georgia; Russia; Turkey

R *Oligodon nikhili*
India: Palni Hills

R *Opheodrys herminae*
(*Liopeltis herminae*)
Sakashima Green Snake
Japan: Nansei-shoto

E *Opisthotropis kikuzatoi*
(*Liopeltis kikuzatoi*)
Kikuzato's Brook Snake
Japan: Nansei-shoto

K *Opisthotropis spenceri*
Smith's Mountain Keelback
Thailand

K *Parahelicops boonsongi*
Boonsong's Keelback
Thailand

R *Pareas iwasakii*
Iwasaki's Snail-eater
Japan: Nansei-shoto

V *Philodryas chamissonis*
Chile

R *Thamnophis gigas*
(*Thamnophis couchi gigas*)
Giant Garter Snake
USA

R *Thamnophis hammondi*
(*Thamnophis couchi hammondi*)
Two-striped Garter Snake
Mexico; USA

R *Thermophis baileyi*
China: Tibet

R *Xenocalamus transvaalensis*
Transvaal Quillsnout Snake
Mozambique; South Africa

Family ELAPIDAE

V *Austrelaps labialis*
Pygmy Copperhead
Australia

V *Denisonia maculata*
Ornamental Snake
Australia

V *Echiopsis atriceps*
Lake Cronin Snake
Australia

V *Echiopsis curta*
Australia

V *Elapognathus minor*
Short-nosed Snake
Australia

V *Furina dunmalli*
Dunmall's Snake
Australia

V *Hoplocephalus bungaroides*
Broad-headed Snake
Australia

K *Naja oxiana*
Central Asian or Oxus Cobra
Afghanistan; India; Iran; Pakistan; Tajikistan;
Turkmenistan; Uzbekistan

I *Ogmodon vitianus*
Fiji Snake
Fiji: Viti Levu

E *Simoselaps calonotus*
Black-striped Snake
Australia

Family HYDROPHIIDAE

R *Laticauda crockeri*
Solomon Islands: Lake Te-Nggana, Rennell
Island

Family VIPERIDAE

R **Bitis inornata**
Plain Mountain Adder
South Africa

K **Bitis schneideri**
Namaqua Dwarf Adder
Namibia; South Africa

I **Bothrops insularis**
Golden Lancehead
Brazil: Queimada Island

R **Crotalus unicolor**
(*Crotalus durissus unicolor*)
Aruba Island Rattlesnake
Aruba

R **Trimeresurus cornutus**
Viet Nam

R **Trimeresurus mangshanensis**
China: Mt Mang, Hunan Province

R **Vipera albizona**
(*V. xanthina albizona*)
Turkey

I **Vipera bornmuelleri**
(*V. xanthina bornmuelleri*)
Lebanon; Syria

I **Vipera bulgardaghica**
Turkey

R **Vipera darevskii**
(*V. kaznakovi darevskii*)
Armenia; Georgia

R **Vipera dinniki**
(*V. kaznakovi dinniki*)
Georgia; Russia

V **Vipera kaznakovi**
Caucasian Viper
Georgia; Russia; Turkey

E **Vipera latifii**
Latifi's Viper
Iran: Lar Valley in Elburz Mts.

K **Vipera pontica**
Georgia?; Turkey

I **Vipera raddei**
(*Vipera xanthina raddei*)
Armenian Viper
Armenia; Iran; Turkey

E **Vipera schweizeri**
(*Macrovipera schweizeri, Vipera lebetina schweizeri*)
Cyclades Blunt-nosed Viper
Greece: Kimolos, Milos, Polyaigos, Siphnos

I **Vipera wagneri**
Iran; Turkey

Class AMPHIBIA

Order ANURA

Family BUFONIDAE

R   ***Bufo amatolica***
Amatola Toad
South Africa

V   ***Bufo atacamensis***
Chile

V   ***Bufo chilensis***
Chile

R   ***Bufo exsul***
(*Bufo boreas exsul*)
Black Toad
USA

E   ***Bufo houstonensis***
Houston Toad
USA

E   ***Bufo periglenes***
Golden Toad
Costa Rica: Cordillera de Tilaran (ex?)

V   ***Bufo retiformis***
Sonoran Green Toad
Mexico; USA

R   ***Capensibufo rosei***
Cape Mountain Toad
South Africa

V   ***Nectophrynoides occidentalis***
(*Nimbaphrynoides occidentalis*)
Mt. Nimba Viviparous Toad
Côte d'Ivoire; Guinea; Liberia?

I   ***Pedostibes kempi***
Garo Hill Tree Toad
India: Assam, Garo Hills

I   ***Pedostibes tuberculosus***
Malabar Tree Toad
India

V   ***Peltophryne lemur***
Puerto Rican Crested Toad
British Virgin Islands; Puerto Rico

Family DISCOGLOSSIDAE

E   ***Alytes muletensis***
(*Baleaphryne muletensis*)
Ferreret
Spain: Mallorca

R   ***Discoglossus jeanneae***
(*Discoglossus galganoi jeanneae*)
Spain

R   ***Discoglossus montalentii***
France: Corsica

Family HELEOPHRYNIDAE

E   ***Heleophryne hewitti***
Hewitt's Ghost Frog
South Africa: Elandsberg Mountains

E   ***Heleophryne rosei***
Table Mountain Ghost Frog
South Africa: Table Mountain

Family HYLIDAE

K   ***Hyla albolineata***
Brazil

R   ***Hyla andersonii***
Pine Barrens Tree Frog
USA

K   ***Hyla izecksohni***
Brazil

K   ***Hyla langei***
Brazil

K   ***Hyla secedens***
Brazil

I   ***Hyla vasta***
Dominican Republic; Haiti

K   ***Litoria aurea***
Green and Golden Bell Frog
Australia

V   ***Litoria brevipalmata***
Green-thighed Frog
Australia

K   ***Litoria dentata***
Bleating Tree Frog
Australia

K   ***Litoria castanea***
Yellow-spotted Tree Frog
Australia

K   ***Litoria lesueuri***
Lesueur's Frog
Australia

V   ***Litoria nannotis***
Torrent Tree Frog
Australia

E   ***Litoria nyakalensis***
Nyakala Frog
Australia

V   ***Litoria pearsoniana***
Pearson's Frog
Australia

V   *Litoria piperata*
Peppered Tree Frog
Australia

K   *Litoria raniformis*
Southern Bell Frog
Australia

V   *Litoria rhencola*
Creek Frog
Australia

E   *Litoria spenceri*
Spotted Frog
Australia

K   *Litoria verreauxii*
Whistling Tree Frog
Australia

V   *Nyctimystes dayi*
Day's Frog
Australia

K   *Phrynomedusa fimbriata*
Brazil

Family HYPEROLIIDAE

R   *Afrixalus aureus*
Golden Dwarf Reed Frog
Mozambique; South Africa; Swaziland

R   *Hyperolius pickersgilli*
Pickersgill's Reed Frog
South Africa

R   *Leptopelis xenodactylus*
Long-toed Tree Frog
South Africa

R   *Tachycnemis seychellensis*
(*Megalixalus seychellensis, Megalixalus infrarufus*)
Seychelle Islands Tree Frog
Seychelle Islands

Family LEIOPELMATIDAE

R   *Leiopelma archeyi*
Archey's Frog
New Zealand: North Island (Coromandel Peninsula)

V   *Leiopelma hamiltoni*
Hamilton's Frog
New Zealand: Stephen Island, Maud Island

R   *Leiopelma hochstetteri*
Hochstetter's Frog
New Zealand: North Island

Family LEPTODACTYLIDAE

R   *Alsodes barrioi*
Chile

E   *Alsodes montanus*
Chile

E   *Alsodes nodosus*
Chile

E   *Alsodes tumultuosos*
Chile

V   *Alsodes vanzolinii*
Chile

K   *Atelognathus grandisonae*
Chile

I   *Atelognathus nitoi*
Argentina: Laguna Verde

R   *Atelognathus reverberii*
Argentina: Somuncurá plateau

R   *Atelognathus solitarius*
Argentina: Las Bayas stream

K   *Batrachophrynus macrostomus*
Lake Junin (Giant) Frog
(Lake Junin)
Bolivia; Peru

V   *Caudiverbera caudiverbera*
Chile

I   *Eleutherodactylus cavernicola*
Jamaica

R   *Eleutherodactylus fuscus*
Jamaica

R   *Eleutherodactylus jasperi*
Golden Coqui Frog
Puerto Rico

I   *Eleutherodactylus junori*
Jamaica

E   *Eleutherodactylus karlschmidtii*
Puerto Rico

I   *Eleutherodactylus semipalmatus*
Haiti

R   *Eleutherodactylus sisyphodemus*
Jamaica

R   *Eupsophus insularis*
Chile

E   *Eupsophus migueli*
Chile

E **Insuetophrymus acarpicus**
   Chile

K **Leptodactylus marambaiae**
   Brazil

I **Paratelmatobius gaigeae**
   Brazil: Serra da Bocaina

V **Somuncuria somuncurensis**
   (Telmatobius somuncurensis)
   Somuncura Frog
      Argentina: Somuncurá plateau

E **Telmatobius atacamensis**
   Argentina

R **Telmatobius halli**
   Chile

R **Telmatobius pefauri**
   Chile

V **Telmatobius peruvianus**
   Chile

R **Telmatobius zapahuirensis**
   Chile

R **Telmatobufo australis**
   Chile

R **Telmatobufo bullocki**
   Chile

R **Telmatobufo venustus**
   Chile

Family MICROHYLIDAE

V **Breviceps gibbosus**
   Cape Rain Frog
   South Africa

R **Breviceps macrops**
   Desert Rain Frog
      Namibia?; South Africa

K **Hyophryne histrio**
   Brazil

I **Melanobatrachus indicus**
   Black Microhylid
   India: Kerala

Family MYOBATRACHIDAE

K **Adelotus brevis**
   Tusked Frog
   Australia

E **Geocrinia alba**
   White-bellied Frog
   Australia

V **Geocrinia vitellina**
   Yellow-bellied Frog
   Australia

K **Heleioporus albopunctatus**
   Western Spotted Frog
   Australia

K **Lechriodus fletcheri**
   Fletcher's Frog
   Australia

K **Mixophyes balbus**
   Stuttering Frog
   Australia

K **Mixophyes fasciolatus**
   Great Barred Frog
   Australia

E **Mixophyes fleayi**
   Fleay's Frog
   Australia

K **Mixophyes iteratus**
   Southern Barred Frog
   Australia

V **Philoria frosti**
   Baw-baw Frog
      Australia: Mt. Baw Baw

K **Pseudophryne australis**
   Red-crowned Toadlet
   Australia

K **Pseudophryne bibronii**
   Bibron's Toadlet
   Australia

V **Pseudophryne corroboree**
   Corroboree Frog
   Australia

E **Rheobatrachus silus**
   Gastric Brooding Frog
      Australia: Conondale and Blackall Ranges
      (ex?)

E **Rheobatrachus vitellinus**
   Northern Gastric-brooding Frog
      Australia: Eungella National Park (ex?)

E **Taudactylus acutirostris**
   Sharp-nosed Torrent Frog
   Australia

E **Taudactylus diurnus**
   Mount Glorious Torrent Frog
   Australia

E **Taudactylus eungellensis**
   Eungella Torrent Frog
   Australia

E **_Taudactylus liemi_**
Liem's Frog
Australia

K **_Taudactylus pleione_**
Pleione's Torrent Frog
Australia

E **_Taudactylus rheophilus_**
Tinkling Frog
Australia

K **_Uperoleia marmorata_**
Marbled Toadlet
Australia

K **_Uperoleia orientalis_**
Alexandra Toadlet
Australia

Family PIPIDAE

E **_Xenopus gilli_**
Cape Platanna
South Africa

Family RANIDAE

R **_Anhydrophryne rattrayi_**
Hogsback Frog
South Africa: Amatola Mountains

R **_Cacosternum capense_**
Cape Caco
South Africa

I **_Cacosternum poyntoni_**
Poynton's Caco
South Africa

V **_Conraua goliath_**
(_Rana goliath, Gigantorana goliath_)
Goliath Frog
Cameroon; Equatorial Guinea

E **_Microbatrachella capensis_**
Micro Frog
South Africa

E **_Platymantis insulatus_**
Philippines: South Gigante

R **_Platymantis spelaeus_**
Philippines: Negros

K **_Platymantis vitiensis_**
Fijian Ground Frog
Fiji

K **_Rana aenea_**
Doichang Frog
Thailand

R **_Rana dracomontana_**
Drakensberg Frog
Lesotho; South Africa?

K **_Rana fasciculispina_**
Spiny-breasted Giant Frog
Thailand

V **_Rana holsti_**
(_Babina holsti_)
Holst's Frog
Japan: Nansei-shoto

R **_Rana holtzi_**
Turkey: Cilician Taurus

V **_Rana ishikawae_**
Ishikawa's Frog
Japan: Nansei-shoto

K **_Rana kohchangae_**
Kohchang Frog
Thailand

V **_Rana latastei_**
Italian Agile Frog
Italy; Slovenia; Switzerland

R **_Rana namiyei_**
Namiye's Frog
Japan: Nansei-shoto (Okinawa)

V **_Rana subaspera_**
(_Babina subaspera_)
Otton Frog
Japan: Nansei-shoto

K **_Rana tasanae_**
Smith's Wrinkled Frog
Thailand

R **_Rana vertebralis_**
Water Frog
Lesotho; South Africa

Family RHINODERMATIDAE

V **_Rhinoderma darwinii_**
Darwin's Toad
Chile

E **_Rhinoderma rufum_**
Chile

Family SOOGLOSSIDAE

R **_Nesomantis thomasseti_**
Thomasset's Seychelles Frog
Seychelles: Mahé, Silhouette

R **_Sooglossus gardineri_**
Gardiner's Seychelles Frog
Seychelles: Cerf, Mahé

R   *Sooglossus sechellensis*
Seychelles Frog
Seychelles: Mahé, Silhouette

Order CAUDATA

Family AMBYSTOMATIDAE

R   *Ambystoma lermaense*
(*Ambystoma lermaensis*)
Lake Lerma Salamander
Mexico: Lake Lerma

R   *Ambystoma mexicanum*
Axolotl
Mexico: Lake Xochimilco region

Family CRYPTOBRANCHIDAE

I   *Andrias davidianus*
(*Megalobatrachus davidianus*)
Chinese Giant Salamander
China: tributaries of Yangzi, Yellow and Pearl Rivers

R   *Andrias japonicus*
(*Megalobatrachus japonicus*)
Japanese Giant Salamander
Japan: south-west Honshu, central Kyushu

Family HYNOBIIDAE

K   *Batrachuperus mustersi*
Afghanistan

E   *Hynobius abei*
Abe's Salamander
Japan: Honshu

R   *Hynobius dunni*
Oita Salamander
Japan: Kyushu

V   *Hynobius hidamontanus*
Hakuba Salamander
Japan

R   *Hynobius okiensis*
Oki Salamander
Japan: Oki Island

R   *Hynobius stejnegeri*
Amber-coloured Salamander
Japan: Kyushu

E   *Hynobius takedai*
Hokuriku Salamander
Japan: Honshu

Family PLETHODONTIDAE

E   *Batrachoseps aridus*
Desert Slender Salamander
USA

R   *Batrachoseps simatus*
Kern Canyon Slender Salamander
USA

R   *Batrachoseps stebbinsi*
Tehachapi Slender Salamander
USA

R   *Eurycea nana*
San Marcos Salamander
USA

R   *Hydromantes brunus*
Limestone Salamander
USA

R   *Hydromantes shastae*
Shasta Salamander
USA

R   *Phaeognathus hubrichti*
Red Hills Salamander
USA

V   *Plethodon larselli*
Larch Mountain Salamander
USA

V   *Plethodon neomexicanus*
Jemez Mountains Salamander
USA

I   *Plethodon nettingi*
(*Plethodon richmondi nettingi*)
Cheat Mountain Salamander
USA

E   *Plethodon shenandoah*
Shenandoah Salamander
USA

K   *Plethodon stormi*
Siskiyou Mts Salamander
USA

R   *Speleomantes flavus*
(*Hydromantes flavus*)
Italy: Sardinia

V   *Speleomantes genei*
(*Hydromantes genei*)
Sardinian or Brown Cave Salamander
Italy: Sardinia

R   *Speleomantes imperialis*
(*Hydromantes imperialis*)
Italy: Sardinia

R   *Speleomantes supramontes*
(*Hydromantes supramontes*)
Italy: Sardinia

E **Typhlomolge rathbuni**
(*Eurycea rathbuni*)
Texas Blind Salamander
USA

K **Typhlotriton spelaeus**
Grotto Salamander
USA

Family PROTEIDAE

V **Proteus anguinus**
Olm
Italy; Slovenia; Yugoslavia
[France; Italy]

Family SALAMANDRIDAE

I **Chioglossa lusitanica**
Gold-striped Salamander
Portugal; Spain

R **Euproctus platycephalus**
Sardinian Brook Salamander
Italy: Sardinia

R **Mertensiella caucasica**
Caucasian Salamander
Georgia; Turkey

R **Mertensiella luschani**
Lycian Salamander
Greece; Turkey

K **Neurergus crocatus**
Turkey

K **Neurergus strauchi**
Turkey

I **Paramesotriton deloustali**
(*Mesotriton deloustali*)
Vietnamese Salamander
Viet Nam: near Hanoi

V **Salamandra aurorae**
(*S. atra aurorae*)
Golden Salamander
Italy: Val d'Assa

R **Salamandra lanzai**
(*S. atra lanzai*)
Large Alpine Salamander
France; Italy

Class CEPHALASPIDOMORPHI

Order PETROMYZONTIFORMES

Family PETROMYZONTIDAE

V　*Eudontomyzon hellenicus*
　　Gavóhelo
　　　Greece

R　*Lampetra hubbsi*
　　Kern Brook Lamprey
　　　USA

R　*Lampetra macrostoma*
　　Lake Lamprey
　　　Canada

K　*Mordacia lapicida*
　　　Chile

K　*Mordacia praecox*
　　Non-parasitic Lamprey
　　　Australia

Class ELASMOBRANCHII

Order ORECTOLOBIFORMES

Family RHINCODONTIDAE

I　*Rhincodon typus*
　　Whale Shark
　　　(Tropical & warm temperate seas)

Order LAMNIFORMES

Family LAMNIDAE

K　*Carcharodon carcharias*
　　Great White Shark
　　　(Sub-tropical & warm temperate seas)

Family CETORHINIDAE

K　*Cetorhinus maximus*
　　Basking Shark
　　　(Temperate waters)

Class ACTINOPTERYGII

Order ACIPENSERIFORMES

Family ACIPENSERIDAE

V　*Acipenser brevirostrum*
　　Shortnose Sturgeon
　　　Canada; USA

V　*Acipenser fulvescens*
　　Lake Sturgeon
　　　Canada; USA

V　*Acipenser schrencki*
　　Amur Sturgeon
　　　(Amur River)
　　　China; Russia

E　*Acipenser sturio*
　　Common Sturgeon
　　　Albania; Algeria; Belgium (ex?); Finland (ex?); France; Germany (ex?); Greece; Iceland (ex?); Ireland (ex?); Italy; Morocco; Netherlands (ex?); Norway (ex?); Poland (ex?); Portugal; Romania; Russia; Spain (ex?); Sweden (ex?); Switzerland?; Turkey; Ukraine; United Kingdom; Yugoslavia (ex?)

R　*Huso dauricus*
　　Kaluga
　　　(Amur River)
　　　China; Russia

E　*Scaphirhynchus albus*
　　Pallid Sturgeon
　　　USA

E　*Scaphirhynchus suttkusi*
　　Alabama Sturgeon
　　　USA: Mobile Bay drainage

Family POLYODONTIDAE

V　*Polyodon spathula*
　　Paddlefish
　　　USA

V　*Psephurus gladius*
　　Chinese Paddlefish
　　　China

Order OSTEOGLOSSIFORMES

Family OSTEOGLOSSIDAE

K　*Arapaima gigas*
　　Pirarucu
　　　Brazil; Guyana; Peru

K　*Scleropages formosus*
　　Asian Bonytongue
　　　Brunei; Cambodia; Indonesia: Bangka, Kalimantan, Sumatra; Malaysia: Peninsular Malaysia, Sabah, Sarawak; Philippines; Singapore; Thailand; Viet Nam

R　*Scleropages leichhardti*
　　Southern Saratoga
　　　Australia

Family NOTOPTERIDAE

R　*Notopterus blanci*
　　Indochina Featherback
　　　Cambodia; Thailand

Order CLUPEIFORMES

Family CLUPEIDAE

R   *Clupeoides papuensis*
Toothed River Herring
Indonesia: Irian Jaya; Papua New Guinea

Family ENGRAULIDAE

K   *Thryssa scratchleyi*
Freshwater Anchovy
Australia

Order CYPRINIFORMES

Family CYPRINIDAE

I   *Acanthorutilus anatolicus*
Yağ Baliği
Turkey

I   *Acanthorutilus crassus*
Turkey

E   *Acanthorutilus handlirschi*
Çiçek
Turkey: Lake Eğridir

I   *Acanthorutilus meandricus*
Turkey

I   *Acanthorhodeus elongatus*
China: Yunnan (Dianchi Lake)

E   *Acheilognathus longipinnis*
Itasenpara Bitterling
Japan: Honshu Island

I   *Alburnus akili*
Turkey

I   *Anabarilius polylepis*
China: Yunnan (Dianchi Lake)

E   *Anaecypris hispanica*
Spain; Portugal

E   *Aulopyge hugeli*
Dalmatian Barbelgudgeon
Yugoslavia

I   *Balantiocheilos melanopterus*
Silver Shark
Brunei; Cambodia; Indonesia: Kalimantan,
Sumatra; Laos; Malaysia: Peninsular Malaysia,
Sabah, Sarawak; Thailand

V   *Barbus andrewi*
Cape Whitefish
South Africa

R   *Barbus brevipinnis*
Shortfin Barb
South Africa

R   *Barbus calidus*
Clanwilliam Redfin
South Africa

R   *Barbus capensis*
Clanwilliam Yellowfish
South Africa

V   *Barbus comiza*
Portugal; Spain

E   *Barbus erubescens*
Twee River Redfin
South Africa

E   *Barbus euboicus*
Petrópsaro
Greece

R   *Barbus guiraonis*
Spain

R   *Barbus haasi*
Spain

I   *Barbus halei*
Malaysia; Thailand

R   *Barbus hospes*
Namaquab Barb
Namibia; South Africa

V   *Barbus kimberleyensis*
Largemouth Yellowfish
Namibia; South Africa

R   *Barbus microcephalus*
Portugal; Spain

K   *Barbus motebensis*
Marico Barb
South Africa

E   *Barbus prespensis*
Briána
Greece

V   *Barbus serra*
Sawfin
South Africa

I   *Barbus somphongsi*
Thailand

V   *Barbus treurensis*
Treur River Barb
South Africa

E   *Barbus trevelyani*
Border Barb
South Africa

E   *Caecobarbus geertsi*
African Blind Barb Fish
Zaire

R   *Caecocypris basimi*
     Iraq

R   *Capoeta antalyensis*
     Turkey

V   *Cephalokompsus pachycheilus*
     Philippines: Mindanao (Lake Lanao)

E   *Chalcalburnus tarichi*
     Incikefali Baliği
     Turkey: Lake Van

R   *Chela caeruleostigmata*
     Thailand

K   *Chondrostoma lemmingii*
     Portugal; Spain

R   *Chondrostoma lusitanicum*
     Portugal

K   *Chondrostoma willkommii*
     Portugal; Spain

V   *Cyprinella bocagrande*
     Sardinita Bocagrande
     Mexico

V   *Cyprinella caerulea*
     Blue Shiner
     USA

V   *Cyprinella callitaenia*
     Bluestripe Shiner
     USA

V   *Cyprinella formosa*
     Beautiful Shiner
     Mexico; USA

V   *Cyprinella monacha*
     Turquoise Shiner
     USA

E   *Cyprinella panarcys*
     Conchos Shiner
     Mexico

V   *Cyprinella proserpina*
     Proserpine Shiner
     Mexico; USA

V   *Cyprinella santamariae*
     Sardinita de Santa Maria
     Mexico

E   *Cyprinella xanthicara*
     Cuatro Cienegas Shiner
     Mexico

V   *Cyprinella* sp.
     Sardinita Nazas
     Mexico

I   *Cyprinus micristius*
     China: Yunnan (Dianchi Lake)

V   *Danio pathirana*
     Barred Danio
     Sri Lanka

V   *Dionda diaboli*
     Devil's River Minnow
     Mexico; USA

R   *Dionda dichroma*
     Sardinita de Rio Verde
     Mexico

E   *Dionda mandibularis*
     Sardinita Quijarrona
     Mexico

V   *Eremichthys acros*
     Desert Dace
     USA

R   *Garra barreimiae*
     Bahrain; Oman

R   *Garra dunsirei*
     Oman

V   *Garra phillipsi*
     Philipps' Garra
     Sri Lanka

V   *Gila alvordensis*
     Alvord Chub
     USA

V   *Gila boraxobius*
     Borax Lake Chub
     USA

E   *Gila cypha*
     Humpback Chub
     USA

V   *Gila ditaenia*
     Charalito Sonorense
     Mexico; USA

E   *Gila elegans*
     Bonytail Chub
     Mexico; USA

R   *Gila intermedia*
     Gila Chub
     Mexico; USA

E   *Gila modesta*
     Charalito Saltillo
     Mexico

V   *Gila nigrescens*
     Charalito Chihuahua
     Mexico; USA

V **Gila purpurea**
Yaqui Chub
Mexico; USA

I **Gobio hettitorum**
Derekaya Baliği
Turkey

I **Hemigrammocapoeta kemali**
Turkey

R **Hemitremia flammea**
Flame Chub
USA

R **Hybognathus amarus**
Rio Grande Minnow
USA

V **Hybopsis cahni**
Slender Chub
USA

V **Hybopsis gelida**
Sturgeon Chub
USA

V **Hybopsis meeki**
Sicklefin Chub
USA

K **Iberocypris palaciosi**
Spain

E **Iotichthys phlegethontis**
Least Chub
USA

R **Iranocypris typhlops**
Iran

E **Labeo fisheri**
Green Labeo
Sri Lanka

E **Labeo seeberi**
Calnwilliam Sandfish
South Africa

V **Ladigesocypris ghigii**
Ghizáni
Greece: Rhodes

E **Lepidomeda albivallis**
White River Spinedace
USA

V **Lepidomeda vittata**
Little Colorado Spinedace
USA

R **Leuciscus carolitertii**
Portugal?; Spain

V **Mandibularca resinus**
Philippines: Mindanao (Lake Lanao)

V **Meda fulgida**
Spikedace
USA

E **Moapa coriacea**
Moapa Dace
USA

V **Notropis aguirrepequenoi**
Sardinita del Pilon
Mexico

R **Notropis buccula**
Smalleye Shiner
USA

E **Notropis cahabae**
Cahaba Shiner
USA

R **Notropis hubbsi**
Bluehead Shiner
USA

R **Notropis imeldae**
Sardinita de Rio Verde
Mexico

I **Notropis jemezanus**
Rio Grande Shiner
USA

E **Notropis mekistocholas**
Cape Fear Shiner
USA

V **Notropis melanostomus**
Blackmouth Shiner
USA

R **Notropis moralesi**
Sardinita de Tepelmene
Mexico

R **Notropis oxyrhynchus**
Sharpnose Shiner
USA

R **Notropis perpallidus**
Colorless Shiner
USA

E **Notropis saladonis**
Sardinita de Salado
Mexico

R **Notropis semperasper**
Roughhead Shiner
USA

E   *Notropis simus*
Bluntnose Shiner
USA

R   *Notropis snelsoni*
Ouachita Mountain Shiner
USA

R   *Notropis welaka*
Bluenose Shiner
USA

V   *Oregonichthys crameri*
Oregon Chub
USA

R   *Oregonichthys kalawatseti*
Umpqua chub
USA

V   *Ospatulus palaemophagus*
Philippines: Mindanao (Lake Lanao)

V   *Ospatulus truncatus*
Philippines: Mindanao (Lake Lanao)

I   *Pararhodeus meandri*
Ot Baliği
Turkey

R   *Phenacobius teretulus*
Kanawha Minnow
USA

I   *Phoxinellus fahirae*
Incilevrek Baliği
Turkey

E   *Phoxinus cumberlandensis*
Mountain Blackside Dace
USA

R   *Phoxinus tennesseensis*
Tennessee Dace
USA

E   *Plagopterus argentissimus*
Woundfin
USA

R   *Pogonichthys macrolepidotus*
Sacramento Splittail
USA

K   *Probarbus jullieni*
Ikan Temoleh
Cambodia;   Laos;   Malaysia: Peninsular
Malaysia; Thailand; Viet Nam

R   *Pseudobarbus afer*
Eastern Cape Redfin
South Africa

R   *Pseudobarbus asper*
Smallscale Redfin
South Africa

R   *Pseudobarbus burchelli*
Burchell's Redfin
South Africa

E   *Pseudobarbus burgi*
Berg River Redfin
South Africa

E   *Pseudobarbus phlegethon*
Fiery Redfin
South Africa

E   *Pseudobarbus quathlambae*
Maluti Minnow
Lesotho

V   *Pseudobarbus tenuis*
Slender Redfin
South Africa

V   *Pseudophoxinus beoticus*
Paskóviza
Greece

V   *Pseudophoxinus stymphalicus*
Dáska
Greece

E   *Ptychocheilus lucius*
Colorado Squafish
USA

V   *Puntius amarus*
Philippines: Mindanao (Lake Lanao)

R   *Puntius asoka*
Asoka Barb
Sri Lanka

V   *Puntius baoulan*
Philippines: Mindanao (Lake Lanao)

V   *Puntius cataractae*
Philippines

V   *Puntius clemensi*
Philippines: Mindanao (Lake Lanao)

V   *Puntius cumingii*
Two Spot Barb
Sri Lanka

V   *Puntius disa*
Philippines: Mindanao (Lake Lanao)

V   *Puntius flavifuscus*
Philippines: Mindanao (Lake Lanao)

V   *Puntius herrei*
Philippines

V *Puntius katalo*
Philippines: Mindanao (Lake Lanao)

V *Puntius lanaoensis*
Philippines: Mindanao (Lake Lanao)

R *Puntius lindong*
Philippines: Mindanao (Lake Lanao)

V *Puntius mamalak*
Philippines: Mindanao (Lake Lanao)

V *Puntius nigrofasciatus*
Black Ruby Barb
Sri Lanka

V *Puntius pleurotaenia*
Side Striped Barb
Sri Lanka

R *Puntius sirang*
Philippines: Mindanao (Lake Lanao)

E *Puntius srilankensis*
Sri Lanka

V *Puntius titteya*
Cherry Barb
Sri Lanka

V *Puntius tras*
Philippines: Mindanao (Lake Lanao)

R *Puntius tumba*
Philippines: Mindanao (Lake Lanao)

V *Rasbora vaterifloris*
Vateria Flower Rasbora
Sri Lanka

R *Relictus solitarius*
Relict Dace
USA

R *Rutilus lemmingii*
Portugal?; Spain

R *Semotilus lumbee*
Sandhills Chub
USA

R *Sinocyclocheilus anophthalmus*
China

V *Spratellicypris palata*
Philippines: Mindanao (Lake Lanao)

E *Tanakia tanago*
Tokyo Bitterling
Japan

V *Tiaroga cobitis*
Loach Minnow
USA

I *Tylognathus klatti*
Saz Baliği
Turkey

R *Typhlobarbus nudiventris*
China

R *Typhlogarra widdowsoni*
Iraq

E *Varicorhinus alticorpus*
Taiwan

R *Vimba melanops*
Malamída
Greece

Family COBITIDAE

V *Cobitis calderoni*
Portugal; Spain

I *Cobitis haasi*
Spain

V *Cobitis paludica*
Portugal; Spain

V *Cobitis stephanidisi*
Greece

E *Lepidocephalichthys jonklaasi*
Spotted Loach
Sri Lanka

E *Leptobotia curta*
Ayumodoki
Japan

Family BALITORIDAE

V *Acanthocobitis urophthalmus*
Banded Mountain Loach
Sri Lanka

R *Nemacheilus troglocataractus*
Thailand: Tham Sai Yok Noi

R *Nemacheilus gejiuensi*
China: Bajianjing, Yunnan Province

R *Nemacheilus smithi*
Iran: Baq-e-Loveh pool, Zagros Mountains

R *Nemacheilus xianggensis*
China: Xiangxi, Hunan Province

R *Oreonectes anophthalmus*
China

R *Schistura jarutanini*
Thailand: Amphoe Sri Sawat, Kanchanaburi Province

R **Schistura oedipus**
   Thailand: Tham Nam Lang, Mae Hong Son Province

R **Schistura sijuensis**
   India

R **Sundoreonectes tiomanensis**
   Malaysia

R **Troglocobitis starostini**
   Turkmenistan: Kugitangtau mountains

E **Yunnanilus nigromaculatus**
   China: Yunnan (Dianchi Lake)

Family CATOSTOMIDAE

V **Catostomus bernardini**
   Yaqui Sucker
   Mexico; USA

V **Catostomus cahita**
   Matalote Cahita
   Mexico

R **Catostomus conchos**
   Matalote Conchos
   Mexico

R **Catostomus leopoldi**
   Matalote del Bavispe
   Mexico

E **Catostomus microps**
   Modoc Sucker
   USA

R **Catostomus santaanae**
   Santa Ana Sucker
   USA

R **Catostomus snyderi**
   Klamath largescale sucker
   USA

E **Catostomus warnerensis**
   Warner Sucker
   USA

R **Catostomus wigginsi**
   Matalote Opata
   Mexico

E **Catostomus sp.**
   Salish Sucker
   Canada; USA

E **Chasmistes brevirostris**
   Shortnose Sucker
   USA

E **Chasmistes cujus**
   Cui-ui
   USA

R **Cycleptus elongatus**
   Blue Sucker
   Mexico; USA

E **Deltistes luxatus**
   Lost River Sucker
   USA

R **Moxostoma ariommumm**
   Bigeye Jumprock
   USA

R **Moxostoma atripinne**
   Blackfin Sucker
   USA

R **Moxostoma congestum**
   Gray Redhorse
   Mexico; USA

R **Moxostoma hamiltoni**
   Rustyside Sucker
   USA

V **Moxostoma hubbsi**
   Copper Redhorse
   Canada

V **Moxostoma sp.**
   Bighead Redhorse
   USA

E **Xyrauchen texanus**
   Razorback Sucker
   USA

Order CHARACIFORMES

Family CHARACIDAE

E **Catabasis acuminatus**
   Brazil

V **Cheirodon australe**
   Chile

V **Cheirodon galusdae**
   Chile

V **Cheirodon kiliani**
   Chile

V **Cheirodon pisciculus**
   Chile

V **Gymnocharacinus bergi**
   Naked Characin
   Argentina

Order SILURIFORMES

Family DIPLOMYSTIDAE

E **Diplomystes camposensis**
   Chile

E   *Diplomystes chilensis*
    Tollo de Agua Dulce
        Chile

E   *Diplomystes nahuelbutensis*
        Chile

Family ICTALURIDAE

R   *Ictalurus australis*
    Bagre del Panuco
        Mexico

R   *Ictalurus lupus*
    Bagre Lobo
        Mexico; USA

R   *Ictalurus mexicanus*
    Bagre de Rio Verde
        Mexico

R   *Ictalurus pricei*
    Bagre de Yaqui
        Mexico

R   *Ictalurus* sp.
    Bagre de Cuatro Cienegas
        Mexico

E   *Noturus baileyi*
    Smoky Madtom
        USA

V   *Noturus flavipinnis*
    Yellowfin Madtom
        USA

R   *Noturus furiosus*
    Carolina Madtom
        USA

V   *Noturus gilberti*
    Orangefin Madtom
        USA

V   *Noturus lachneri*
    Ouachita Madtom
        USA

V   *Noturus munitus*
    Frecklebelly Madtom
        USA

V   *Noturus placidus*
    Neosho Madtom
        USA

E   *Noturus stanauli*
    Pygmy Madtom
        USA

V   *Noturus taylori*
    Caddo Madtom
        USA

E   *Noturus trautmani*
    Scioto Madtom
        USA

E   *Prietella phreatophila*
    Bagre de Muzquiz
        Mexico

V   *Satan eurystomus*
    Widemouth Blindcat
        USA

V   *Trogloglanis pattersoni*
    Toothless Blindcat
        USA

Family BAGRIDAE

E   *Austroglanis barnardi*
    Barnard's Rock-catfish
        South Africa

R   *Austroglanis gilli*
    Clanwilliam Rock-catfish
        South Africa

I   *Austroglanis sclateri*
    Rock-catfish
        South Africa

E   *Coreobagrus ichikawai*
    Nekogigi
        Japan

I   *Leiocassis medianalis*
        China: Yunnan (Dianchi Lake)

R   *Pardiglanis tarabinii*
    Giant Catfish
        Somalia: Jubba River

E   *Pseudobagrus* sp.
    Gibachi
        Japan: Kyushu Island

Family SILURIDAE

K   *Silurus mento*
        China: Yunnan (Dianchi Lake)

Family PANGASIIDAE

V   *Pangasianodon gigas*
    Giant Catfish
        Cambodia; China: Yunnan Province; Laos;
        Myanmar; Thailand; Viet Nam

R   *Pangasius sanitwongsei*
    Pla Thepa
        Cambodia; Laos; Thailand; Viet Nam

Family AMBLYCIPITIDAE

I   *Liobagrus nigricauda*
        China: Yunnan (Dianchi Lake)

Family SISORIDAE

I   *Oreoglanis siamensis*
    Thailand

Family CLARIIDAE

E   *Clarias cavernicola*
    Cave Catfish
    Namibia

R   *Horaglanis krishnai*
    Cave Catfish
    India

Family HETEROPNEUSTIDAE

V   *Heteropnuestes microps*
    Sri Lanka

Family ARIIDAE

K   *Ancharius brevibarbus*
    Madagascar

V   *Arius taylori*
    Taylor's Catfish
    Indonesia: Irian Jaya; Papua New Guinea

K   *Cinetodus froggatti*
    Small Mouthed Catfish
    Australia

I   *Tetranesodon conorhynchus*
    Lorentz Catfish
    Indonesia: Irian Jaya

Family PLOTOSIDAE

R   *Neosilurus* sp. 1
    Dalhousie Catfish
    Australia

R   *Neosilurus* sp. 2
    Cooper Creek Tandan
    Australia

K   *Neosilurus* sp. 3
    False Spine Catfish
    Australia

V   *Oloplotosus torobo*
    Kutubu Tandan
    Papua New Guinea

R   *Tandanus* sp.
    Belinger River Tandan
    Australia

Family MOCHOKIDAE

V   *Chiloglanis bifurcus*
    Incomati Rock Catlet
    South Africa

K   *Chiloglanis swierstrai*
    Lowveld Rock Catlet
    Mozambique; South Africa; Zimbabwe

Family PIMELODIDAE

V   *Rhamdia reddelli*
    Juil Ciego
    Mexico

Family TRICHOMYCTERIDAE

V   *Bullockia maldonadoi*
    Chile

I   *Eremophilus mutisii*
    Colombia: Bogotá area

E   *Nematogenys inermis*
    Chile

V   *Trichomycterus areolatus*
    Chile

E   *Trichomycterus chiltoni*
    Chile

E   *Trichomycterus chungarensis*
    Chile

E   *Trichomycterus laucaensis*
    Chile

E   *Trichomycterus rivulatus*
    Chile

Order SALMONIFORMES

Family UMBRIDAE

R   *Novumbra hubbsi*
    Olympic Mudminnow
    USA

Family LEPIDOGALAXIIDAE

R   *Lepidogalaxias salamandroides*
    Salmanderfish
    Australia

Family OSMERIDAE

V   *Hypomesus transpacificus*
    Delta Smelt
    USA

R   *Osmerus spectrum*
    Pygmy Smelt
    Canada; USA

Family SALANGIDAE

E   *Neosalanx regani*
    Ariakehimeshirauo
    Japan: Kyushu Island

Family RETROPINNIDAE

V **_Prototroctes maraena_**
Australian Grayling
Australia: Tasmania

Family GALAXIIDAE

K **_Aplochiton marinus_**
Chile

V **_Brachygalaxias bullocki_**
Chile

V **_Brachygalaxias gothei_**
Chile

E **_Galaxias fontanus_**
Swan Galaxias
Australia: Tasmania

E **_Galaxias fuscus_**
Barred Galaxias
Australia

E **_Galaxias globiceps_**
Chile

V **_Galaxias gracilis_**
Dwarf Inanga
New Zealand

E **_Galaxias johnstoni_**
Clarence Galaxias
Australia: Tasmania

K **_Galaxias parvus_**
Small Pedder Galaxias
Australia: Tasmania

E **_Galaxias pedderensis_**
Pedder Galaxias
Australia: Tasmania

R **_Galaxias postvectis_**
Shortjawed Kokopu
New Zealand

R **_Galaxias rostratus_**
Murray Jollytail
Australia

V **_Galaxias sp._**
New Zealand: Waipori River

V **_Galaxias tanycephalus_**
Saddled Galaxias
Australia: Tasmania

R **_Galaxiella nigrostriata_**
Black-Striped Minnow
Australia

V **_Galaxiella pusilla_**
Dwarf Galaxias
Australia: Tasmania

V **_Neochanna burrowsius_**
Canterbury Mudfish
New Zealand

R **_Neochanna diversus_**
Black Mudfish
New Zealand

R **_Paragalaxias mesotes_**
Arthurs Paragalaxias
Australia

Family SALMONIDAE

R **_Coregonus artedii_**
Cisco
(Great Lakes)
Canada; USA

E **_Coregonus canadensis_**
Atlantic Whitefish
(Great Lakes)
Canada; USA

R **_Coregonus hoyi_**
Bloater
(Great Lakes)
Canada; USA

V **_Coregonus kiyi_**
Kiyi
(Great Lakes)
Canada; USA

E **_Coregonus nigripinnis_**
Blackfin Cisco
(Great Lakes)
Canada; USA

E **_Coregonus oxyrhynchus_**
Houting
Denmark; Estonia; Finland; Germany; Ireland;
Latvia; Lithuania; Norway; Poland; Russia;
Sweden; United Kingdom

E **_Coregonus reighardi_**
Shortnose Cisco
(Great Lakes)
Canada; USA

E **_Coregonus zenithicus_**
Shortjaw Cisco
(Great Lakes)
Canada; USA

E **_Coregonus sp._** 1
Opeongo Whitefish
Canada

V *Coregonus* sp. 2
Squanga Whitefish
 Canada

E *Hucho hucho*
Danube Salmon
 Austria; Czech Republic; France; Germany;
 Italy; Moldavia?; Poland; Romania; Slovakia;
 Switzerland; Ukraine; Yugoslavia

V *Onchorhynchus apache*
Apache Trout
 USA

V *Onchorhynchus chrysogaster*
Mexican Golden Trout
 Mexico

V *Onchorhynchus gilae*
Gila Trout
 USA

E *Onchorhynchus ishikawai*
Satsukimasu Salmon
 Japan: Nagara River, Honshu Island

E *Onchorhynchus iwame*
Iwame Trout
 Japan

R *Onchorhynchus* sp.
Trucha de Yaqui
 Mexico

I *Salmo platycephalus*
Ala Balik
 Turkey

E *Salmothymus obtusirostris*
Adriatic Salmon
 Yugoslavia

R *Salvelinus anaktuvukensis*
Angayukaksurak Char
 USA

I *Salvelinus confluentus*
Bull Trout
 Canada; USA

E *Salvelinus japonicus*
Kirikuchi Char
 Japan: Totsukawa River, Honshu Island

Order PERCOPSIFORMES

Family AMBLYOPSIDAE

V *Amblyopsis rosae*
Ozark Cavefish
 USA

V *Amblyopsis spelaea*
Northern Cavefish
 USA

E *Speoplatyrhinus poulsoni*
Alabama Cavefish
 USA

Order OPHIDIIFORMES

Family BYTHITIDAE

I *Lucifuga spelaeotes*
New Providence Cusk-eel
 Bahamas: Mermaids Pool, New Providence
 Island

E *Typhliasina pearsei*
Dama Ciega Blanca
 Mexico

E *Typhliasina* sp.
Nueva Dama Ciega
 Mexico

Order CYPRINODONTIFORMES

Family APLOCHEILIDAE

E *Campellolebias brucei*
Santa Catarina Sabrefin
 Brazil

R *Cynolebias boitonei*
Brasilia Lyrefin
 Brazil

V *Cynolebias constanciae*
 Brazil

E *Cynolebias marmoratus*
Ginger Pearlfish
 Brazil

I *Cynolebias minimus*
Minute Pearlfish
 Brazil

E *Cynolebias opalescens*
Opalescent Pearlfish
 Brazil

E *Cynolebias splendens*
Splendid Pearlfish
 Brazil

E *Nothobranchius* sp.
Caprivi Killifish
 Namibia

K *Pachypanchax homalonotus*
 Madagascar

K *Pachypanchax sakaramyi*
 Madagascar

R   *Rivulus marmoratus*
Rivulus
USA

R   *Rivulus robustus*
Rivulus Almirante
Mexico

Family CYPRINODONTIDAE

I   *Aphanius anatolias*
Dislisazancik Baliği
Turkey

I   *Aphanius burduricus*
Turkey

I   *Aphanius chantrei*
Dislisazancik Baliği
Turkey

E   *Aphanius iberus*
Spain

R   *Crenichthys baileyi*
White River Springfish
USA

V   *Crenichthys nevadae*
Railroad Valley Springfish
USA

E   *Cualac tessellatus*
Cachorrito de Media Luna
Mexico

V   *Cyprinodon alvarezi*
Perrito de Potosi
Mexico

R   *Cyprinodon atrorus*
Perrito del Bolson
Mexico

V   *Cyprinodon beltrani*
Cachorrito Lodero
Mexico

R   *Cyprinodon bifasciatus*
Perrito de Cuatro Cienegas
Mexico

E   *Cyprinodon bovinus*
Leon Springs Pupfish
USA

V   *Cyprinodon diabolis*
Devils Hole Pupfish
USA

E   *Cyprinodon elegans*
Comanche Springs Pupfish
USA

E   *Cyprinodon fontinalis*
Perrito de Carbonera
Mexico

V   *Cyprinodon labiosus*
Cachorrito Cangrejero
Mexico

V   *Cyprinodon macrolepis*
Largescale Pupfish
Mexico

V   *Cyprinodon maya*
Cachorrito Gigante
Mexico

E   *Cyprinodon meeki*
Cachorrito de Mezquital
Mexico

V   *Cyprinodon nazas*
Cachorrito del Aguanaval
Mexico

E   *Cyprinodon pachycephalus*
Cachorrito Cabezon
Mexico

V   *Cyprinodon pecosensis*
Pecos Pupfish
USA

E   *Cyprinodon radiosus*
Owens Pupfish
USA

V   *Cyprinodon simus*
Cachorrito Boxeador
Mexico

R   *Cyprinodon tularosa*
White Sands Pupfish
USA

V   *Cyprinodon verecundus*
Cachorrito de Dorsal Larga
Mexico

R   *Fundulus julisia*
Barrens Topminnow
USA

V   *Fundulus lima*
Killifish
Mexico

V   *Fundulus waccamensis*
Waccamaw Killifish
USA

E   *Lucania interioris*
Sardinilla Cuatro Cienegas
Mexico

V **Kosswigichthys asquamatus**
Scaleless Killifish
Turkey

E **Megupsilon aporus**
Cachorrito Enano de Potosi
Mexico

I **Micropanchax schoelleri**
Egypt

E **Orestias chungarensis**
Chile

E **Orestias cuvieri**
Bolivia

E **Orestias laucaensis**
Chile

E **Orestias parinacotensis**
Chile

K **Pantanodon madagascariensis**
Madagascar

E **Valencia hispanica**
Valencia Toothcarp
Spain

E **Valencia letourneuxi**
Zournás
Greece

Family GOODEIDAE

E **Allotoca maculata**
Opal Goodeid
Mexico

E **Ameca splendens**
Goodeid
Mexico

E **Ataeniobius toweri**
Striped Goodeid
Mexico

V **Characodon audax**
Bold Characodon
Mexico

E **Characodon lateralis**
Rainbow Goodeid
Mexico

E **Girardinichthys multiradiatus**
Mexico

E **Girardinichthys viviparus**
Mexclapique
Mexico

V **Goodea gracilis**
Mexico

E **Hubbsina turneri**
Mexico

E **Skiffia francesae**
Tiro
Mexico

E **Xenoophorus captivus**
Solo Goodeido
Mexico

Family POECILIIDAE

I **Gambusia aestiputeus**
Colombia: San Andrés

V **Gambusia alvarezi**
Guayacon de San Gregorio
Mexico

R **Gambusia eurystoma**
Guayacon Bocon
Mexico

E **Gambusia gaigei**
Big Bend Gambusia
USA

V **Gambusia heterochir**
Clear Creek Gambusia
USA

V **Gambusia hurtadoi**
Guayacon de Hacienda Dolores
Mexico

I **Gambusia krumholzi**
Mexico

V **Gambusia longispinis**
Guayacon de Cuatro Cienegas
Mexico

V **Gambusia nobilis**
Pecos Gambusia
USA

R **Gambusia senilis**
Guayacon Pinto
Mexico; USA

I **Gambusia speciosa**
USA

V **Poecilia latipunctata**
Molly del Tamesi
Mexico

V **Poecilia sulphuraria**
Molly del Teapa
Mexico

I **Poecilia vetiprovidentiae**
Colombia: Isla de Providencia

I *Poeciliopsis monacha*
Mexico

R *Poeciliopsis occidentalis*
Charalito
Mexico; USA

R *Xiphophorus clemenciae*
Espada de Clemencia
Mexico

E *Xiphophorus couchianus*
Platy Monterrey
Mexico

E *Xiphophorus gordoni*
Platy Cuatro Cienegas
Mexico

E *Xiphophorus meyeri*
Platy de Muzquiz
Mexico

Order BELONIFORMES

Family ADRIANICHTHYIDAE

E *Adrianichthys kruyti*
Duck-billed Buntingi
Indonesia: Sulawesi (Lake Poso)

V *Oryzias marmoratus*
Indonesia: Sulawesi

V *Oryzias matanensis*
Indonesia: Sulawesi (Malili Lakes)

V *Oryzias nigrimas*
Black Buntingi
Indonesia: Sulawesi (Lake Poso)

E *Oryzias orthognathus*
Sharp-jawed Buntingi
Indonesia: Sulawesi (Lake Poso)

V *Oryzias profundicola*
Indonesia: Sulawesi (Malili Lakes)

E *Xenopoecilus oophorus*
Egg-carrying Buntingi
Indonesia: Sulawesi (Lake Poso)

E *Xenopoecilus poptae*
Popta's Buntingi
Indonesia: Sulawesi (Lake Poso)

E *Xenopoecilus sarasinorum*
Indonesia: Sulawesi

Family HEMIRAMPHIDAE

V *Dermogenys megarramphus*
Indonesia: Sulawesi (Malili Lakes)

V *Dermogenys weberi*
Indonesia: Sulawesi (Malili Lakes)

R *Nomoramphus celebensis*
Poso Halfbeak
Indonesia: Sulawesi (Lake Poso)

R *Zenarchopterus alleni*
Allen's River Garfish
Indonesia: Irian Jaya

R *Zenacrchopterus robertsi*
Robert's River Garfish
Papua New Guinea

Order ATHERINIFORMES

Family ATHERINIDAE

V *Austromenidia gracilis*
Chile

V *Basilichthys australis*
Chile

E *Basilichthys microlepidotus*
Chile

K *Bedotia geayi*
Madagascar

K *Bedotia longianalis*
Madagascar

K *Bedotia madagascariensis*
Madagascar

R *Cairnsichthys rhombosomoides*
Cairns Rainbowfish
Australia

V *Cauque mauleanum*
Chile

R *Chilatherina axelrodi*
Axelrod's Rainbowfish
Indonesia: Irian Jaya; Papau New Guinea

R *Chilatherina bleheri*
Bleher's Rainbowfish
Indonesia: Irian Jaya

R *Chilatherina bulolo*
Bulolo Rainbowfish
Papua New Guinea

R *Chilatherina sentaniensis*
Sentani Rainbowfish
Indonesia: Irian Jaya

K *Chirostoma bartoni*
Charal de la Caldera
Mexico

E *Chirostoma regani*
Charal del Valle de Mexico
Mexico

R **Craterocephalus amniculus**
Darling River Hardyhead
Australia

R **Craterocephalus centralis**
Finke River Hardyhead
Australia

R **Craterocephalus dalhousiensis**
Dalhousie Hardyhead
Australia

V **Craterocephalus fluviatillis**
Murray Hardyhead
Australia

R **Craterocephalus gloveri**
Glovers Hardyhead
Australia

R **Craterocephalus helenae**
Drysdale Hardyhead
Australia

R **Craterocephalus kailolae**
Kailola's Hardyhead
Papua New Guinea

V **Craterocephalus lacustris**
Kutubu Hardyhead
Papua New Guinea

R **Craterocephalus lentiginosus**
Prince Regent Hardyhead
Australia

K **Craterocephalus marianae**
Magela Hardyhead
Australia

R **Craterocephalus pimatuae**
Pima Hardyhead
Papua New Guinea

R **Glossolepis incisus**
Red Rainbowfish
Indonesia: Irian Jaya

R **Glossolepis maculosus**
Spotted Rainbowfish
Papua New Guinea

R **Glossolepis pseudoincisus**
Tami River Rainbowfish
Indonesia: Irian Jaya; Papua New Guinea

R **Glossolepis ramuensis**
Ramu Rainbowfish
Papua New Guinea

R **Glossolepis wanamensis**
Lake Wanam Rainbowfish
Papua New Guinea

V **Kiunga ballochi**
Glass Blue-Eye
Indonesia: Irian Jaya; Papua New Guinea

R **Melanotaenia ajamaruensis**
Ajamaru Lakes Rainbowfish
Indonesia: Irian Jaya

R **Melanotaenia angfa**
Yakati Rainbowfish
Indonesia: Irian Jaya

R **Melanotaenia arfakensis**
Arfak Rainbowfish
Indonesia: Irian Jaya

V **Melanotaenia boesemani**
Boeseman's Rainbowfish
Indonesia: Irian Jaya

R **Melanotaenia catherinae**
Waigeo Rainbowfish
Indonesia: Irian Jaya

R **Melanotaenia corona**
Corona Rainbowfish
Indonesia: Irian Jaya

R **Melanotaenia exquisita**
Exquisite Rainbowfish
Australia

R **Melanotaenia gracilis**
Slender Rainbowfish
Australia

R **Melanotaenia herbertaxelrodi**
Lake Tebera Rainbowfish
Papua New Guinea

R **Melanotaenia iris**
Strickland Rainbowfish
Papua New Guinea

V **Melanotaenia lacustris**
Lake Kutubu Rainbowfish
Papua New Guinea

R **Melanotaenia maylandi**
Mayland's Rainbowfish
Indonesia: Irian Jaya

R **Melanotaenia misoolensis**
Misool Rainbowfish
Indonesia: Irian Jaya

R **Melanotaenia monticola**
Mountain Rainbowfish
Papua New Guinea

I **Melanotaenia ogilbyi**
Ogilby's Rainbowfish
Indonesia: Irian Jaya

V *Melanotaenia oktediensis*
Oktedi Rainbowfish
Papua New Guinea

R *Melanotaenia papuae*
Papuan Rainbowfish
Papua New Guinea

R *Melanotaenia parva*
Lake Kurumoi Rainbowfish
Indonesia: Irian Jaya

R *Melanotaenia pimanensis*
Pima River Rainbowfish
Papua New Guinea

R *Melanotaenia praecox*
Dwarf Rainbowfish
Indonesia: Irian Jaya

R *Melanotaenia pygmaea*
Pygmy Rainbowfish
Australia

V *Melanotaenia sexlineata*
Fly River Rainbowfish
Indonesia: Irian Jaya; Papua New Guinea

R *Melanotaenia vanheurni*
Van Heurn's Rainbowfish
Indonesia: Irian Jaya

V *Menidia conchorum*
Key Silverside
USA

V *Menidia extensa*
Waccamaw Silverside
USA

V *Poblana alchichica*
Charal de Alchichica
Mexico

R *Poblana ferdebueni*
Mexico

V *Poblana letholepis*
Charal de la Preciosa
Mexico

V *Poblana squamata*
Charal de Quechulac
Mexico

R *Pseudomugil connieae*
Popondetta Blue-Eye
Papua New Guinea

R *Pseudomugil furcatus*
Forktail Blue-Eye
Papua New Guinea

I *Pseudomugil majusculus*
Cape Blue-Eye
Papua New Guinea

V *Pseudomugil mellis*
Honey Blue-eye
Australia

V *Pseudomugil paskai*
Paska's Blue-Eye
Indonesia: Irian Jaya; Papua New Guinea

V *Rheocles alaotrensis*
Katrana
Madagascar

R *Rheocles lateralis*
Madagascar: Nosivolo River

I *Rheocles pellegrini*
Madagascar: near Andapa

E *Rheocles sikorae*
Sardine d'eau douce
Madagascar: near Anosibe, Manambola River

E *Rheocles wrightae*
Madagascar: near Anosibe, Manambola River

K *Teramulus kieneri*
Madagascar

E *Scaturiginichthys vermeilipinnis*
Red-finned Blue-eye
Australia

Family PHALLOSTETHIDAE

I *Phallostethus dunckeri*
Malaysia

Family TELMATHERINIDAE

V *Paratherina cyanea*
Indonesia: Sulawesi (Malili Lakes)

V *Paratherina labiosa*
Indonesia: Sulawesi (Malili Lakes)

V *Paratherina striata*
Indonesia: Sulawesi

V *Paratherina wolterecki*
Indonesia: Sulawesi (Malili Lakes)

V *Telmatherina abendanoni*
Indonesia: Sulawesi (Malili Lakes)

V *Telmatherina bonti*
Indonesia: Sulawesi

V *Telmatherina celebensis*
Indonesia: Sulawesi

R   *Telmatherina ladigesi*
Celebes Rainbow
Indonesia: Sulawesi

Order GASTEROSTEIFORMES

Family GASTEROSTEIDAE

V   *Gasterosteus* sp. 1
Giant Stickleback
Canada

V   *Gasterosteus* sp. 2
Enos Stickleback
Canada

E   *Pungitius hellenicus*
Ellinopygósteos
Greece

E   *Pungitius* sp.
Musashitomiyo
Japan: near Kumagaya city

Order SYNGNATHIFORMES

Family SYNGNATHIDAE

V   *Hippocampus capensis*
Knysna Seahorse
South Africa

I   *Microphis caudocarinatus*
Slender Pipefish
Indonesia: Irian Jaya

I   *Microphis spinachoides*
Spinach Pipefish
Papua New Guinea

Order SYNBRANCHIFORMES

Family SYNBRANCHIDAE

K   *Ophisternon candidum*
Blind Cave Eel
Australia

E   *Ophisternon infernale*
Anguila Ciega
Mexico

Family MASTACEMBELIDAE

E   *Macrognathus aral*
Spiny Eel
Sri Lanka

Order SCORPAENIFORMES

Family COTTIDAE

R   *Cottus asperrimus*
Rough Sculpin
USA

R   *Cottus extensus*
Bear Lake Sculpin
USA

V   *Cottus greenei*
Shoshone Sculpin
USA

R   *Cottus leiopomus*
Wood River Sculpin
USA

R   *Cottus princeps*
Klamath Lake Sculpin
USA

E   *Cottus pygmaeus*
Pygmy Sculpin
USA

R   *Cottus tenuis*
Slender Sculpin
USA

V   *Myoxocephalus quadricornis*
Fourhorn Sculpin
Canada

Order PERCIFORMES

Family AMBASSIDAE

R   *Ambassis agassizi*
Agassiz's Perchlet
Australia

K   *Ambassis elongatus*
Yellow-Fin Perchlet
Australia

I   *Parambassis altipinnis*
High-Finned Glass Perchlet
Indonesia: Irian Jaya

R   *Tetracentrum caudovittatus*
Kokoda Glass Perchlet
Papua New Guinea

Family PERCICHTHYIDAE

V   *Edelia obscura*
Yarra Pygmy Perch
Australia

E   *Maccullochella ikei*
Eastern Freshwater Cod
Australia

E   *Maccullochella macquariensis*
Trout Cod
Australia

E   *Maccullochella* sp. 1
Mary River Cod
Australia

E   *Maccullochella* sp. 2
Clarence River Cod
Australia

K   *Macquaria australasica*
Macquarie Perch
Australia

R   *Nannatherina balstoni*
Balston's Pygmy Perch
Australia

V   *Nannoperca oxleyana*
Oxleyan Pygmy Perch
Australia

V   *Nannoperca variegata*
Ewen's Pygmy Perch
Australia

E   *Percichthys melanops*
Chile

V   *Percilia gillissi*
Chile

E   *Percilla irwini*
Chile

Family TERAPONTIDAE

R   *Hannia greenwayi*
Greenway's Grunter
Australia

V   *Hephaestus adamsoni*
Adamson's Grunter
Papua New Guinea

R   *Hephaestus epirrhinos*
Long-Nose Sooty Grunter
Australia

I   *Hephaestus obtusifrons*
Striped Grunter
Indonesia: Irian Jaya; Papua New Guinea

R   *Hephaestus trimaculatus*
Threespot Grunter
Papua New Guinea

R   *Leiopotherapon aheneus*
Fortescus Grunter
Australia

R   *Leiopotherapon macrolepis*
Large-Scale Grunter
Australia

K   *Pingalla gilberti*
Gilberts Grunter
Australia

R   *Pingalla midgleyi*
Midgley's Grunter
Australia

K   *Scortum hilli*
Leathery Grunter
Australia

R   *Scortum parviceps*
Small-Headed Grunter
Australia

K   *Scortum* sp.
Angalarri Grunter
Australia

K   *Syncomistes kimberleyensis*
Kimberley Grunter
Australia

R   *Syncomistes rastellus*
Drysdale Grunter
Australia

R   *Varia jamoerensis*
Jamur Lake Grunter
Indonesia: Irian Jaya

Family KHULIIDAE

K   *Kuhlia marginata*
Spotted Flagtail
Australia

Family CENTRARCHIDAE

R   *Ambloplites cavifrons*
Roanoke Bass
USA

R   *Micropterus notius*
Suwannee Bass
USA

R   *Micropterus treculi*
Guadalupe Bass
USA

Family ELASSOMATIDAE

R   *Elassoma boehlkei*
Carolina Pygmy Sunfish
USA

R   *Elassoma okatie*
Bluebarred Pygmy Sunfish
USA

V   *Elassoma* sp.
Spring Pygmy Sunfish
USA

Family PERCIDAE

R   *Ammocrypta asprella*
Crystal Darter
USA

V   *Ammocrypta pellucida*
Eastern Sand Darter
Canada; USA

R   *Etheostoma acuticeps*
Sharphead Darter
USA

V   *Etheostoma aquali*
Coppercheek Darter
USA

E   *Etheostoma australe*
Dardo de Conchos
Mexico

V   *Etheostoma boschungi*
Slackwater Darter
USA

R   *Etheostoma cinereum*
Ashy Darter
USA

R   *Etheostoma cragini*
Arkansas Darter
USA

V   *Etheostoma ditrema*
Coldwater Darter
USA

E   *Etheostoma fonticola*
Fountain Darter
USA

R   *Etheostoma grahami*
Rio Grande Darter
Mexico; USA

R   *Etheostoma kanawhae*
Kanawha Darter
USA

R   *Etheostoma luteovinctum*
Redband Darter
USA

R   *Etheostoma maculatum*
Spotted Darter
USA

R   *Etheostoma mariae*
Pinewoods Darter
USA

V   *Etheostoma moorei*
Yellowcheek Darter
USA

V   *Etheostoma nianguae*
Niangua Darter
USA

E   *Etheostoma nuchale*
Watercress Darter
USA

V   *Etheostoma okaloosae*
Okaloosa Darter
USA

R   *Etheostoma osburni*
Finescale Saddled Darter
USA

V   *Etheostoma pallididorsum*
Paleback Darter
USA

V   *Etheostoma pottsi*
Mexican Darter
Mexico

V   *Etheostoma rubrum*
Bayou Darter
USA

R   *Etheostoma striatulum*
Striated Darter
USA

V   *Etheostoma trisella*
Trispot Darter
USA

V   *Etheostoma tuscumbia*
Tuscumbia Darter
USA

V   *Etheostoma wapiti*
Boulder Darter
USA

E   *Etheostoma* sp.
Dardo de Cuatro Cienegas
Mexico

R   *Perca schrenki*
Balkhash Perch
China?; Kazakhstan; Kirgizia?

E   *Percina antesella*
Amber Darter
USA

V   *Percina aurolineata*
Goldline Darter
USA

R   *Percina burtoni*
Blotchside Logperch
USA

R   *Percina cymatotaenia*
Bluestripe Darter
USA

E   *Percina jenkinsi*
Conasauga Logperch
USA

V   *Percina lenticula*
Freckled Darter
USA

V   *Percina macrocephala*
Longhead Darter
USA

V   *Percina nasuta*
Longnose Darter
USA

V   *Percina pantherina*
Leopard Darter
USA

E   *Percina rex*
Roanoke Logperch
USA

V   *Percina tanasi*
Snail Darter
USA

R   *Percina uranidea*
Stargazing Darter
USA

E   *Romanichthys valsanicola*
Asprete
Romania

E   *Zingel asper*
Asper
France

V   *Zingel streber*
Streber
Austria; Bulgaria; Czech Republic; Germany;
Hungary; Moldavia?; Slovakia; Switzerland;
Ukraine; Yugoslavia

Family SCIAENIDAE

E   *Totoaba macdonaldi*
Totoaba
Mexico

Family TOXOTIDAE

K   *Toxotes oligolepis*
Large-Scale Archerfish
Australia

Family CICHLIDAE

R   *Chetia brevis*
Orange-fringed Largemouth
South Africa

E   *Cichlasoma bartoni*
Mojarra Caracolera
Mexico

E   *Cichlasoma labridens*
Mojarra
Mexico

E   *Cichlasoma minckleyi*
Mojarra Caracolera de Cuatro Cienegas
Mexico

R   *Cichlasoma pantostictum*
Mojarra
Mexico

R   *Cichlasoma steindachneri*
Mojarra
Mexico

E   *Cichlasoma* sp.
Mojarra Caracolera de Media Luna
Mexico

V   *Konia dikume*
Dikume
Cameroon: Lake Barombi Mbo

V   *Konia eisentrauti*
Konye
Cameroon: Lake Barombi Mbo

V   *Myaka myaka*
Myaka myaka
Cameroon: Lake Barombi Mbo

R   *Oxylapia polli*
Madagascar: Marolambo Rapids, Nosivolo
River

V   *Paratilapia polleni*
Marakely
Madagascar

K   *Paretroplus dami*
Damba
Madagascar

K   *Paretroplus kieneri*
Kotsovato
Madagascar

K *Paretroplus maculatus*
Masovoatoaka
Madagascar

K *Paretroplus petiti*
Kotso
Madagascar

E *Ptychochromoides betsileanus*
Trondo Mainty
Madagascar

R *Ptychochromoides* sp.
Madagascar: Nosivolo River

V *Pungu maclareni*
Pungu
Cameroon: Lake Barombi Mbo

V *Sarotherodon caroli*
Fissi
Cameroon: Lake Barombi Mbo

V *Sarotherodon linnellii*
Unga
Cameroon: Lake Barombi Mbo

V *Sarotherodon lohbergeri*
Leka Keppe
Cameroon: Lake Barombi Mbo

V *Sarotherodon steinbachi*
Kululu
Cameroon: Lake Barombi Mbo

R *Serranochromis meridianus*
Lowveld Largemouth
South Africa

V *Stomatepia mariae*
Nsess
Cameroon: Lake Barombi Mbo

V *Stomatepia mongo*
Mongo
Cameroon: Lake Barombi Mbo

V *Stomatepia pindu*
Pindu
Cameroon: Lake Barombi Mbo

R *Tilapia bakossiorum*
Cameroon: Lake Bermin

R *Tilapia bemini*
Cameroon: Lake Bermin

R *Tilapia bythobathes*
Cameroon: Lake Bermin

R *Tilapia flava*
Cameroon: Lake Bermin

E *Tilapia guinasana*
Otjikoto Tilapia
Namibia

R *Tilapia gutturosa*
Cameroon: Lake Bermin

R *Tilapia imbriferna*
Cameroon: Lake Bermin

R *Tilapia snyderae*
Cameroon: Lake Bermin

R *Tilapia spongotroktis*
Cameroon: Lake Bermin

R *Tilapia thysi*
Cameroon: Lake Bermin

Family MUGILIDAE

R *Liza luciae*
Saint Lucia Mullet
South Africa

R *Myxus capensis*
Freshwater Mullet
South Africa

Family CLINIDAE

R *Clinus spatulatus*
Bot River Klipfish
South Africa

Family ELEOTRIDAE

R *Bostrichthys aruensis*
Island Gudgeon
Indonesia: Aru Islands

I *Bostrichthys zonatus*
Barred Gudgeon
Indonesia: Irian Jaya

R *Eleotris sandwicensis*
Oopu
USA

R *Gobiomorphus alpinus*
Tarndale Bully
New Zealand

R *Hypseleotris aurea*
Golden Gudgeon
Australia

R *Hypseleotris dayi*
Golden Sleeper
South Africa

K *Hypseleotris ejuncida*
Slender Gudgeon
Australia

K   *Hypseleotris kimberleyensis*
     Barnett River Gudgeon
     Australia

K   *Hypseleotris regalis*
     Prince Regent Gudgeon
     Australia

R   *Kimberleyeleotris hutchinsi*
     Mitchell Gudgeon
     Australia

R   *Kimberleyeleotris notata*
     Drysdale Gudgeon
     Australia

R   *Milyeringa veritas*
     Blind Gudgeon
     Australia

R   *Mogurnda adspersa*
     Purple Spotted Gudgeon
     Australia

V   *Mogurnda furva*
     Black Mogurnda
     Papua New Guinea

R   *Mogurnda lineata*
     Kokoda Mogurnda
     Papua New Guinea

R   *Mogurnda orientalis*
     Eastern Mogurnda
     Papua New Guinea

V   *Mogurnda spilota*
     Blotched Mogurnda
     Papua New Guinea

V   *Mogurnda variegata*
     Variegated Mogurnda
     Papua New Guinea

V   *Mogurnda vitta*
     Striped Mogurnda
     Papua New Guinea

R   *Mogurnda* sp. 1
     False-Spotted Gudgeon
     Australia

R   *Mogurnda* sp. 2
     Flinders Ranges Gudgeon
     Australia

R   *Mogurnda* sp. 3
     Karamui Gudgeon
     Papua New Guinea

R   *Mogurnda* sp. 4
     Wau Gudgeon
     Papua New Guinea

R   *Mogurnda* sp. 5
     Highlands Gudgeon
     Papua New Guinea

R   *Mogurnda* sp. 6
     Malas Gudgeon
     Papua New Guinea

R   *Oxyeleotris wisselensis*
     Paniai Gudgeon
     Indonesia: Irian Jaya

V   *Ratsirakia legendrei*
     Madagascar

Family GOBIIDAE

R   *Awaous stamineus*
     Oopu Nakea
     USA

E   *Chlamydogobius* sp. 1
     Elizabeth Springs Goby
     Australia

K   *Chlamydogobius* sp. 2
     Edgbaston Goby
     Australia

R   *Chlamydogobius* sp. 3
     Dalhousie Goby
     Australia

I   *Croilia mossambica*
     Burrowing Goby
     South Africa

R   *Economidichthys trichonis*
     Nanogoviós
     Greece

R   *Eucyclogobius newberryi*
     Tidewater Goby
     USA

R   *Glossogobius hoesei*
     Hoese's Goby
     Indonesia: Irian Jaya

V   *Glossogobius intermedius*
     Indonesia: Sulawesi

V   *Glossogobius matanensis*
     Indonesia: Sulawesi

R   *Glossogobius* sp. 1
     Mountain Goby
     Papua New Guinea

I   *Glossogobius* sp. 2
     Irian Goby
     Indonesia: Irian Jaya

V   *Glossogobius* sp. 3
Robert's Goby
Indonesia: Irian Jaya; Papua New Guinea

V   *Glossogobius* sp. 4
Bluntsnout Goby
Papua New Guinea

R   *Glossogobius* sp. 5
Sentani Goby
Indonesia: Irian Jaya

R   *Glossogobius* sp. 6
Fly River Goby
Indonesia: Irian Jaya; Papua New Guinea

V   *Glossogobius* sp. 7
Kutubu Goby
Papua New Guinea

R   *Glossogobius* sp. 8
Bighead Goby
Papua New Guinea

R   *Glossogobius* sp. 9
Ramu Goby
Papua New Guinea

R   *Glossogobius* sp. 10
Mulgrave Goby
Australia

I   **Gobius tigerellus**
Tiger Goby
Indonesia: Irian Jaya

I   **Knipowitschia goerneri**
Greece

V   **Knipowitschia milleri**
Greece

R   **Knipowitschia punctatissima**
Greece

V   **Knipowitschia thessala**
Thessalogovinós
Greece

V   **Loentipes concolor**
Oopu Alamoo
USA

V   **Mistichthys luzonensis**
Sinarapan
Philippines

V   **Mugilogobius latifrons**
Indonesia: Sulawesi

V   **Mugilogobius sp.**
Indonesia: Sulawesi

V   **Padogobius nigricans**
Greece

I   **Pandaka pygmaea**
Dwarf Pygmy Goby
Philippines: Malabon River

I   **Pseudogobiopsis sp.**
Red-spotted Goby
Papua New Guinea

R   **Redigobius dewaali**
Checked Goby
Mozambique; South Africa

R   **Schismatogobius deraniyagalai**
Redneck Goby
Sri Lanka

R   **Sicydium stimpsoni**
Oopu Nopili
USA

R   **Sicyopterus halei**
Red-tailed Goby
Sri Lanka

R   **Sicyopus jonklaasi**
Lipstick Goby
Sri Lanka

R   **Silhouettea sibayi**
Sibayi Goby
South Africa

V   **Stupidogobius flavipinnis**
Indonesia: Sulawesi (Malili Lakes)

R   **Taenioides jacksoni**
Bearded Goby
South Africa

V   **Tamanka sarasinorum**
Sarasin's Goby
Indonesia: Sulawesi (Malili Lakes)

E   **Weberogobius amadi**
Poso Bungu
Indonesia: Sulawesi (Lake Poso)

Family ANABANTIDAE

E   **Sandelia bainsii**
Eastern Province Rocky
South Africa

Family BELONTIIDAE

R   **Belontia signata**
Combtail
Sri Lanka

V   **Malpulutta kretseri**
Ornate Paradisefish
Sri Lanka

Class SARCOPTERYGII

Order COELACANTHIFORMES

Family LATIMERIIDAE

V   *Latimeria chalumnae*
     Coelacanth
       Comoros; South Africa

Phylum CNIDARIA

Class ANTHOZOA

Order GORGONACEA

Family PLEXAURIDAE

K   *Eunicella verrucosa*
Broad Sea Fan
(Mediterranean Sea; N.E. Atlantic Ocean)

Order ACTINIARIA

Family EDWARDSIIDAE

E   *Edwardsia ivelli*
Ivell's Sea Anemone
United Kingdom

V   *Nematostella vectensis*
Starlet Sea Anemone
Canada; United Kingdom; USA

Phylum PLATYHELMINTHES

Class TURBELLARIA

Order TRICLADIDA

Family KENKIIDAE

R   *Kenkia rhynchida*
Malheur Cave Planarian
USA

E   *Sphalloplana holsingeri*
Holsinger's Groundwater Planarian
USA

E   *Sphalloplana subtilis*
Biggers' Groundwater Planarian
USA

Phylum NEMERTEA

Class ENOPLA

Order HOPLONEMERTEA

E   *Antiponemertes allisonae*
New Zealand

R   *Argonemertes hillii*
Australia

R   *Argonemertes stocki*
Australia

R   *Geonemertes rodericana*
Mauritius: Rodrigues

R   *Katechonemertes nightingaleensis*
Saint Helena: Tristan da Cunha

E   *Pantinonemertes agricola*
Bermuda

Phylum MOLLUSCA

Class GASTROPODA

Order ARCHAEOGASTROPODA

Family NERITIDAE

I   *Neritilia hawaiiensis*
Anchialine Pool Snail
USA: Hawaiian Islands

V   *Theodoxus transversalis*
Austria; Bulgaria; Germany; Hungary; Moldova; Romania; Slovakia; Ukraine; Yugoslavia?

Family HYDROCENIDAE

V   *Georissa biangulata*
Guam

V   *Georissa elegans*
Guam

V   *Georissa laevigata*
Guam

R   *Georissa laseroni*
Australia: New South Wales

V   *Georissa rufula*
Federated States of Micronesia: Pohnpei

V   *Monterissa gowerensis*
Australia: Lord Howe Island

Family HELICINIDAE

V   *Ogasawarana arata*
Japan: Ogasawara

V   *Ogasawarana capsula*
Japan: Ogasawara

V   *Ogasawarana comes*
Japan: Ogasawara

R   *Ogasawarana discrepans*
Japan: Ogasawara

R   *Ogasawarana microtheca*
Japan: Ogasawara

R   *Ogasawarana nitida*
Japan: Ogasawara

R   *Ogasawarana ogasawarana*
Japan: Ogasawara

V **Ogasawarana optima**
   Japan: Ogasawara

V **Sturanyella carolinarum**
   Federated States of Micronesia: Pohnpei

V **Sturanyella epicharis**
   Federated States of Micronesia: Chuuk Islands
   (Lukunor)

Order MESOGASTROPODA

Family CYCLOPHORIDAE

V **Craspedoma costata**
   Spain: Canary Islands (El Hierro, La Gomera)

V **Craspedoma hespericum**
   Portugal: Azores

R **Craspedoma lyonnetianum**
   Portugal: Madeira

R **Ditropis whitei**
   Australia: Queensland (Islands off Cape York
   Peninsula)

Family POTERIIDAE

V **Kondoraphe kiyokoae**
   Federated States of Micronesia: Chuuk Islands

V **Ostodes brazieri**
   Federated States of Micronesia: Chuuk Islands

V **Paramiella incisa**
   Federated States of Micronesia: Chuuk Islands

V **Paramiella kondoi**
   Federated States of Micronesia: Chuuk Islands
   (Moen, Fefan)

Family DIPLOMMATINIDAE

V **Diplommatina alata**
   Palau: Ngemelis

V **Diplommatina aurea**
   Palau: Koror

V **Diplommatinaa crassilabris**
   Palau: Koror

V **Diplommatina gibboni**
   Palau: Koror

V **Diplommatina hyalina**
   Guam

V **Diplommatina inflatula**
   Palau: Peleliu

V **Diplommatina lamellata**
   Palau: Peleliu

V **Diplommatina lutea**
   Palau: Koror

V **Diplommatina pyramis**
   Palau: Peleliu

V **Diplommatina ringens**
   Palau: Peleliu

V **Hungerfordia pelewensis**
   Palau: Koror

V **Palaina albata**
   Palau: Koror

V **Palaina dimorpha**
   Palau: Peleliu

V **Palaina dohrni**
   Palau: Palau

V **Palaina doliolum**
   Federated States of Micronesia: Pohnpei

V **Palaina kubaryi**
   Federated States of Micronesia: Pohnpei

V **Palaina moussoni**
   Palau: Ngcheangel

V **Palaina ovatula**
   Federated States of Micronesia: Pohnpei

V **Palaina patula**
   Palau: Koror, Peleliu

V **Palaina platycheilus**
   Palau: Koror

V **Palaina pupa**
   Palau: Peleliu

V **Palaina pusilla**
   Palau: Peleliu

V **Palaina rubella**
   Palau: Koror

V **Palaina scalarina**
   Federated States of Micronesia: Pohnpei

V **Palaina strigata**
   Palau: Peleliu

V **Palaina striolata**
   Palau

V **Palaina taeniolata**
   Guam

V **Palaina wilsoni**
   Palau

V **Palaina xiphidium**
   Federated States of Micronesia: Pohnpei

V **Pseudopalaina polymorpha**
   Palau: Peleliu

Family PUPINIDAE

R **Hedleya coxeni**
(*Signepupina coxeni*)
Australia: Queensland

R **Hedleya macleayi**
Australia: Queensland

R **Hedleya pfeifferi**
(Signepupina pfeifferi)
Australia: Queensland

V **Pupina brenchleyi**
Federated States of Micronesia: Chuuk Islands
(Lukunor)

V **Pupina complanata**
Federated States of Micronesia: Kosrae,
Pohnpei; Marshall Islands: Jaluit, Ebon

V **Pupina difficilis**
Palau

R **Pupina splendens**
(*Suavocallia splendens*)
Australia: Queensland (Lizard Islands)

Family LIAREIDAE

R **Cytora hirsutissima**
New Zealand

Family VIVIPARIDAE

I **Lioplax cyclostomaformis**
Cylindrical Lioplax
USA

E **Tulotoma magnifica**
Tulotoma
USA

V **Viviparus acerosus**
Austria; Bulgaria; Germany; Hungary;
Romania; Slovakia

Family VALVATIDAE

E **Valvata utahensis**
Utah Valvata
USA

Family POMATIASIDAE

R **Pomatias raricosta**
Spain: Canary Islands (Tenerife)

E **Tropidophora articulata**
Mauritius: Rodrigues

R **Tropidophora deburghiae**
Madagascar

Family ACICULIDAE

R **Acicula norrisi**
Gibraltar

R **Platyla foliniana**
France

R **Renea gormonti**
France

R **Renea paillona**
France

Family HYDROBIIDAE

V **Alzoniella hartwigschuetti**
Austria

I **Antrobia breweri**
USA

I **Antrobia culveri**
Tumbllng Creek Cavesnail
USA

I **Apachecoccus arizonae**
Bylas Springsnail
USA

I **Aphaostracon asthenes**
Blue Spring Hydrobe
USA

I **Aphaostracon monas**
Wekiwa Hydrobe
USA

I **Aphaostracon pycnum**
Dense Hydrobe
USA

I **Aphaostracon xynoelictus**
Fenney Spring Hydrobe
USA

I **Arganiella exilis**
France

K **Avenionia brevis**
France; Belgium; Netherlands; Germany

V **Beddomeia angulata**
Australia: Tasmania

V **Beddomeia averni**
Australia: Tasmania

V **Beddomeia bellii**
Australia: Tasmania

V **Beddomeia bowryensis**
Australia: Tasmania

V **Beddomeia briansmithi**
Australia: Tasmania

V **Beddomeia camensis**
Australia: Tasmania

V **Beddomeia capensis**
Australia: Tasmania

V **Beddomeia fallax**
Australia: Tasmania

V **Beddomeia forthensis**
Australia: Tasmania

V **Beddomeia franklandensis**
Australia: Tasmania

V **Beddomeia fromensis**
Australia: Tasmania

V **Beddomeia fultoni**
Australia: Tasmania

V **Beddomeia gibba**
Australia: Tasmania

V **Beddomeia hallae**
Australia: Tasmania

V **Beddomeia hermansi**
Australia: Tasmania

V **Beddomeia hullii**
Australia: Tasmania

V **Beddomeia inflata**
Australia: Tasmania

V **Beddomeia kershawi**
Australia: Tasmania

V **Beddomeia kessneri**
Australia: Tasmania

V **Beddomeia krybetes**
Australia: Tasmania

V **Beddomeia launcestonensis**
Australia: Tasmania

V **Beddomeia lodderae**
Australia: Tasmania

V **Beddomeia mesiboyi**
Australia: Tasmania

V **Beddomeia minima**
Australia: Tasmania

V **Beddomeia petterdi**
Australia: Tasmania

V **Beddomeia phasianella**
Australia: Tasmania

V **Beddomeia protuberata**
Australia: Tasmania

V **Beddomeia ronaldi**
Australia: Tasmania

V **Beddomeia salmonis**
Australia: Tasmania

V **Beddomeia tasmanica**
Australia: Tasmania

V **Beddomeia topsiae**
Australia: Tasmania

V **Beddomeia trochiformis**
Australia: Tasmania

E **Beddomeia tumida**
Australia: Tasmania

V **Beddomeia turnerae**
Australia: Tasmania

V **Beddomeia waterhouseae**
Australia: Tasmania

V **Beddomeia wilmotensis**
Australia: Tasmania

V **Beddomeia wiseae**
Australia: Tasmania

V **Beddomeia zeehanensis**
Australia: Tasmania

E **Belgrandiella austriana**
Austria

E **Belgrandiella fuchsi**
Austria

E **Belgrandiella komenskyi**
Czech Republic

V **Belgrandiella lacheineri**
Austria

E **Belgrandiella parreyssi**
Austria

V **Belgrandiella pupula**
Austria

I **Belgrandiella pyrenaica**
France

E **Belgrandiella styriaca**
Austria

E **Bythinella badensis**
Germany

E **Bythinella bavarica**
Germany

I **Bythinella bicarinata**
France

I **Bythinella carinulata**
France

E **Bythinella compressa**
Germany

R **Bythinella cylindrica**
Austria

E **Bythinella dunkeri**
Belgium; Germany

I **Bythinella pupoides**
France; Switzerland

I **Bythinella reyniesii**
Andorra; France

I **Bythinella vesontiana**
France

I **Bythinella viridis**
Belgium; France

E **Bythiospeum acicula**
Germany

R **Bythiospeum alpinum**
Switzerland

I **Bythiospeum articense**
France

I **Bythiospeum bressanum**
France

E **Bythiospeum cisterciensorum**
Austria

I **Bythiospeum diaphanum**
France, Switzerland

E **Bythiospeum elseri**
Austria

I **Bythiospeum garneri**
France

E **Bythiospeum geyeri**
Austria

E **Bythiospeum noricum**
Austria

E **Bythiospeum quenstedti**
Germany

E **Bythiospeum reisalpense**
Austria

E **Bythiospeum sandbergeri**
Germany

I **Cincinnatia helicogyra**
Crystal Siltsnail
USA

I **Cincinnatia mica**
Ichetucknee Siltsnail
USA

I **Cincinnatia monroensis**
Enterprise Siltsnail
USA

I **Cincinnatia parva**
Pygmy Siltsnail
USA

I **Cincinnatia ponderosa**
Ponderous Siltsnail
USA

I **Cincinnatia vanhyningi**
Seminole Siltsnail
USA

I **Cincinnatia wekiwae**
Wekiwa Siltsnail
USA

I **Clappia cahabensis**
Cahaba Pebblesnail
USA

V **Coahuilix hubbsi**
Coahuilix de Hubbs Snail
Mexico

I **Cochliopa texana**
Phantom Cavesnail
USA

V **Cochliopina milleri**
Miller's Snail
Mexico

I **Coxiella striata**
Australia: Tasmania

V **Durangonella coahuilae**
Durangonella de Coahuila Snail
Mexico

I **Fissuria boui**
France

I **Fluminicola avernalis**
Moapa Pebblesnail
USA

I **Fluminicola columbiana**
Columbia Pebblesnail
USA

I **Fluminicola merriami**
Pahranagat Pebblesnail
USA

V **Fluvidona anodonta**
Australia: Queensland

E   *Fluvidona dunrobinensis*
Australia: Tasmania

E   *Fluvidona dulvertonensis*
Australia: Tasmania

V   *Fluvidona dyeriana*
Australia: Tasmania

V   *Fluvidona elongatus*
Australia: Tasmania

V   *Fluvidona grampianensis*
Australia: Victoria

I   *Fluvidona petterdi*
Australia: New South Wales

E   *Fluvidona pontvillensis*
Australia: Tasmania

E   *Fluvidona simsoniana*
Australia: Tasmania

I   *Fluviopupa gracilis*
Australia: Lord Howe Island

I   *Fluviopupa ramsayi*
Australia: Lord Howe Island

V   *Fonscochlea accepta*
Australia

V   *Fonscochlea aquatica*
Australia

V   *Fonscochlea conica*
Australia

V   *Fonscochlea billakalina*
Australia

V   *Fonscochlea zeidleri*
Australia

I   *Fontigens holsingeri*
Tapered Cavesnail
USA

I   *Fontigens turretella*
Greenbrier Cavesnail
USA

E   *Hauffenia kerschneri*
Austria

K   *Hauffenia minuta*
France; Switzerland

V   *Hemistoma beaumonti*
Australia: Lord Howe Island

V   *Hemistoma flexicolumella*
Australia: Lord Howe Island

V   *Hemistoma gemma*
Australia: Lord Howe Island

V   *Hemistoma minutissima*
Australia: Lord Howe Island

V   *Hemistoma pusillior*
Australia: Lord Howe Island

E   *Hemistoma whiteleggei*
Australia: Lord Howe Island

I   *Heterocyclus perroquini*
New Caledonia

I   *Heterocyclus petiti*
New Caledonia

I   *Hydrobia scamandri*
France

E   *Jardinella acuminata*
Australia

E   *Jardinella carnarvonensis*
Australia

E   *Jardinella colmani*
Australia

E   *Jardinella coreena*
Australia

E   *Jardinella corrugata*
Australia

E   *Jardinella edgbastonensis*
Australia

E   *Jardinella eulo*
Australia

E   *Jardinella exigua*
Australia

E   *Jardinella isolata*
Australia

E   *Jardinella jesswiseae*
Australia

E   *Jardinella pallida*
Australia

E   *Jardinella zeidlerorum*
Australia

I   *Lepyrium showalteri*
Flat Pebblesnail
USA

I   *Litthabitella elliptica*
France

E   *Lobaunia danubialis*
Austria

V   *Mexipyrgus carranzae*
Mexipyrgus de Carranza Snail
Mexico

V *Mexipyrgus churinceanus*
   Mexipyrgus de Churince Snail
   Mexico

V *Mexipyrgus escobedae*
   Mexipyrgus de Escobeda Snail
   Mexico

V *Mexipyrgus lugoi*
   Mexipyrgus de Lugo Snail
   Mexico

V *Mexipyrgus mojarralis*
   Mexipyrgus de West El Mojarral Snail
   Mexico

V *Mexipyrgus multilineatus*
   Mexipyrgus de East El Mojarral Snail
   Mexico

V *Mexithauma quadripaludium*
   Mexithauma de Cienegas Snail
   Mexico

I *Moitessieria juvenisanguis*
   France

I *Moitessieria lineolata*
   France

I *Moitessieria locardi*
   France

I *Moitessieria puteana*
   France

I *Moitessieria rayi*
   France

I *Moitessieria rolandiana*
   France

I *Moitessieria simoniana*
   France; Spain

V *Nanocochlea monticola*
   Australia: Tasmania

V *Nanocochlea pupoides*
   Australia: Tasmania

V *'Nanocochlea' parva*
   Australia: Tasmania

V *Neohoratia minuta*
   Switzerland

V *Nymphophilus minckleyi*
   Nymphophilus de Minckley Snail
   Mexico

I *Palacanthilhiopsis vervierii*
   France

R *Paladilhia hungarica*
   Hungary

I *Paladilhia pleurotoma*
   France

I *Paladilhiopis bourguignati*
   France

V *Paludinella conica*
   Guam; Northern Marianas: Saipan

V *Paludinella minima*
   Japan: Ogasawara

V *Paludinella semperi*
   Marshall Islands: Jaluit; Palau

V *Paludinella vitrea*
   Palau: Peleliu

V *Paludiscala caramba*
   Paludiscala de Oro Snail
   Mexico

V *Phrantela annamurrayae*
   Australia: Tasmania

V *Phrantela conica*
   Australia: Tasmania

V *Phrantela kutikina*
   Australia: Tasmania

V *Phrantela marginata*
   Australia: Tasmania

V *Phrantela pupiformis*
   Australia: Tasmania

V *Phrantela richardsoni*
   Australia: Tasmania

V *Phrantela umbilicata*
   Australia: Tasmania

I *Phreatodrobia imatata*
   Mimic Cavesnail
   USA

I *Plagigeyeria conilis*
   France

V *Potamopyrgus oscitans*
   Australia: Lord Howe Island

I *Pseudamnicola anteisensis*
   France

I *Pseudamnicola klemmi*
   France

E *Pseudamnicola melitensis*
   Malta

V *Pseudotricula eberhardi*
   Australia: Tasmania

I   *Pyrgulopsis agarhecta*
Ocmulgee Marstonia
USA

I   *Pyrgulopsis bacchus*
Grand Wash Springsnail
USA

E   *Pyrgulopsis bruneauensis*
Bruneau Hot Springsnail
USA

I   *Pyrgulopsis castor*
Beaver Pond Marstonia
USA

I   *Pyrgulopsis chupaderae*
(*Fontelicella chupaderae*)
Chupadera Springsnail
USA

I   *Pyrgulopsis conicus*
Kingman Springsnail
USA

I   *Pyrgulopsis cristalis*
Crystal Spring Springsnail
USA

I   *Pyrgulopsis davisi*
(*Fontelicella davisi*)
Davis County Springsnail
USA

I   *Pyrgulopsis erythopoma*
Ash Meadows Pebblesnail
USA

I   *Pyrgulopsis fairbanksensis*
Fairbanks Springsnail
USA

I   *Pyrgulopsis gilae*
(*Fontelicella gilae*)
Gila Springsnail
USA

I   *Pyrgulopsis glandulosus*
Verde Rim Springsnail
USA

E   *Pyrgulopsis idahoensis*
(*Fontelicella idahoensis*)
Idaho Springsnail
USA

I   *Pyrgulopsis isolatus*
Elongate-gland Springsnail
USA

I   *Pyrgulopsis metcalfi*
(*Fontelicella metcalfi*)
Presidio County Springsnail
USA

I   *Pyrgulopsis micrococcus*
Oasis Valley Springsnail
USA

I   *Pyrgulopsis montezumensis*
Montezuma Well Springsnail
USA

I   *Pyrgulopsis morrisoni*
Page Springsnail
USA

I   *Pyrgulopsis nanus*
Distal-gland Springsnail
USA

E   *Pyrgulopsis neomexicana*
Socorro Snail
USA

I   *Pyrgulopsis ogmoraphe*
Royal Marstonia
USA

I   *Pyrgulopsis olivacea*
Olive Marstonia
USA

I   *Pyrgulopsis ozarkensis*
Ozark Pyrg
USA

I   *Pyrgulopsis pachyta*
Armored Marstonia
USA

I   *Pyrgulopsis pecosensis*
(*Pyrgulopsis fontelicella*)
Pecos Springsnail
USA

I   *Pyrgulopsis pisteri*
Median-gland Nevada Springsnail
USA

I   *Pyrgulopsis robusta*
Jackson Lake Springsnail
USA

I   *Pyrgulopsis roswellensis*
(*Fontelicella roswellensis*)
Roswell Springsnail
USA

I   *Pyrgulopsis simplex*
Fossil Springsnail
USA

I **Pyrgulopsis solus**
Brown Springsnail
USA

I **Pyrgulopsis thermalis**
(*Fontelicella thermalis*)
New Mexico Hotspring Snail
USA

I **Pyrgulopsis thompsoni**
Huachuca Springsnail
USA

I **Pyrgulopsis trivialis**
(*Fontelicella trivialis*)
Three Forks Springsnail
USA

E **Sadleriana pannonica**
Hungary; Slovakia

I **Somatogyrus amnicoloides**
Oachita Pebblesnail
USA

I **Somatogyrus aureus**
Goldend Pebblesnail
USA

I **Somatogyrus biangulatus**
Angular Pebblesnail
USA

I **Somatogyrus constrictus**
Knotty Pebblesnail
USA

I **Somatogyrus coosaensis**
Coosa Pebblesnail
USA

I **Somatogyrus crassilabris**
Thick-lipped Pebblesnail
USA

I **Somatogyrsus crassus**
Stocky Pebblesnail
USA

I **Somatogyrus currierianus**
Tennessee Pebblesnail
USA

I **Somatogyrus deciphens**
Hidden Pebblesnail
USA

I **Somatogyrus excavatus**
Ovate Pebblesnail
USA

I **Somatogyrus hendersoni**
Fluted Pebblesnail
USA

I **Somatogyrus hinkleyi**
Granite Pebblesnail
USA

I **Somatogyrus humerosus**
Atlas Pebblesnail
USA

I **Somatogyrus nanus**
Dwarf Pebblesnail
USA

I **Somatogyrus obtusus**
Moom Pebblesnail
USA

I **Somatogyrus parvulus**
Sparrow Pebblesnail
USA

I **Somatogyrus pilsbryanus**
Tallapoosa Pebblesnail
USA

I **Somatogyrus pygmaeus**
Pygmy Pebblesnail
USA

I **Somatogyrus quadrulus**
Quadrate Pebblesnail
USA

I **Somatogyrus sergenti**
Mud Pebblesnail
USA

I **Somatogyrus strengi**
Rolling Pebblesnail
USA

I **Somatogyrus tenax**
Savannah Pebblesnail
USA

I **Somatogyrus tennesseensis**
Opaque Pebblesnail
USA

I **Somatogyrus wheeleri**
Channeled Pebblesnail
USA

I **Stiobia nana**
Sculpin Snail
USA

V **Trochidrobia punicea**
Australia

V **Trochidrobia smithi**
Australia

E **Trochidrobia inflata**
Australia

V   *Trochidrobia minuta*
Australia

I   *Tryonia adamantina*
Diamond Y Springsnail
USA

E   *Tryonia alamosae*
Alamosa Springsnail
USA

I   *Tryonia angulata*
Sportingoods Tryonia
USA

I   *Tryonia brunei*
Brune's Tryonia
USA

I   *Tryonia cheatumi*
Phantom Tryonia
USA

I   *Tryonia clathrata*
Grated Tryonia
USA

I   *Tryonia elata*
Point of Rocks Tryonia
USA

I   *Tryonia ericae*
Minute Tryonia
USA

I   *Tryonia gilae*
Gila Tryonia
USA

I   *Tryonia imitator*
Mimic Tryonia
USA

I   *Tryonia kosteri*
Koster's Tryonia
USA

I   *Tryonia quitobaquitae*
Quitabaquito Tryonia
USA

I   *Tryonia stocktonensis*
Gonzales Spring Tryonia
USA

I   *Tryonia variegata*
Amargossa Tryonia
USA

V   *Victodrobia burni*
Australia: Victoria

V   *Victodrobia elongata*
Australia: Victoria

V   *Victodrobia millerae*
Australia: Victoria

V   *Victodrobia victoriensis*
Australia: Victoria

I   *Yaquicoccus bernardinus*
San Bernadino Springsnail
USA

Family TRUNCATELLIDAE

V   *Taheitia alata*
Guam

V   *Taheitia lamellicosta*
Guam

V   *Taheitia mariannarum*
Guam

V   *Taheitia parvula*
Guam

V   *Truncatella guerinii*
Japan: Ogasawara

Family ASSIMINEIDAE

I   *Assiminea infirma*
Badwater Snail
USA

V   *Assiminea palauensis*
Palau

I   *Assiminea pecos*
Pecos Assiminea
USA

E   *Austroassiminea letha*
Australia

V   *Heteropoma fulvum*
Guam

V   *Heteropoma glabratum*
Guam

V   *Heteropoma pyramis*
Guam

V   *Heteropoma quadrasi*
Guam

V   *Heteropoma tuberculatum*
Guam

V   *Heteropoma turritum*
Guam

V   *Kubaryia pilikia*
Palau: Koror

E   *Omphalotropis albocarinata*
Australia: Norfolk Island

V **Omphalotropis carolinensis**
   Federated States of Micronesia: Chuuk Islands
   (Lukunor)

V **Omphalotropis cheynei**
   Palau

V **Omphalotropis cookei**
   Guam; Northern Marianas: Saipan

V **Omphalotropis elegans**
   Guam

V **Omphalotropis elongatula**
   Guam

V **Omphalotropis erosa**
   Guam

V **Omphalotropis exquisita**
   Australia: Lord Howe Island

V **Omphalotropis fragilis**
   Federated States of Micronesia: Kosrae,
   Pohnpei

V **Omphalotropis gracilis**
   Guam

V **Omphalotropis guamensis**
   Guam

V **Omphalotropis howeinsulae**
   Australia: Lord Howe Island

V **Omphalotropis innesi**
   Australia: Lord Howe Island

V **Omphalotropis laevigata**
   Guam

V **Omphalotropis laticosta**
   Guam

V **Omphalotropis latilabris**
   Guam

V **Omphalotropis mutica**
   Palau

V **Omphalotropis ochthogyra**
   Guam

V **Omphalotropis picta**
   Guam

V **Omphalotropis pilosa**
   Guam

V **Omphalotropis quadrasi**
   Guam

V **Omphalotropis semicostata**
   Guam

V **Omphalotropis striatipila**
   Palau

V **Omphalotropis submaritima**
   Guam

V **Omphalotropis suturalis**
   Guam

E **Omphalotropis suteri**
   Australia: Norfolk Island

V **Omphalotropis tumidula**
   Federated States of Micronesia: Pohnpei

V **Ponapella pihapiha**
   Federated States of Micronesia: Pohnpei

V **Quadrasiella clathrata**
   Guam

V **Quadrasiella mucronata**
   Guam

V **Thaanumella angulosa**
   Federated States of Micronesia: Pohnpei

V **Thaanumella cookei**
   Federated States of Micronesia: Pohnpei

V **Wrayanna soluta**
   Federated States of Micronesia: Pohnpei

Family MELANOPSIDAE

V **Fagotia esperi**
   Austria; Belarus; Hungary; Moldova; Slovakia;
   Ukraine

Family PLEUROCERIDAE

I **Anculosa ampla**
   (*Leptoxis ampla*)
   Round Rocksnail
   USA

I **Anculosa compacta**
   (*Leptoxis compacta*)
   Oblong Rocksnail
   USA

I **Anculopsis crassa**
   (*Leptoxis crassa*)
   Boulder Snail
   USA

I **Anculosa formosa**
   (*Leptoxis formosa*)
   Maiden Rocksnail
   USA

I **Anculosa melanoidus**
   (*Leptoxis melanoidus*)
   Black Mudalia
   USA

I *Anculosa minor*
(*Leptoxis minor*)
Knob Mudalia
USA

I *Anculosa picta*
(*Leptoxis picta*)
Spotted Rocksnail
USA

I *Anculosa plicata*
(*Leptoxis plicata*)
Plicate Rocksnail
USA

I *Anculosa taeniata*
(*Leptoxis taeniata*)
Painted Rocksnail
USA

I *Anculosa virgata*
(*Leptoxis virgata*)
Smooth Rocksnail
USA

I *Goniobasis albanyensis*
(*Elimia albanyensis*)
Black-crest Elimia
USA

I *Goniobasis ampla*
(*Elimia ampla*)
Ample Elimia
USA

I *Goniobasis annettae*
(*Elimia annettae*)
Lily Shoals Elimia
USA

I *Goniobasis annulifera*
(*Elimia annulifera*)
USA

I *Goniobasis bellula*
(*Elimia bellula*)
Walnut Elimia
USA

I *Goniobasis boykiniana*
(*Elimia boykiniana*)
Flaxen Elimia
USA

I *Goniobasis brevis*
(*Elimia brevis*)
Short-spired Elimia
USA

I *Goniobasis cahawbensis*
(*Elimia cahawbensis*)
Cahaba Elimia
USA

I *Goniobasis capillaris*
(*Elimia capillaris*)
Spindle Elimia
USA

I *Goniobasis crenatella*
(*Elimia crenatella*)
Lacy Elimia
USA

I *Goniobasis fascinans*
(*Elimia fascinans*)
Banded Elimia
USA

I *Goniobasis gerhardti*
(*Elimia gerhardti*)
Coldwater Elimia
USA

I *Goniobasis haysiana*
(*Elimia haysiana*)
Silt Elimia
USA

I *Goniobasis hydei*
(*Elimia hydei*)
Gladiator Elimia
USA

I *Goniobasis interrupta*
(*Elimia interrupta*)
Knotty Elimia
USA

I *Goniobasis interveniens*
(*Elimia interveniens*)
Slowwater Elimia
USA

I *Goniobasis nassula*
(*Elimia nassula*)
Round-rib Elimia
USA

I *Goniobasis olivula*
(*Elimia olivula*)
Caper Elimia
USA

I *Goniobasis showalteri*
(*Elimia showalteri*)
Compact Elimia
USA

I **Goniobasis vanuxemiana**
(*Elimia vanuxemiana*)
Cobble Elimia
USA

I **Goniobasis variata**
(*Elimia variata*)
Squat Elimia
USA

I **Io fluvialis**
Spiny River Snail
USA

I **Lithasia armigera**
Armored Rocksnail
USA

I **Lithasia curta**
Knobby Rocksnail
USA

I **Lithasia duttoniana**
Helmet Rocksnail
USA

I **Lithasia geniculata**
Ornate Rocksnail
USA

E **Lithasia jayana**
Rugose Rocksnail
USA

E **Lithasia lima**
Warty Rocksnail
USA

E **Lithasia salebrosa**
Muddy Rocksnail
USA

I **Lithasia verrucosa**
Varicose Rocksnail
USA

I **Pleurocera alveare**
Rugged Hornsnail
USA

I **Pleurocera annulifera**
Ringed Hornsnail
USA

I **Pleurocera brumbyi**
Spiral Hornsnail
USA

I **Pleurocera corpulenta**
Corpulent Hornsnail
USA

I **Pleurocera curta**
Shortspire Hornsnail
USA

I **Pleurocera foremani**
Rough Hornsnail
USA

I **Pleurocera posteri**
Broken Hornsnail
USA

I **Pleurocera pyrenella**
Skirted Hornsnail
USA

I **Pleurocera showalteri**
Upland Hornsnail
USA

I **Pleurocera walkeri**
Telescope Hornsnail
USA

Order BASOMMATOPHORA

Family ACROLOXIDAE

I **Acroloxus coloradensis**
Rocky Mountain Capshell
USA

Family LYMNAEIDAE

E **Erinna carinata**
Réunion

V **Myxas glutinosa**
Austria; Belarus; Belgium; Czech Republic;
Estonia; Finland; Germany; Kazakhstan;
Latvia; Lithuania; Moldova; Netherlands;
Norway; Poland; Russia; Sweden; Ukraine;
United Kingdom

I **Stagnicola utahensis**
Thickshell Pondsnail
USA

Family LANCIDAE

E **Lanx** sp.
Banbury Springs Limpet
USA

Family GLACIDORBIDAE

V **Glacidorbis occidentalis**
Australia

I **Glacidorbis pawpela**
Australia: Tasmania

I **Glacidorbis pedderi**
Australia: Tasmania

Family PHYSIDAE

I   **Physa microstriata**
    (*Physella microstriata*)
    Fish Lake Physa
      USA

E   **Physa natricina**
    Snake River Physa Snail
      USA

I   **Physa spelunca**
    (*Physella spelunca*)
    Cave Physa
      USA

I   **Physa utahensis**
    (*Physella utahensis*)
    Utah Physa
      USA

I   **Physa zionis**
    (*Physella zionis*)
    Wet Rock Physa
      USA

Family PLANORBIDAE

E   **Ancylastrum cumingianus**
    Australian Freshwater Limpet
    Australia: Tasmania

I   **Glyptophysa petiti**
    New Caledonia

I   **Helisoma jacksonense**
    Jackson Lake Snail
      USA

E   **Miratesta celebensis**
    Indonesia: Sulawesi

I   **Planorbella magnifica**
    Magnificent Ramshorn
      USA

I   **Planorbella multivolvis**
    Acorn Ramshorn
      USA

Family NEOPLANORBIDAE

I   **Amphigyra alabamensis**
    Shoal Sprite
      USA

I   **Neoplanorbis carinatus**
      USA

I   **Neoplanorbis smithi**
      USA

I   **Neoplanorbis tantilus**
      USA

I   **Neoplanorbis umbilicatus**
      USA

Family ANCYLIDAE

I   **Ferrissia mcneili**
    Hood Ancylid
      USA

I   **Rhodacmaea elatior**
    Domed Ancylid
      USA

I   **Rhodacmaea filosa**
    Wicker Ancylid
      USA

Order STYLOMMATOPHORA

Family ACHATINELLIDAE

E   **Achatinella apexfulva**
      USA: Hawaiian Islands (Oahu)

E   **Achatinella bellula**
      USA: Hawaiian Islands (Oahu)

E   **Achatinella bulimoides**
      USA: Hawaiian Islands (Oahu)

E   **Achatinella byronii**
      USA: Hawaiian Islands (Oahu)

E   **Achatinella cestus**
      USA: Hawaiian Islands (Oahu)

E   **Achatinella concavospira**
      USA: Hawaiian Islands (Oahu)

E   **Achatinella curta**
      USA: Hawaiian Islands (Oahu)

E   **Achatinella decipiens**
      USA: Hawaiian Islands (Oahu)

E   **Achatinella fulgens**
      USA: Hawaiian Islands (Oahu)

E   **Achatinella fuscobasis**
      USA: Hawaiian Islands (Oahu)

E   **Achatinella leucorrhaphe**
      USA: Hawaiian Islands (Oahu)

E   **Achatinella lila**
      USA: Hawaiian Islands (Oahu)

E   **Achatinella lorata**
      USA: Hawaiian Islands (Oahu)

E   **Achatinella mustelina**
      USA: Hawaiian Islands (Oahu)

E   **Achatinella phaeozona**
      USA: Hawaiian Islands (Oahu)

E   *Achatinella pulcherrima*
    USA: Hawaiian Islands (Oahu)

E   *Achatinella pupukanioe*
    USA: Hawaiian Islands (Oahu)

E   *Achatinella sowerbyana*
    USA: Hawaiian Islands (Oahu)

E   *Achatinella stewartii*
    USA: Hawaiian Islands (Oahu)

E   *Achatinella swiftii*
    USA: Hawaiian Islands (Oahu)

E   *Achatinella taeniolata*
    USA: Hawaiian Islands (Oahu)

E   *Achatinella turgida*
    USA: Hawaiian Islands (Oahu)

E   *Achatinella viridans*
    USA: Hawaiian Islands (Oahu)

E   *Achatinella vulpina*
    USA: Hawaiian Islands (Oahu)

E   *Auriculella ambusta*
    USA: Hawaiian Islands (Oahu)

E   *Auriculella castanea*
    USA: Hawaiian Islands (Oahu)

E   *Auriculella crassula*
    USA: Hawaiian Islands (Maui)

E   *Auriculella malleata*
    USA: Hawaiian Islands (Oahu)

E   *Auriculella perpusilla*
    USA: Hawaiian Islands (Oahu)

E   *Auriculella pulchra*
    USA: Hawaiian Islands (Oahu)

E   *Auriculella tenella*
    USA: Hawaiian Islands (Oahu)

I   *Elasmias kitaiwojimanum*
    Japan: Ogasawara

V   *Elasmias quadrasi*
    Guam; Northern Marianas: Saipan, Rota

E   *Gulickia alexandri*
    USA: Hawaiian Islands (Maui)

I   *Lamellidea biplicata*
    Japan: Ogasawara

V   *Lamellidea microstoma*
    Guam; Northern Marianas: Saipan, Rota

R   *Lamellidea ogasawarana*
    Japan: Ogasawara

V   *Lamellidea subcylindrica*
    Guam; Northern Marianas: Rota

E   *Partulina confusa*
    USA: Hawaiian Islands

E   *Partulina dolei*
    USA: Hawaiian Islands (Maui)

E   *Partulina dubia*
    USA: Hawaiian Islands (Oahu)

E   *Partulian dwightii*
    USA: Hawaiian Islands (Molokai)

V   *Partulina fusoidea*
    USA: Hawaiian Islands (Maui)

E   *Partulina kaaeana*
    USA: Hawaiian Islands (Maui)

E   *Partulina mighelsiana*
    USA: Hawaiian Islands (Molokai)

E   *Partulina nattii*
    USA: Hawaiian Islands (Maui)

V   *Partulina perdix*
    USA: Hawaiian Islands (Maui)

E   *Partulina physa*
    USA: Hawaiian Islands (Hawaii)

E   *Partulina porcellana*
    USA: Hawaiian Islands (Maui)

E   *Partulina proxima*
    USA: Hawaiian Islands (Molokai)

E   *Partulina redfieldi*
    USA: Hawaiian Islands (Molokai)

E   *Partulina semicarinata*
    USA: Hawaiian Islands (Lanai)

E   *Partulina splendida*
  Splendid Partulina
    USA: Hawaiian Islands (Maui)

E   *Partulina talpina*
    USA: Hawaiian Islands

E   *Partulina tappaniana*
    USA: Hawaiian Islands (Maui)

E   *Partulina terebra*
    USA: Hawaiian Islands (Maui)

E   *Partulina tessellata*
    USA: Hawaiian Islands (Molokai)

E   *Partulina ustulata*
    USA: Hawaiian Islands (Maui)

E   *Partulina variabilis*
    USA: Hawaiian Islands (Lanai)

E   *Partulina virgulata*
    USA: Hawaiian Islands (Maui)

E   *Perdicella carinella*
    USA: Hawaiian Islands (Maui)

E   *Perdicella helena*
    USA: Hawaiian Islands (Molokai)

E   *Perdicella kuhnsi*
    USA: Hawaiian Islands (Maui)

E   *Perdicella ornata*
    USA: Hawaiian Islands (Maui)

V   *Tornatellinops ponapensis*
    Federated States of Micronesia: Pohnpei

Family COCHLICOPIDAE

K   *Cochlicopa nitens*
    Armenia;   Austria;   Azerbaijan;   Belarus;
    Bulgaria;   Denmark;   Estonia;   Georgia;
    Germany;   Hungary;   Kazakhstan;   Latvia;
    Lithuania;   Moldova;   Netherlands;   Poland;
    Romania;   Russia;   Slovakia;   Sweden;
    Switzerland;   Turkmenistan;   Ukraine;
    Yugoslavia

E   *Cryptazeca monodonta*
    France; Spain

E   *Cryptazeca subcylindrica*
    France

I   *Hypnophila remyi*
    France: Corsica

Family AMASTRIDAE

E   *Amastra cylindrica*
    USA: Hawaiian Islands (Oahu)

E   *Amastra micans*
    USA: Hawaiian Islands (Oahu)

E   *Amastra rubens*
    USA: Hawaiian Islands (Oahu)

E   *Amastra spirizona*
    USA: Hawaiian Islands (Oahu)

E   *Armsia petasus*
    USA: Hawaiian Islands (Oahu)

E   *Laminella sanguinea*
    USA: Hawaiian Islands (Oahu)

I   *Leptachatina lepida*
    USA: Hawaiian Islands (Maui)

E   *Leptachatina* sp. 1
    USA: Hawaiian Islands (Oahu)

E   *Leptachatina* sp. 2
    USA: Hawaiian Islands

E   *Tropidoptera heliciformis*
    (*Pterodiscus heliciformis*)
    USA: Hawaiian Islands (Oahu)

Family PUPILLIDAE

E   *Lauria fanalensis*
    Portugal: Madeira

E   *Leiostyla callathiscus*
    Portugal: Madeira

I   *Leiostyla cheiligona*
    Portugal: Madeira

E   *Leiostyla concinna*
    Portugal: Madeira

E   *Leiostyla corneocostata*
    Portugal: Madeira

E   *Leiostyla degenerata*
    Portugal: Madeira

E   *Leiostyla ferraria*
    Portugal: Madeira

E   *Leiostyla filicum*
    Portugal: Madeira

V   *Leiostyla fusca*
    Portugal: Madeira

I   *Leiostyla laevigata*
    Portugal: Madeira

R   *Leiostyla laurinea*
    Portugal: Madeira

E   *Leiostyla monticola*
    Portugal: Madeira

R   *Leiostyla relevata*
    Portugal: Madeira

R   *Leiostyla vincta*
    Portugal: Madeira

E   *Pupilla ficulnea*
    Australia: Northern Territory

I   *Pupilla pupula*
    Réunion

Family VALLONIIDAE

R   *Acanthinula spinifera*
    Spain: Canary Islands (La Palma)

E   *Spelaeodiscus tatricus*
    Slovakia

E   *Vallonia allamanica*
    Germany

V   *Vallonia declivis*
Austria; France; Germany; Poland; Slovakia;
Switzerland

K   *Vallonia enniensis*
Austria; Belgium; Czech Republic; France;
Germany; Greece; Hungary; Italy; Poland;
Romania; Russia; Spain: including Balearic
Islands, Canary Islands; Slovakia; Switzerland;
Ukraine

E   *Vallonia suevica*
Germany

Family VERTIGINIDAE

K   *Cylindrovertilla kingi*
Australia: New South Wales

I   *Gastrocopta boninensis*
Japan: Ogasawara

R   *Gyliotrachela catherina*
Australia: Northern Territory

V   *Nesopupa eapensis*
Palau

V   *Nesopupa ponapica*
Federated States of Micronesia: Pohnpei

V   *Nesopupa quadrasi*
Guam

V   *Ptychalaea dedecora*
Japan: Ogasawara

V   *Pupisoma orcula*
Federated States of Micronesia: Kosrae,
Pohnpei

I   *Sterkia clementina*
Insular Birddrop
USA

K   *Truncatellina atomus*
Spain: Canary Islands (Tenerife)

I   *Vertigo alabamensis*
USA

K   *Vertigo angustior*
Armenia;   Austria;   Azerbaijan;   Belarus;
Belgium; Czech Republic; Denmark; Estonia;
Finland; France; Georgia; Germany; Hungary;
Ireland;   Italy;   Liechtenstein;   Lithuania;
Netherlands;   Norway;   Poland;   Romania;
Russia;   Slovakia;   Sweden;   Switzerland;
Ukraine; United Kingdom

V   *Vertigo genesii*
Finland; Germany; Norway; Poland; Romania;
Russia; Sweden; Switzerland; United Kingdom

V   *Vertigo geyerii*
Austria; Czech Republic; Denmark; Finland;
Germany; Ireland; Latvia; Lithuania; Norway;
Poland; Slovakia; Sweden; Switzerland; United
Kingdom

I   *Vertigo hebardi*
USA

Family ORCULIDAE

V   *Orcula austriaca*
Austria

R   *Orcula fuchsi*
Austria

V   *Orcula pseudodolium*
Austria

Family CHONDRINIDAE

I   *Solatopupa guidoni*
France: Corsica; Italy: Sardinia

I   *Solatopupa psarolena*
France; Italy

Family BULIMINIDAE

E   *Boninena callistoderma*
Japan: Ogasawara

V   *Boninena hiraseana*
Japan: Ogasawara

E   *Boninena ogasawarae*
Japan: Ogasawara

R   *'Napaeus' alabastrinus*
Portugal: Azores

V   *Napaeus isletae*
Spain: Canary Islands (Gran Canaria)

R   *Napaeus nanodes*
Spain: Canary Islands (Tenerife)

I   *Napaeus pygmaeus*
Spain: Canary Islands (La Gomera)

I   *Napaeus tagmichensis*
Spain: Canary Islands (La Gomera)

I   *Napaeus tagulichensis*
Spain: Canary Islands (La Gomera)

R   *Napaeus tarnerianus*
Spain: Canary Islands (Tenerife)

Family CLAUSILIIDAE

R   *Boettgeria obesiuscula*
Portugal: Madeira

V   *Charpentieria dyodon*
Italy; Switzerland

R *Lamnifera pauli*
France; Spain

E *Lampedusa imitratix*
Malta

E *Lampedusa melitensis*
Malta

R *Muticaria macrostoma*
Malta

Family PARTULIDAE

E *Eua zebrina*
American Samoa: Tutuila

E *Partula arguta*
French Polynesia: Huahine

V *Partula calypso*
Palau: Peleliu

E *Partula dentifera*
French Polynesia: Raiatea

V *Partula emersoni*
Federated States of Micronesia: Pohnpei

E *Partula faba*
French Polynesia: Raiatea

E *Partula gibba*
Fat Guam Partula
Guam; Northern Marianas: Rota

V *Partula guamensis*
Federated States of Micronesia: Pohnpei

E *Partula hebe*
French Polynesia: Raiatea

E *Partula labrusca*
French Polynesia: Raiatea

E *Partula langfordi*
Northern Marianas: Aguijan

V *Partula leucothoe*
Palau

V *Partula martensiana*
Federated States of Micronesia: Kosrae

V *Partula radiolata*
Radiolate Partula
Guam

E *Partula rosea*
French Polynesia: Huahine

V *Partula thetis*
Palau: Koror

E *Partula varia*
French Polynesia: Huahine

E *Samoana annectens*
French Polynesia: Huahine

E *Samoana attenuata*
French Polynesia: BoraBora, Moorea, Tahiti, Raiatea

E *Samoana conica*
American Samoa: Tutuila

E *Samoana diaphana*
French Polynesia: Moorea

E *Samoana fragilis*
Guam

E *Samoana solitaria*
French Polynesia: Moorea

E *Samoana thurstoni*
American Samoa: Ofu

Family ORTHALICIDAE

V *Bothriembryon angasianus*
Australia: South Australia

V *Bothriembryon brazieri*
Australia: Western Australia

V *Bothriembryon glauerti*
Australia: Western Australia

V *Bothriembryon irvineanus*
Australia: Western Australia

E *Bothriembryon praecelcus*
Australia: Western Australia

V *Bothriembryon spenceri*
Australia: Northern Territory

V *Bothriembryon tasmanicus*
Australia: Tasmania

E *Bulimulus adelphus*
Ecuador: Galapagos Islands

E *Bulimulus akamatus*
Ecuador: Galapagos Islands

E *Bulimulus alethorhytidus*
Ecuador: Galapagos Islands

E *Bulimulus amastroides*
Ecuador: Galapagos Islands

E *Bulimulus blombergi*
Ecuador: Galapagos Islands

E *Bulimulus calvus*
Ecuador: Galapagos Islands

E *Bulimulus cavagnaroi*
Ecuador: Galapagos Islands

E **Bulimulus darwini**
  Ecuador: Galapagos Islands

E **Bulimulus eos**
  Ecuador: Galapagos Islands

E **Bulimulus eschariferus**
  Ecuador: Galapagos Islands

E **Bulimulus hirsutus**
  Ecuador: Galapagos Islands

E **Bulimulus jacobi**
  Ecuador: Galapagos Islands

E **Bulimulus lycodus**
  Ecuador: Galapagos Islands

E **Bulimulus nesioticus**
  Ecuador: Galapagos Islands

E **Bulimulus nux**
  Ecuador: Galapagos Islands

E **Bulimulus ochsneri**
  Ecuador: Galapagos Islands

E **Bulimulus reibischi**
  Ecuador: Galapagos Islands

E **Bulimulus rugiferus**
  Ecuador: Galapagos Islands

E **Bulimulus saeronius**
  Ecuador: Galapagos Islands

E **Bulimulus sculpturatus**
  Ecuador: Galapagos Islands

E **Bulimulus sp. 1**
  Ecuador: Galapagos Islands

E **Bulimulus sp. 2**
  Ecuador: Galapagos Islands

E **Bulimulus sp. 3**
  Ecuador: Galapagos Islands

E **Bulimulus sp. 4**
  Ecuador: Galapagos Islands

E **Bulimulus sp. 5**
  Ecuador: Galapagos Islands

E **Bulimulus tanneri**
  Ecuador: Galapagos Islands

E **Bulimulus unifasciatus**
  Ecuador: Galapagos Islands

E **Bulimulus ustulatus**
  Ecuador: Galapagos Islands

E **Bulimulus wolfi**
  Ecuador: Galapagos Islands

E **Leuchocharis pancheri**
  New Caledonia

V **Orthalicus reses**
  Stock Island Tree Snail
  USA

V **Placostylus ambagiosus**
  Pupuharakeke, Flax Snail
  New Zealand

R **Placostylus bollonsi**
  Pupuharakeke
  New Zealand

V **Placostylus hongii**
  Pupuharakeke, Flax Snail
  New Zealand

Family FERUSSACIIDAE

R **Amphorella melampoides**
  Portugal: Madeira (Port Santo)

R **Amphorella producta**
  Portugal: Madeira

I **Cecilioides connollyi**
  Gibraltar

K **Cecilioides nyctelia**
  Portugal: Madeira

V **Cylichnidia ovuliformis**
  Portugal: Madeira (Porto Santo)

R **Sculptiferussacia clausiliaeformis**
  Spain: Canary Islands (Fuerteventura)

Family COELIAXIDAE

I **Pyrgina umbilicata**
  São Tomé and Príncipe: São Tomé

I **Thomea newtoni**
  São Tomé and Príncipe: São Tomé

Family THYROPHORELLIDAE

I **Thyrophorella thomensis**
  São Tomé and Príncipe: São Tomé

Family STREPTAXIDAE

V **Gonospira bourguignati**
  Réunion

V **Gonospira cylindrella**
  Réunion

E **Gonospira deshayesi**
  Réunion

E **Gonospira duponti**
  Mauritius

V *Gonospira funicula*
Réunion

V *Gonospira turgidula*
Réunion

E *Gonospira uvula*
Réunion

V *Gulella plantii*
South Africa

E *Imperturbatia violescens*
Seychelles

Family CARYODIDAE

E *Anoglypta launcestonensis*
Granulated Tasmanian Snail
Australia: Tasmania

Family MEGOMPHICIDAE

I *Ammonitella yatesii*
Tight Coin
USA

Family RHYTIDIDAE

V *Delos oualanensis*
Federated States of Micronesia: Kosrae

R *Ougapia spaldingi*
(*Torresiropa spaldingi*)
Australia: Queensland (Cape York & Torres Strait Islands)

R *Paryphanta busbyi*
Kauri Snail, Pupurangi
New Zealand

V *Paryphanta gilliesi*
Gillies' Land Snail
New Zealand

V *Paryphanta hochstetteri*
Hochstetter's Land Snail
New Zealand

V *Paryphanta lignaria*
Woodformed Land Snail
New Zealand

V *Paryphanta rossiana*
Ross' Land Snail
New Zealand

V *Paryphanta traversi*
Travers' Land Snail
New Zealand

R *Rhytida clarki*
(*Wainuia clarki*)
New Zealand

V *Rhytida lamproides*
(*Tasmaphena lamproides*)
Australia: Tasmania, Victoria

R *Rhytida oconnori*
New Zealand

V *Victaphanta atramentaria*
Australia: Victoria

V *Victaphanta compacta*
Australia: Victoria

Family ENDODONTIDAE

V *Aaadonta angaurana*
Palau: Angaur

V *Aaadonta constricta*
Palau

V *Aaadonta fuscozonata*
Palau

V *Aaadonta irregularis*
Palau: Peleliu

V *Aaadonta kinlochi*
Palau: Angaur

V *Aaadonta pelewana*
Palau: Koror, Peleliu

V *Anguispira picta*
Painted Snake-coiled Forest Snail
USA

E *Cookeconcha* sp.
USA: Hawaiian Islands

E *Endodonta* sp.
USA: Hawaiian Islands

I *Helicodiscus diadema*
USA

I *Helicodiscus hexodon*
USA

E *Hirasea acutissima*
Japan: Ogasawara

E *Hirasea chichijimana*
Japan: Ogasawara

E *Hirasea diplomphalus*
Japan: Ogasawara

E *Hirasea insignis*
Japan: Ogasawara

E *Hirasea operculina*
Japan: Ogasawara

E *Thaumatodon hystricelloides*
Western Samoa: Upolu

I   ***Theskelomensor creon***
     Australia: Queensland

I   ***Theskelomensor lizardensis***
     Australia: Queensland (Lizard Island)

Family PUNCTIDAE

V   ***Pasmaditta jungermanniae***
     Australia: Tasmania

Family CHAROPIDAE

V   ***Allocharopa erskinensis***
     Australia: Victoria

V   ***Allocharopa okeana***
     Australia: Victoria

V   ***Allocharopa tarravillensis***
     Australia: Victoria

E   ***Bischoffena bischoffensis***
     Australia: Tasmania

R   ***Coenocharopa yessabahensis***
     Australia: New South Wales

E   ***Cralopa colliveri***
     Australia: Victoria

R   ***Cralopa kaputarensis***
     Australia: New South Wales

R   ***Dipnelix pertricosa***
     Australia: South Australia

E   ***Discocharopa mimosa***
     Australia: Tasmania

V   ***Dupucharopa millestriata***
     Australia: Western Australia

V   ***Geminoropa scindocataracta***
     Australia: Victoria

R   ***Hedleyoconcha ailaketoae***
     Australia: Queensland

E   ***Helenoconcha relicta***
     Saint Helena

V   ***Himeroconcha fusca***
     Guam

V   ***Himeroconcha lamlanensis***
     Guam

V   ***Himeroconcha quadrasi***
     Guam

V   ***Himeroconcha rotula***
     Guam

V   ***Jokajdon callizonus***
     Federated States of Micronesia: Pohnpei

V   ***Jokajdon tumidulus***
     Federated States of Micronesia: Pohnpei

V   ***Kubaryiellus kubaryi***
     Federated States of Micronesia: Pohnpei

V   ***Ladronellum mariannarum***
     Guam

V   ***Letomola barrenensis***
     Australia: Bass Strait islands

R   ***Letomola contortus***
     Australia: New South Wales

R   ***Ngairea murphyi***
     Australia: New South Wales

R   ***Oreokera cumulus***
     Australia: Queensland

R   ***Oreokera nimbus***
     Australia: Queensland

V   ***Oreomava cannfluviatilus***
     Australia: Victoria

V   ***Oreomava otwayensis***
     Australia: Victoria

V   ***Palikirus cosmetus***
     Federated States of Micronesia: Pohnpei

V   ***Palikirus ponapicus***
     Federated States of Micronesia: Pohnpei

V   ***Palline micramyla***
     Federated States of Micronesia: Pohnpei

V   ***Palline notera***
     Palau

V   ***Pernagera gatliffi***
     Australia: Victoria

R   ***Pillomena aemula***
     Australia: Northern Territory

V   ***Pilsbrycharopa tumida***
     Australia: Western Australia

V   ***Pilula praetumida***
     Réunion

E   ***Planilaoma luckmanii***
     Australia: Tasmania

R   ***Rhophodon kempseyensis***
     Australia: New South Wales

V   ***Rhophodon problematica***
     Australia: Victoria

V   ***Roimontis tolotomensis***
     Federated States of Micronesia: Pohnpei

V *Russatus nigrescens*
  Federated States of Micronesia: Pohnpei

V *Semperdon heptaptychius*
  Guam

V *Semperdon kororensis*
  Palau: Koror

V *Semperdon rotanus*
  Guam; Northern Marianas: Rota

V *Semperdon uncatus*
  Palau

V *Semperdon xyleborus*
  Palau

R *Setomedea nudicostata*
  Australia: Queensland

V *Sinployea kusaieana*
  Federated States of Micronesia: Kosrae

V *Trukcharopa trukana*
  Federated States of Micronesia: Chuuk Islands
  (Tol, Lukunor)

Family DISCIDAE

R *Discus engonata*
  Spain: Canary Islands (Tenerife)

E *Discus macclintocki*
  Iowa Pleistocene Snail
  USA

K *Discus marmorensis*
  Marbled Disc
  USA

R *Discus scutula*
  Spain: Canary Islands (Tenerife)

Family OREOHELICIDAE

V *Oreohelix jugalis*
  Boulder Pile Mountain Snail
  USA

R *Oreohelix vortex*
  Whorled Mountain Snail
  USA

I *Oreohelix waltoni*
  Lava Rock Mountain Snail
  USA

V *Radiocentrum avalonense*
  Catalina Mountain Snail
  USA

Family SUCCINEIDAE

I *Boninosuccinea ogasawarae*
  Japan: Ogasawara

I *Boninosuccinea punctulispira*
  Japan: Ogasawara

V *Catinella arenaria*
  Belgium; France; Germany; Ireland;
  Netherlands; Norway; Poland; Slovakia;
  Sweden; Switzerland; United Kingdom

E *Oxyloma kanabense*
  Kanab Amber Snail
  USA

V *Succinea chittenangoensis*
  Chittenango Ovate Amber Snail
  USA

V *Succinea philippinica*
  Palau

E *Succinea piratarum*
  Guam

E *Succinea quadrasi*
  Guam

V *Succinea sanctaehelenae*
  Saint Helena

Family EUCONULIDAE

V *Palaua babelthuapi*
  Palau: Babeldaob

V *Palaua margaritacea*
  Palau

V *Palaua minor*
  Palau

V *Palaua ngarduaisi*
  Palau: Babeldaob

V *Palaua straminea*
  Palau: Angaur

V *Palaua wilsoni*
  Palau

E *Caldwellia boryi*
  Mauritius

V *Caldwellia imperfecta*
  Mauritius; Réunion

E *Ctenophila caldwelli*
  Mauritius

R *Ctenophila salaziensis*
  Réunion

E *Ctenophila setiliris*
  Réunion

V *Ctenophila vorticella*
  Réunion

V   **Dendrotrochus ponapensis**
    Federated States of Micronesia: Pohnpei

I   **Diastole matafaoi**
    American Samoa: Tutuila

E   **Hacrochlamys lineolatus**
    Japan: Ogasawara

V   **Harmogenanina argentea**
    Réunion

E   **Harmogenanina detecta**
    Réunion

E   **Harmogenanina implicata**
    Mauritius

R   **Helixarion australis**
    (*Helicarion australis*)
    Australia: New South Wales, Queensland

R   **Helixarion leopardina**
    (*Helicarion leopardina*)
    Australia: New South Wales

R   **Helixarion porrectus**
    (*Helicarion porrectus*)
    Australia: New South Wales

E   **Helixarion rubicundus**
    (*Helicarion rubicundus*)
    Australia: Tasmania

R   **Helixarion semoni**
    (*Fastosarion semoni*)
    Australia: Queensland

R   **Helixarion submissus**
    (*Peloparion submissus*)
    Australia: New South Wales

V   **Kusaiea frivola**
    Federated States of Micronesia: Kosrae

V   **Lamprocystis denticulata**
    Guam; Northern Marianas: Saipa, Rota

V   **Lamprocystis fastigata**
    Guam; Northern Marianas: Rota

V   **Lamprocystis hahajimana**
    Japan: Ogasawara

V   **Lamprocystis hornbosteli**
    Northern Marianas: Tinian

V   **Lamprocystis misella**
    Guam

E   **Liardetia boninensis**
    Japan: Ogasawara

V   **Liardetia tenuisculpta**
    Federated States of Micronesia: Kosrae,
    Pohnpei

V   **Plegma caelatura**
    Réunion

V   **Plegma rodriguezensis**
    Mauritius: Rodrigues

V   **Ryssota pachystoma**
    Federated States of Micronesia: Chuuk Islands

V   **Tengchiena euroxestus**
    (*Echonitor euroxestus*)
    Australia: South Australia

E   **Thapsia snelli**
    Mauritius: Rodrigues

E   **Trochochlamys ogasawarana**
    Japan: Ogasawara

Family TROCHOMORPHIDAE

V   **Brazieria entomostoma**
    Federated States of Micronesia: Chuuk Islands
    (Dublon)

V   **Brazieria erasa**
    Federated States of Micronesia: Chuuk Islands
    (Dublon)

V   **Brazieria lutaria**
    Federated States of Micronesia: Chuuk Islands
    (Dublon)

V   **Brazieria minuscula**
    Federated States of Micronesia: Chuuk Islands
    (Tol)

V   **Brazieria obesa**
    Federated States of Micronesia: Chuuk Islands
    (Tol)

V   **Brazieria velata**
    Federated States of Micronesia: Chuuk Islands

V   **Hongolua kondorum**
    Federated States of Micronesia: Chuuk Islands
    (Moen, Dublon)

V   **Kondoa kondorum**
    Federated States of Micronesia: Chuuk Islands
    (Dublon)

E   **Trochomorpha apia**
    American Samoa: Tutuila

V   **Trochomorpha approximata**
    Federated States of Micronesia: Chuuk Islands
    (Dublon)

V   **Trochomorpha carolinae**
    Federated States of Micronesia: Pohnpei

V   **Trochomorpha conoides**
    Federated States of Micronesia: Pohnpei

V   *Trochomorpha contigua*
    Federated States of Micronesia: Pohnpei

V   *Trochomorpha kuesteri*
    Federated States of Micronesia: Pohnpei

R   *Trochomorpha melvillensis*
    Australia: Northern Territory

V   *Trochomorpha nigritella*
    Federated States of Micronesia: Pohnpei

V   *Videna electra*
    Palau: Peleliu

V   *Videna oleacina*
    Palau: Peleliu

V   *Videna pagodula*
    Palau: Peleliu

V   *Videna pumila*
    Palau: Peleliu

Family VITRINIDAE

R   *Insulivitrina machadoi*
    Spain: Canary Islands (Gran Canaria)

R   *Insulivitrina mascaensis*
    Spain: Canary Islands (Tenerife)

V   *Insulivitrina reticulata*
    Spain: Canary Islands (Tenerife)

R   *Insulivitrina tuberculata*
    Spain: Canary Islands (Tenerife)

R   *Phenacolimax atlantica*
    Portugal: Azores

R   *Vitrea pseudotrolli*
    France; Italy

K   *Vitrea striata*
    Spain: Ibiza

Family ZONITIDAE

I   *Glyphyalinia pecki*
    USA

E   *Oxychilus agostinhoi*
    Portugal: Azores

K   *Oxychilus basajauna*
    Spain

I   *Paravitrea clappi*
    USA

R   *Retinella stabilei*
    Italy

Family PARMACELLIDAE

V   *Parmacella tenerifensis*
    Spain: Canary Islands (Tenerife)

Family MILACIDAE

V   *Tandonia nigra*
    Switzerland

Family LIMACIDAE

K   *Deroceras fatrense*
    Slovakia

V   *Malacolimax wiktori*
    Spain: Canary Islands (Tenerife)

Family POLYGYRIDAE

I   *Ashmunella pasonis*
    Franklin Mountain Woodland Snail
    USA

I   *Cryptomastix magnidenta*
    Mission Creek Oregonian
    USA

I   *Mesodon archeri*
    Archer's Toothed Land Snail
    USA

I   *Mesodon clenchi*
    Clench's Middle-toothed Land Snail
    USA

I   *Mesodon jonesianus*
    Jones' Middle-toothed Land Snail
    USA

I   *Mesodon magazinensis*
    Magazine Mountain Middle-toothed Snail
    USA

I   *Polygyra hippocrepis*
    USA

I   *Polygyra peregrina*
    Strange Many-whorled Land Snail
    USA

E   *Polygyriscus virginianus*
    Virginia Fringed Mountain Snail
    USA

I   *Stenotrema hubrichti*
    USA

I   *Stenotrema pilsbryi*
    Pilsbry's Narrow-apertured Land Snail
    USA

I   *Triodopsis occidentalis*
    Western Three-toothed Land Snail
    USA

E   *Triodopsis platysayoides*
     Flat-spired Three-toothed Snail
     USA

V   *Vespericola karokorum*
     Karok Hesperion
     USA

Family CAMAENIDAE

R   *Amphidromus cognatus*
     Australia: Northern Territory

E   *Amplirhagada astuta*
     Australia: Western Australia (Koolan Island)

V   *Amplirhagada elevata*
     Australia: Western Australia

I   *Amplirhagada herbertena*
     Australia: Western Australia

I   *Amplirhagada montalivetensis*
     Australia: Western Australia (Montalivet
     Island)

R   *Amplirhagada novelta*
     Australia: Western Australia

E   *Amplirhagada questroana*
     Australia: Western Australia

R   *Austrochloritis ascensa*
     Australia: New South Wales

R   *Austrochloritis pusilla*
     Australia: Queensland

I   *Baccalena squamulosa*
     Australia: Northern Territory

V   *Badistes benneti*
     (*Meridolum benneti*)
     Australia: Queensland

V   *Badistes corneovirens*
     (*Meridolum corneovirens*)
     Australia: New South Wales

R   *Badistes depressa*
     (*Meridolum depressa*)
     Australia: New South Wales

R   *Badistes marshalli*
     (*Meridolum marshalli*)
     Australia: New South Wales

I   *Baudinella baudinensis*
     Australia: Western Australia (Baudin Island)

V   *Carinotrachia carsoniana*
     Australia: Western Australia

R   *Cooperconcha centralis*
     Australia: South Australia

R   *Craterodiscus pricei*
     Australia: Queensland

E   *Cristilabrum bubulum*
     Australia: Western Australia

E   *Cristilabrum buryillum*
     Australia: Western Australia

E   *Cristilabrum grossum*
     Australia: Western Australia

V   *Cristilabrum isolatum*
     Australia: Western Australia

V   *Cristilabrum monodon*
     Australia: Western Australia

V   *Cristilabrum primum*
     Australia: Western Australia

V   *Cristilabrum rectum*
     Australia: Western Australia

V   *Cristilabrum simplex*
     Australia: Western Australia

E   *Cristilabrum solitudum*
     Australia: Western Australia

I   *Cristilabrum spectaculum*
     Australia: Western Australia

R   *Cupedora broughami*
     Australia: South Australia

E   *Cupedora evandaleana*
     Australia: South Australia

R   *Cupedora luteofusca*
     Australia: South Australia

R   *Cupedora marcidum*
     Australia: New South Wales

E   *Cupedora nottensis*
     Australia: South Australia

I   *Cupedora sutilosa*
     Australia: Kangaroo Island

E   *Cupedora tomsetti*
     Australia: Kangaroo Island

E   *Damochlora millepunctata*
     Australia: Western Australia

V   *Damochlora spina*
     Australia: Western Australia

E   *Divellomelon hillieri*
     Australia: Northern Territory

K   *Glyptorhagada asperrima*
     (*Eximiorhagada asperrima*)
     Australia: South Australia

E *Glyptorhagada bordaensis*
   Australia: Kangaroo Island

E *Glyptorhagada euglypta*
   Australia: South Australia

R *Glyptorhagada janaslini*
   Australia: South Australia

E *Glyptorhagada kooringensis*
   Australia: South Australia

R *Glyptorhagada silveri*
   Australia: South Australia

R *Glyptorhagada tattawuppana*
   Australia: South Australia

V *Granulomelon grandituberculatum*
   Australia: Northern Territory

V *Hadra wilsoni*
   Australia: Western Australia

R *Jacksonena delicata*
   Australia: Queensland

R *Jacksonena rudis*
   Australia: Queensland

E *Kimboraga exanimus*
   Australia: Western Australia

V *Kimboraga koolanensis*
   Australia: Western Australia (Koolan Island)

V *Kimboraga micromphala*
   Australia: Western Australia

V *Kimboraga yammerana*
   Australia: Western Australia

R *Lacustrelix minor*
   Australia: South Australia

R *Lacustrelix yerelinana*
   Australia: South Australia

E *Mandarina anijimana*
   Japan: Ogasawara

E *Mandarina aureola*
   Japan: Ogasawara

V *Mandarina chichijimana*
   Japan: Ogasawara

E *Mandarina exoptata*
   Japan: Ogasawara

V *Mandarina hahajimana*
   Japan: Ogasawara

V *Mandarina hirasei*
   Japan: Ogasawara

V *Mandarina mandarina*
   Japan: Ogasawara

E *Mandarina polita*
   Japan: Ogasawara

E *Mandarina ponderosa*
   Japan: Ogasawara

E *Mandarina suenoae*
   Japan: Ogasawara

R *Meliobba shafferyi*
   Australia: Queensland

R *Mesodontrachia desmonda*
   Australia: Northern Territory

R *Mesodontrachia fitzroyana*
   Australia: Northern Territory

V *Mouldingia occidentalis*
   Australia: Western Australia

E *Mouldingia orientalis*
   Australia: Western Australia

R *Mussonena campbelli*
   Australia: Queensland

V *Ningbingia australis*
   Australia: Western Australia

V *Ningbingia bulla*
   Australia: Western Australia

V *Ningbingia dentiens*
   Australia: Western Australia

V *Ningbingia laurina*
   Australia: Western Australia

V *Ningbingia octava*
   Australia: Western Australia

V *Ningbingia res*
   Australia: Western Australia

R *Noctepuna muensis*
   Australia: Queensland

E *Occirhenea georgiana*
   Australia: Western Australia.

R *Offachloritis dryanderensis*
   Australia: Queensland

R *Ordtrachia australis*
   Australia: Northern Territory

V *Ordtrachia elegans*
   Australia: Western Australia

R *Ordtrachia septentrionalis*
   Australia: Northern Territory

R *Papuexul bidwilli*
   Australia: New South Wales, Queensland

R   *Papustyla pulcherrima*
     Papua New Guinea: Manus Island

K   *Planispira wesselensis*
     (*Cristigibba wesselensis*)
     Australia: Northern Territory

R   *Pleuroxia arcigerens*
     Australia: Northern Territory

E   *Pleuroxia hinsbyi*
     Australia: New South Wales

R   *Pleuroxia italowiana*
     Australia: South Australia

R   *Posorites turneri*
     Australia: Queensland

R   *Prototrachia sedula*
     Australia: Northern Territory

V   *Prymnbriareus nimberlinus*
     Australia: Western Australia

V   *Rhagada gibbensis*
     Australia: Western Australia

E   *Rhagada harti*
     Australia: Western Australia

I   *Semotrachia euzyga*
     Australia: Northern Territory

V   *Semotrachia sublevata*
     Australia: Northern Territory

R   *Semotrachia winneckeana*
     Australia: Northern Territory

V   *Setobaudinia collingii*
     Australia: Western Australia (Parry Island)

R   *Setobaudinia victoriana*
     Australia: Northern Territory

V   *Sinumelon bednalli*
     Australia: Northern Territory

R   *Sphaerospira macleayi*
     Australia: Queensland (Whitsunday Islands)

R   *Sphaerospira rockhamptonensis*
     Australia: Queensland

R   *Sphaerospira whartoni*
     Australia: Queensland (Holbourne Island)

E   *Thersites mitchellae*
     Australia: New South Wales

V   *Torresitrachia crawfordi*
     Australia: Western Australia

K   *Torresitrachia funium*
     Australia: Northern Territory

V   *Torresitrachia thedana*
     Australia: Western Australia

V   *Turgenitubulus aslini*
     Australia: Western Australia

V   *Turgenitubulus christenseni*
     Australia: Western Australia

V   *Turgenitubulus costus*
     Australia: Western Australia

V   *Turgenitubulus depressus*
     Australia: Western Australia

V   *Turgenitubulus foramenus*
     Australia: Western Australia

V   *Turgenitubulus opiranus*
     Australia: Western Australia

V   *Turgenitubulus pagodula*
     Australia: Western Australia

V   *Turgenitubulus tanmurrana*
     Australia: Western Australia

V   *Vidumelon wattii*
     Australia: Northern Territory

V   *Westraltrachia alterna*
     Australia: Western Australia

V   *Westraltrachia inopinata*
     Australia: Western Australia

V   *Westraltrachia lievreana*
     Australia: Western Australia

V   *Westraltrachia porcata*
     Australia: Western Australia

V   *Westraltrachia recta*
     Australia: Western Australia

V   *Westraltrachia subtila*
     Australia: Western Australia

V   *Westraltrachia turbinata*
     Australia: Western Australia

Family HYGROMIIDAE

V   *Petasina subtecta*
     Austria

I   *Plentusia vendia*
     Spain

V   *Trichia biconica*
     Switzerland

R   *Trichia caelata*
     Switzerland

R   *Trichia gramnicola*
     Germany

E   *Trichia oreinos*
     Austria

Family HELICELLIDAE

I   *Candidula setubalensis*
     Portugal

I   *Cyrnotheba corsica*
     France: Corsica

V   *Trochoidea gharlapsi*
     Malta

R   *Trochoidea spratti*
     Malta

Family HELICIDAE

V   *Actinella actinophora*
     Portugal: Madeira

V   *Actinella anaglyptica*
     Portugal: Madeira

V   *Actinella armitageana*
     Portugal: Madeira

R   *Actinella carinofausta*
     Portugal: Madeira

E   *Actinella effugiens*
     Portugal: Madeira (Porto Santo)

E   *Actinella fausta*
     Portugal: Madeira

V   *Actinella giramica*
     Portugal: Madeira

R   *Actinella laciniosa*
     Portugal: Madeira

V   *Actinella obserata*
     Portugal: Madeira

E   *Actinella robusta*
     Portugal: Madeira

V   *Canariella leprosa*
     Spain: Canary Islands (Tenerife)

V   *Canariella pthonera*
     Spain: Canary Islands (Tenerife)

R   *Caseolus abjectus*
     Portugal: Madeira (Porto Santo)

V   *Caseolus calculus*
     Portugal: Madeira (Porto Santo)

R   *Caseolus commixtus*
     Portugal: Madeira (Porto Santo)

R   *Caseolus consors*
     Portugal: Madeira (Porto Santo)

R   *Caseolus hartungi*
     Portugal: Madeira

V   *Caseolus leptostictus*
     Portugal: Madeira

V   *Caseolus subcalliferus*
     Portugal: Madeira (Porto Santo)

R   *Chilostoma cingulellum*
     Poland; Slovakia

R   *Chilostoma rossmaessleri*
     Poland; Slovakia

R   *Codringtonia codringtonii*
     Rock Snail
     Greece

V   *Cylindrus obtusus*
     Austria

R   *Discula bicarinata*
     Portugal: Madeira (Porto Santo)

V   *Discula bulweri*
     Portugal: Madeira (Porto Santo)

R   *Discula cheiranticola*
     Portugal: Madeira (Porto Santo)

R   *Discula echinulata*
     Portugal: Madeira (Porto Santo)

R   *Discula leacockiana*
     Portugal: Madeira (Porto Santo)

V   *Discula oxytropis*
     Portugal: Madeira (Porto Santo)

V   *Discula tabellata*
     Portugal: Madeira

R   *Discula tectiformis*
     Portugal: Madeira (Porto Santo)

E   *Discula testudinalis*
     Portugal: Madeira (Porto Santo)

V   *Discula turricula*
     Portugal: Madeira (Porto Santo)

R   *Disculella maderensis*
     Portugal: Madeira

V   *Disculella spirulina*
     Portugal: Madeira

R   *Elona quimperiana*
     France; Spain

R   *Geomitra moniziana*
     Portugal: Madeira

E   *Geomitra tiarella*
     Portugal: Madeira

K **Gittenbergeri turriplana**
Portugal

I **Helix ceratina**
France: Corsica

E **Helix godetiana**
Greece: Cyclades

V **Hemicycla adansoni**
Spain: Canary Islands (Tenerife)

R **Hemicycla berkeleyi**
Spain: Canary Islands

V **Hemicycla glyceia**
Spain: Canary Islands (Tenerife)

V **Hemicycla inutilis**
Spain: Canary Islands (Tenerife)

V **Hemicycla mascaensis**
Spain: Canary Islands (Tenerife)

E **Hemicycla modesta**
Spain: Canary Islands (Tenerife)

E **Hemicycla plicaria**
Spain: Canary Islands (Tenerife)

V **Hemicycla pouchet**
Spain: Canary Islands (Tenerife)

V **Idiomela subplicata**
Portugal: Madeira (Porto Santo)

V **Lampadia webbiana**
Portugal: Madeira (Porto Santo)

R **Lemniscia calva**
Portugal: Madeira

E **Lemniscia galeata**
Portugal: Madeira

V **Lemniscia michaudi**
Portugal: Madeira (Porto Santo)

R **Leptaxis furva**
Portugal: Madeira

V **Leptaxis portosancti**
Portugal: Madeira (Porto Santo)

E **Leptaxis wollastoni**
Portugal: Madeira (Porto Santo)

R **Pseudocampylaea portosanctana**
Portugal: Madeira (Porto Santo)

R **Spirorbula latens**
Portugal: Madeira

R **Spirorbula obtecta**
Portugal: Madeira

R **Spirorbula squalida**
Portugal: Madeira

I **Tacheocampylaea raspaili**
France: Corsica

V **Tacheocampylaea tacheoides**
Italy

R **Trissexodon constrictus**
France; Spain

R **Tyrrheniella josephi**
Italy

Family HELMINTHOGLYPTIDAE

K **Eremarionta immaculata**
White Desrt Snail
USA

K **Eremarionta millepalmarum**
Thousand Palms Desert Snail
USA

K **Eremarionta morongoana**
Morongo Desert Snail
USA

R **Helminthoglypta allynsmithi**
Merced Canyon Shoulderband
USA

I **Helminthoglypta callistoderma**
Kern Shoulderband
USA

K **Helminthoglypta coelata**
Mesa Shoulderband
USA

K **Helminthoglypta mohaveana**
Victorville Shoulderband
USA

E **Helminthoglypta walkeriana**
Morro Shoulderband
USA

K **Micrarionta facta**
Santa Barbara Island Snail
USA

E **Micrarionta feralis**
San Nicolas Island Snail
USA

K **Micrarionta gabbi**
San Clemente Island Snail
USA

K **Micrarionta opuntia**
Prickly Pear Island Snail
USA

R   *Monadenia circumcarinata*
    Keeled Sideband
    USA

V   *Monadenia setosa*
    Trinity Bristle Snail
    USA

K   *Monadenia troglodytes*
    Shasta Sideband
    USA

I   *Sonorella eremita*
    Sax Xavier Talus Snail
    USA

I   *Sonorella metcalfi*
    Franklin Mountain Talus Snail
    USA

K   *Xerarionta intercisa*
    Plain Cactus Snail
    USA

K   *Xerarionta redimita*
    Wreathed Cactus Snail
    USA

K   *Xerarionta tryoni*
    Bicolor Cactus Snail
    USA

Family ARIONIDAE

R   *Arion obesoductus*
    Austria

K   *Arion vejdorskyi*
    Czech Republic

V   *Binneya notabilis*
    Santa Barbara Shelled Slug
    USA

V   *Geomalacus maculosus*
    Ireland; Portugal; Spain

Class BIVALVIA

Order UNIONOIDA

Family MARGARITIFERIDAE

E   *Margaritifera auricularia*
    Belgium; Czech Republic; France; Germany;
    Italy; Luxembourg; Netherlands; Portugal;
    Spain; United Kingdom

E   *Margaritifera hembeli*
    Louisiana Pearlshell
    USA

V   *Margaritifera margaritifera*
    Austria; Belgium; Czech Republic; Denmark;
    Finland; France; Germany; Iceland; Ireland;
    Luxembourg; Norway; Poland; Portugal;
    Russia: Spain; Sweden; United Kingdom

I   *Margaritifera marrianae*
    Alabama Pearl Shell
    USA

I   *Margaritifera monodonta*
    (*Cumberlandia monodonta*)
    Spectacle Case
    USA

Family UNIONIDAE

I   *Alasmidonta arcula*
    Altamaha Arcmussel
    USA

I   *Alasmidonta atropurpurea*
    Cumberland Elktoe
    USA

E   *Alasmidonta heterodon*
    Dwarf Wedge Mussel
    USA

I   *Alasmidonta raveneliana*
    Appalacian Elktoe
    USA

I   *Alismodonta varicosa*
    Brook Floater
    USA

I   *Alasmidonta wrightiana*
    Ochlockonee Arcmussel
    USA

I   *Amblema neislerii*
    Fat Threeridge
    USA

I   *Anodonta californensis*
    California Floater
    USA

E   *Arkansia wheeleri*
    Ouachita Rock Pocketbook
    USA

E   *Carunculina cylindrellus*
    (*Toxolasma cylindrellus*)
    Pale Lilliput
    USA

I   *Carunculina lividus*
    (*Toxolasma lividus*)
    Purple Lilliput
    USA

I	***Carunculina pullus*** (*Toxolasma pullus*) Savannah Lilliput USA
I	***Cyprogenia aberti*** Western Fan-shell USA
E	***Cyprogenia stegaria*** Fanshell USA
E	***Dromus dromas*** Dromedary Pearly Mussel USA
I	***Dysnomia brevidens*** (*Epioblasma brevidens*) Cumberlandian Combshell USA
I	***Dysnomia capsaeformis*** (*Epioblasma capsaeformis*) Oyster Mussel USA
E	***Dysnomia metastriata*** (*Epioblasma metastriata*) Upland Combshell USA
E	***Dysnomia othcaloogensis*** (*Epioblasma othcaloogensis*) Southern Acornshell USA
E	***Dysnomia penita*** (*Epioblasma penita*) Southern Combshell USA
I	***Dysnomia triquetra*** (*Epioblasma triquetra*) Snuffbox USA
E	***Dysnomia turgidula*** (*Epioblasma turgidula*) Turgid-blossom USA
I	***Elliptio jayensis*** Flat Spike USA
I	***Elliptio lanceolata*** Yellow Lance USA
I	***Elliptio marsupiobesa*** Cape Fear Spike USA

I	***Elliptio nigella*** Winged Spike USA
I	***Elliptio shepardiana*** Altamaha Lance USA
I	***Elliptio spinosa*** Altamaha Spinymussel USA
E	***Elliptio steinstansana*** Tar River Spinymussel USA
I	***Elliptio waccamawensis*** Waccamaw Spike USA
E	***Fusconaia cor*** Shiny Pigtoe USA
E	***Fusconaia cuneolus*** Fine-rayed Pigtoe USA
I	***Fusconaia escambia*** Narrow Pigtoe USA
I	***Fusconaia masoni*** Atlantic Pigtoe USA
E	***Hemistena lata*** Cracking Pearlymussel USA
E	***Lampsilis abrupta*** Pink Mucket USA
V	***Lampsilis altilis*** Fine-lined Pocketbook USA
I	***Lampsilis australis*** Southern Sandshell USA
I	***Lampsilis binominata*** Lined Pocketbook USA
I	***Lampsilis cariosa*** Yellow Lampmussel USA
I	***Lampsilis fullerkati*** Waccamaw Fatmucket USA

E   *Lampsilis higginsii*
Higgin's Eye
USA

V   *Lampsilis perovalis*
Orangenacre Mucket
USA

V   *Lampsilis powellii*
Arkansas Fatmucket
USA

I   *Lampsilis rafinesqueana*
Neosho Mucket
USA

I   *Lampsilis salinasensis*
(*Disconaias salinasensis*)
Salina Mucket
USA

E   *Lampsilis streckeri*
Speckled Pocketbook
USA

I   *Lampsilis subangulata*
Shinyrayed Pocketbook
USA

E   *Lampsilis virescens*
Alabama Lampmussel
USA

E   *Lasmigona decorata*
Carolina Heelsplitter
USA

I   *Lasmigona holstonia*
Tennessee Heelsplitter
USA

I   *Lasmigona subviridis*
Green Floater
USA

V   *Leguminaia compressa*
(*Microcondylaea compressa*)
Italy; Switzerland; Yugoslavia

E   *Lemiox rimosus*
Birdwing Pearlymussel
USA

I   *Leptodea leptodon*
Scaleshell
USA

I   *Lexingtonia dolabelloides*
Slabside Pearlymussel
USA

V   *Medionidus acutissimus*
Alabama Moccasinshell
USA

E   *Medionidus parvulus*
Coosa Moccasinshell
USA

I   *Nephronaias sloatianus*
(*Elliptoideus sloatianus*)
Purple Bankclimber
USA

E   *Obovaria retusa*
Ring Pink
USA

I   *Obovaria rotulata*
Round Ebonyshell
USA

E   *Pegias fabula*
Littlewing Pearlymussel
USA

E   *Plethobasus cicatricosus*
White Wartyback
USA

E   *Plethobasus cooperianus*
Orangefoot Pimpleback
USA

E   *Pleurobema clava*
Clubshell
USA

E   *Pleurobema collina*
James River Spinymussel
USA

E   *Pleurobema curtum*
Black Clubshell
USA

E   *Pleurobema decisum*
Southern Clubshell
USA

E   *Pleurobema furvum*
Dark Pigtoe
USA

E   *Pleurobema georgianum*
Southern Pigtoe
USA

E   *Pleurobema gibberum*
Cumberland Pigtoe
USA

E   *Pleurobema marshalli*
Flat Pigtoe
USA

I   *Pleurobema oviforme*
Tennessee Clubshell
USA

I   ***Pleurobema perovatum***
Ovate Clubshell
USA

E   ***Pleurobema plenum***
Rough Pigtoe
USA

I   ***Pleurobema pyriforme***
Oval Pigtoe
USA

I   ***Pleurobema rubellum***
Warrior Pigtoe
USA

I   ***Pleurobema rubrum***
Pyramid Pigtoe
USA

E   ***Pleurobema taitianum***
Heavy Pigtoe
USA

I   ***Pleurobema verum***
True Pigtoe
USA

I   ***Potamilus amphiehaenus***
Texas Heelsplitter
USA

E   ***Potamilus capax***
Fat Pocketbook
USA

V   ***Potamilus inflatus***
Alabama Heelsplitter
USA

K   ***Pseudanodonta complanata***
Austria; Belarus; Belgium; Bulgaria; Czech Republic; Estonia; Finland; Germany; Hungary; Kazakhstan; Latvia; Lithuania; Moldova; Norway; Poland; Romania; Russia; Sweden; Switzerland; Slovakia; Ukraine; United Kingdom

E   ***Ptychobranchus greenii***
Triangular Kidneyshell
USA

I   ***Ptychobranchus jonesi***
Southern Kidneyshell
USA

I   ***Quadrula cylindrica strigillata***
Rough Rabbitsfoot
USA

E   ***Quadrula fragosa***
Winged Mapleleaf
USA

E   ***Quadrula intermedia***
Cumberland Monkeyface
USA

E   ***Quadrula sparsa***
Appalachian Monkeyface
USA

E   ***Quadrula stapes***
Stirrupshell
USA

I   ***Quincuncina mitchelli***
False Spike
USA

I   ***Simpsoniconcha ambigua***
(*Simpsonaias ambigua*)
Salamander Mussel
USA

I   ***Truncilla cognata***
Mexican Fawnsfoot
USA

E   ***Unio cariei***
(*Nodularia cariei*)
Réunion

E   ***Unio crassus***
Austria; Belarus; Belgium; Bulgaria; Czech Republic; Denmark; Estonia; Finland; France; Germany; Hungary; Kazakhstan; Latvia; Liechtenstein; Lithuania; Luxembourg; Moldova: Netherlands; Poland; Romania; Russia; Slovakia; Sweden; Switzerland; Ukraine

V   ***Unio elongatulus***
France; Italy; Spain; Switzerland; Yugoslavia

R   ***Unio turtoni***
France: Corsica

I   ***Villosa choctawensis***
Choctaw Bean
USA

I   ***Villosa fabalis***
Rayed Bean
USA

I   ***Villosa ortmanni***
Kentucky Creekshell
USA

I   ***Villosa perpurpurea***
Purple Bean
USA

E   ***Villosa trabalis***
Cumberland Bean
USA

Family HYRIIDAE

I   *Hyridella moretonicus*
     (*Velesunio moretonicus*)
     Australia: Tasmania

Order VENEROIDA

Family TRIDACNIDAE

I   *Hippopus hippopus*
     Bear Paw Clam
     (Indo-Pacific: including Bay of Bengal, South
     China Sea, East China Sea, Coral Sea)
     American Samoa (ex?); Australia: Queensland,
     Western; Federated States of Micronesia; Fiji
     (ex?); Guam (ex?); India?: Andaman and
     Nicobar Islands; Indonesia; Japan: Ogasawara-
     shoto (Bonin Islands) (ex?), Ryukyu Islands
     (ex?); Kiribati: Gilbert Islands; Malaysia;
     Marshall Islands; Myanmar; New Caledonia;
     Northern Marianas (ex?); Palau; Philippines;
     Papua New Guinea; Paracel Islands?; Samoa
     (ex?); Singapore; Solomon Islands; Taiwan
     (ex?); Thailand?; Tonga (ex?); Tuvalu;
     Vanuatu

I   *Hippopus porcellanus*
     China Clam
     (Indo-Pacific: including Flores Sea, South
     China Sea)
     Indonesia; Palau; Philippines: Sulu
     Archipelago, Masbate Island; South China Sea
     reefs

K   *Tridacna crocea*
     Crocus Clam
     (Indo-Pacific: including South China Sea,
     Coral Sea)
     Australia; Guam (ex?); Indonesia; Japan:
     Ryukyu Islands; Malaysia; Northern Marianas
     (ex?); Palau; Papua New Guinea; Philippines;
     Singapore; Solomon Islands; Thailand;
     Tuvalu?; Vanuatu?; Viet Nam

V   *Tridacna derasa*
     Southern Giant clam
     (Indo-Pacific: Coral Sea)
     Australia: Queensland; Cocos (Keeling)
     Islands?; Fiji; French Polynesia?: Tuamotu
     Archipelago; Guam (ex?); Indonesia: Irian
     Jaya, Taka Bone Rate in Sulawesi; New
     Caledonia; Northern Marianas (ex?); Palau;
     Papua New Guinea; Philippines;
     Solomon Islands; Tonga: Tongatapu; Tuvalu?;
     Vanuatu?
     [American Samoa; Cook Islands; Federated
     States of Micronesia; Marshall Islands]

V   *Tridacna gigas*
     Giant Clam
     (Indo-Pacific: including South China Sea,
     Coral Sea)
     Australia: Queensland, Western; Federated
     States of Micronesia: Lamotrek Atoll, Wesy
     Fagu; Fiji (ex?); Indonesia; Japan: Ryukyu
     Islands (ex?); Kiribati: Gilbert Islands;
     Malaysia; Marshall Islands; Myanmar; New
     Caledonia (ex?); Northern Marianas (ex?);
     Palau; Papua New Guinea; Philippines;
     Solomon Islands; Taiwan (ex?); Thailand;
     Tuvalu; Vanuatu (ex?)
     [Guam (ex?); USA: including Hawaiian
     Islands]

K   *Tridacna maxima*
     Small Giant Clam
     (Indian Ocean; Pacific Ocean)
     American Samoa; Australia: including Lord
     Howe Island; British Indian Ocean Territory:
     Chagos Archipelago; China; Cook Islands;
     Egypt; Federated States of Micronesia; Fiji;
     French Polynesia; Guam; India: Andaman and
     Nicobar Islands, Lakshadweep; Indonesia;
     Japan; Kenya; Kiribati: Gilbert, Phoenix, Line
     Islands; Madagascar; Malaysia; Maldives;
     Marshall Islands; Mauritius; Mozambique;
     Myanmar; New Caledonia; Northern Marianas;
     Palau; Papua New Guinea; Philippines;
     Pitcairn Islands: Henderson Island; Samoa;
     Saudi Arabia; Seychelles; Singapore; Solomon
     Islands; South Africa; Sri Lanka; Taiwan;
     Thailand; Tokelau; Tonga; Tuvalu; USA
     Pacific Islands; Vanuatu; Viet Nam

I   *Tridacna squamosa*
     Scaly Clam, Fluted Clam
     (Indian Ocean; Pacific Ocean)
     American Samoa; Australia; British Indian
     Ocean Territory: Chagos Archipelago; Egypt;
     Federated States of Micronesia; Fiji; French
     Polynesia: Tuamotu Archipelago; India:
     Andaman and Nicobar Islands, Lakshadweep;
     Indonesia; Japan (ex?); Kenya; Kiribati:
     Gilbert Islands; Madagascar; Malaysia;
     Maldives; Marshall Islands; Mauritius;
     Mozambique; Myanmar; New Caledonia;
     Northern Marianas (ex?); Palau; Papua New
     Guinea; Philippines; Samoa; Saudi Arabia;
     Seychelles; Singapore; Solomon Islands; South
     Africa; Sri Lanka; Thailand; Tokelau; Tonga;
     Tuvalu; Vanuatu; Viet Nam
     [Guam (ex?); USA: including Hawaiian
     Islands]

K   ***Tridacna tevoroa***
Tevoro Clam
(South Pacific)
Fiji: Lau Islands; Tonga: Ha'apai and Vava'u
Groups

Family PISIDIIDAE

I   ***Pisidium sanguinichristi***
USA

I   ***Pisidium ultramontanum***
Montane Peaclam
USA

Phylum ANNELIDA

Class POLYCHAETA

Order EUNICIDA

Family EUNICIDAE

K   ***Eunice viridis***
Palolo Worm
(South Pacific)

Class HIRUDINEA

Order ARHYNCHOBDELLAE

Family HIRUDINIDAE

I   ***Hirudo medicinalis***
Medicinal Leech
Albania; Armenia; Austria; Azerbaijan?;
Belarus?; Belgium; Bulgaria; Czech Republic?;
Denmark; Estonia?; Finland; France; Georgia;
Germany; Greece; Hungary; Italy;
Kazakhstan?; Latvia?; Lithuania; Luxembourg;
Moldova; Netherlands; Norway; Poland;
Portugal; Romania; Russia; Spain; Sweden;
Switzerland; Turkey; Ukraine; United
Kingdom; Yugoslavia

Class OLIGOCHAETA

Order HAPLOTAXIDA

Family KOMAREKIONIDAE

V   ***Komarekiona eatoni***
USA

Family LUTODRILIDAE

R   ***Lutodrilus multivesiculatus***
USA

Family MEGASCOLECIDAE

E   ***Driloleirus americanus***
(*Megascolides americanus*)
Washington Giant Earthworm
USA

E   ***Driloleirus macelfreshi***
(*Megascolides macelfreshi*)
Oregon Giant Earthworm
USA

V   ***Megascolides australis***
Giant Gippsland Earthworm
Australia

Phylum ARTHROPODA

Class MEROSTOMATA

Order XIPHOSURA

Family LIMULIDAE

K   ***Carcinoscorpius rotundicauda***
Horseshoe Crab
Coastal waters - India; Indonesia; Malaysia;
Philippines; Singapore; Thailand

K   ***Limulus polyphemus***
Horseshoe Crab
Coastal waters - Canada; Mexico; USA

K   ***Tachypleus gigas***
Horseshoe Crab
Coastal waters - India; Indonesia; Malaysia;
Singapore; Thailand

K   ***Tachypleus tridentatus***
Horseshoe Crab
Coastal waters - China; Indonesia; Japan;
Malaysia; Philippines; Taiwan; Viet Nam

Class ARACHNIDA

Order ARANEAE

Family THERAPHOSIDAE

K   ***Euathlus smithi***
(*Brachypelma smithi*)
Red-kneed Tarantula
Mexico

Family HEXATHELIDAE

I   ***Macrothele cretica***
Greece: Crete

Family CTENIZIDAE

I   *Cyclocosmia torreya*
    Torreya Trap-door Spider
    USA

Family GRADUNGULIDAE

I   *Spelungula cavernicola*
    Nelson Cave Spider
    New Zealand

Family LEPTONETIDAE

E   *Leptoneta myopica*
    Tooth Cave Spider
    USA

Family LINYPHIIDAE

R   *Troglohyphantes gracilis*
    Kocevje Subterranean Spider
    Yugoslavia

R   *Troglohyphantes similis*
    Kocevje Subterranean Spider
    Yugoslavia

R   *Troglohyphantes spinipes*
    Kocevje Subterranean Spider
    Yugoslavia

Family ARANEIDAE

I   *Meta dolloff*
    Dolloff Cave Spider
    USA

Family GNAPHOSIDAE

I   *Cesonia irvingi*
    Key Gnaphosid Spider
    Bahamas; USA

Family LYCOSIDAE

E   *Adelocosa anops*
    No-eyed Big-eyed Wolf Spider
    USA: Hawaiian Islands

I   *Lycosa ericeticola*
    Rosemary Wolf Spider
    USA

R   *Pardosa diuturna*
    Glacier Bay Wolf Spider
    USA

I   *Sosippus placidus*
    Lake Placid Funnel Wolf Spider
    USA

Family ASAURIDAE

V   *Dolomedes plantarius*
    Great Raft Spider
        Austria; Belarus?; Belgium; Denmark; France;
        Georgia?; Germany; Hungary; Italy; Latvia;
        Lithuania; Netherlands; Poland; Romania;
        Russia; Slovakia; Sweden;

Order PSEUDOSCORPIONIDA

Family NEOBISIIDAE

I   *Microcreagris imperialis*
    Empire Cave Pseudoscorpion
    USA

E   *Microcreagris texana*
    Tooth Cave Pseudoscorpion
    USA

Order OPILIONES

Family PHALANGODIDAE

V   *Banksula melones*
    Melones Cave Harvestman
    USA

Class CRUSTACEA

Order CLADOCERA

Family DAPHNIDAE

R   *Daphnia jollyi*
    Water Flea
        Australia: Western Australia

R   *Daphnia occidentalis*
    Water Flea
        Australia: Western Australia

R   *Daphnia nivalis*
    Water Flea
        Australia: New South Wales

Family CHYDORIDAE

R   *Rhynchochydorus australiensis*
    Water Flea
        Australia: New South Wales

Order ANOSTRACA

Family ARTEMIIDAE

I   *Artemia monica*
    Mono Lake Brine Shrimp
    USA

Family BRANCHINECTIDAE

I   *Branchinecta gigas*
    Giant Fairy Shrimp
        Canada; USA

Family BRANCHIPODIDAE

I   *Parartemia contracta*
Brine Shrimp
Australia: Western Australia

Family THAMNOCEPHALIDAE

K   *Branchinella apophysata*
Fairy Shrimp
Australia: Western Australia

K   *Branchinella basispina*
Fairy Shrimp
Australia: Western Australia

K   *Branchinella denticulata*
Fairy Shrimp
Australia: Western Australia

K   *Branchinella simplex*
Brine Shrimp
Australia: Western Australia

K   *Branchinella wellardi*
Fairy Shrimp
Australia: Western Australia

Order MYODOCOPINA

Family CYPRIDINIDAE

K   *Zonocypretta kalimna*
Seed Shrimp
Australia: Western Australia

Family NOTODROMADIDAE

K   *Newnhamia fuscata*
Seed Shrimp
Australia: New South Wales

K   *Newnhamia insolita*
Seed Shrimp
Australia: New South Wales

Order PODOCOPINA

Family LIMNOCYTHERIDAE

K   *Limnocythere porphyretica*
Seed Shrimp
Australia: Western Australia

Order CALANOIDA

Family CENTROPAGIDAE

R   *Boeckella nyoraensis*
Australia

R   *Calamoecia australica*
Australia: Victoria

R   *Calamoecia elongata*
Australia: Western Australia

Order HARPACTICOIDA

Family CANTHOCAMPTIDAE

K   *Canthocamptus echinopyge*
Australia: Tasmania

K   *Canthocamptus dedeckkeri*
Australia: Victoria

K   *Canthocamptus tasmaniae*
Australia: Tasmania

K   *Canthocamptus longipes*
Australia: Victoria

K   *Canthocamptus mammillifurca*
Australia: Victoria

K   *Canthocamptus sublaevis*
Australia: Victoria

K   *Fibulacamptus gracilior*
Australia: Victoria

K   *Fibulacamptus bisetosus*
Australia: Western Australia

Order THORACICA

Family BALANIDAE

I   *Armatobalanus nefrens*
USA

I   *Balanus aquila*
USA

Order ANASPIDACEA

Family ANASPIDIDAE

I   *Allanaspides helonomus*
Syncarid Shrimp
Australia: Tasmania

V   *Allanaspides hickmani*
Syncarid Shrimp
Australia: Tasmania

K   *Anaspides* sp.
Syncarid Shrimps
Australia: Tasmania

I   *Paranaspides lacustris*
Great Lake Shrimp
Australia: Tasmania

Family PSAMMASPIDIDAE

K   *Eucrenonaspides oinotheke*
Australia: Tasmania

Order ISOPODA

Family CIROLANIDAE

V *Antrolana lira*
Madison Cave Isopod
USA

I *Arubolana imula*
Aruba

K *Mexilana saluposi*
Mexico

K *Speocirolana affinis*
Mexico

K *Speocirolana interstitialis*
Mexico

K *Speocirolana thermydromis*
Mexico

Family SPHAEROMATIDAE

K *Thermosphaeroma dugesi*
Mexico

K *Thermosphaeroma milleri*
Mexico

K *Thermosphaeroma smithi*
Mexico

K *Thermosphaeroma subequalum*
Mexico

E *Thermosphaeroma thermophilum*
Socorro Isopod
USA

Family TRICHONISCIDAE

K *Metatrichoniscoides celticus*
United Kingdom

Family STYLONISCIDAE

I *Styloniscus* sp.
Australia: Tasmania

Family ARMADILLIDAE

I *Echinodillo cavaticus*
Australia: Tasmania

Family PHREATOICIDAE

I *Mesacanthotelson setosis*
Australia: Tasmania

R *Onchotelson brevicaudatus*
Australia: Tasmania

R *Onchotelson spatulatus*
Australia: Tasmania

R *Uramphisopus pearsoni*
Australia: Tasmania

Family ASELLIDAE

I *Caecidotea barri*
Clifton Cave Isopod
USA

I *Caecidotea macropoda*
Bat Cave Isopod
USA

I *Caecidotea nickajackensis*
Nickajack Cave Isopod
USA

I *Lirceus culveri*
Rye Cove Cave Isopod
USA

E *Lirceus usdagalun*
Lee County Cave Isopod
USA

Family STENASELLIDAE

I *Mexistenasellus coahuila*
Mexico

R *Mexistenasellus parzefalli*
Parzefall's Stenasellid
Mexico

R *Mexistenasellus wilkensi*
Wilken's Stenasellid
Mexico

Order AMPHIPODA

Family GAMMARIDAE

I *Gammarus acheronytes*
Illinois Cave Amphipod
USA

I *Gammarus bousfieldi*
Bousfield's Amphipod
USA

I *Gammarus desperatus*
Noel's Amphipod
USA

I *Gammarus hyalieioides*
Diminutive Amphipod
USA

I *Gammarus pecos*
Pecos Amphipod
USA

Family ORCHESTIIDAE

I   *Spelasorchestia koloana*
Kaui Cave Amphipod
USA: Hawaiian Islands

Family CRANGONYCTIDAE

I   *Allocrangonyx hubrichti*
Central Missouri Cave Amphipod
USA

I   *Allocrangonyx pellucidus*
Oklahoma Cave Amphipod
USA

I   *Crangonyx dearolfi*
Pennsylvania Cave Amphipod
USA

I   *Crangonyx grandimanus*
Florida Cave Amphipod
USA

I   *Crangonyx hobbsi*
Hobb's Cave Amphipod
USA

I   *Stygobromus araeus*
Tidewater Interstitial Amphipod
USA

I   *Stygobromus arizonensis*
Arizona Cave Amphipod
USA

I   *Stygobromus balconius*
Balcones Cave Amphipod
USA

I   *Stygobromus barri*
Barr's Cave Amphipod
USA

I   *Stygobromus bifurcatus*
Bifurcated Cave Amphipod
USA

I   *Stygobromus bowmani*
Bowman's Cave Amphipod
USA

I   *Stygobromus clantoni*
Clanton's Cave Amphipod
USA

I   *Stygobromus conradi*
Burnsville Cove Cave Amphipod
USA

I   *Stygobromus cooperi*
Cooper's Cave Amphipod
USA

I   *Stygobromus dejectus*
Cascade Cave Amphipod
USA

I   *Stygobromus elatus*
Elevated Spring Amphipod
USA

I   *Stygobromus emarginatus*
Greenbrier Cave Amphipod
USA

I   *Stygobromus ephemerus*
Ephemeral Cave Amphipod
USA

I   *Stygobromus flagellatus*
Ezell's Cave Amphipod
USA

I   *Stygobromus gradyi*
Grady's Cave Amphipod
USA

I   *Stygobromus hadenoecus*
Devil's Sinkhole Amphipod
USA

I   *Stygobromus harai*
Hara's Cave Amphipod
USA

E   *Stygobromus hayi*
Hay's Spring Amphipod
USA

I   *Stygobromus heteropodus*
Pickle Springs Amphipod
USA

I   *Stygobromus hubbsi*
Malheur Cave Amphipod
USA

I   *Stygobromus identatus*
Tidewater Stygonectid Amphipod
USA

I   *Stygobromus longipes*
Long-legged Cave Amphipod
USA

I   *Stygobromus mackenziei*
Mackenzie's Cave Amphipod
USA

I   *Stygobromus montanus*
Mountain Cave Amphipod
USA

I   *Stygobromus morrisoni*
Morrison's Cave Amphipod
USA

I   *Stygobromus mundas*
    Bath County Cave Amphipod
    USA

I   *Stygobromus nortoni*
    Norton's Cave Amphipod
    USA

I   *Stygobromus onondagaensis*
    Onondaga Cave Amphipod
    USA

I   *Stygobromus ozarkensis*
    Ozark Cave Amphipod
    USA

I   *Stygobromus parvus*
    Minute Cave Amphipod
    USA

I   *Stygobromus pecki*
    Peck's Cave Amphipod
    USA

I   *Stygobromus pizzinii*
    Pizzini's Amphipod
    USA

I   *Stygobromus putealis*
    Wisconsin Well Amphipod
    USA

I   *Stygobromus reddelli*
    Reddell's Cave Amphipod
    USA

I   *Stygobromus smithii*
    Alabama Well Amphipod
    USA

I   *Stygobromus spinatus*
    Spring Cave Amphipod
    USA

I   *Stygobromus stellmacki*
    Stellmack's Cave Amphipod
    USA

I   *Stygobromus subtilis*
    Subtle Cave Amphipod
    USA

I   *Stygobromus wengerorum*
    Wengeror's Cave Amphipod
    USA

Order DECAPODA

Family ATYIDAE

E   *Palaemonias alabamae*
    Alabama Cave Shrimp
    USA

E   *Palaemonias ganteri*
    Kentucky Cave Shrimp
    USA

E   *Syncaris pacifica*
    California Freshwater Shrimp
    USA

I   *Typhlatya monae*
    Mona Cave Shrimp
    Puerto Rico

Family PALAEMONIDAE

I   *Palaemonetes antrorum*
    Balcones Cave Shrimp
    USA

V   *Palaemonetes cummingi*
    Squirrel Chimney Cave Shrimp
    USA

Family CAMBARIDAE

I   *Cambarus batchi*
    Bluegrass Crayfish
    USA

I   *Cambarus bouchardi*
    Big South Fork Crayfish
    USA

I   *Cambarus catagius*
    Greenshorn Burrowing Crayfish
    USA

I   *Cambarus chasmodactylus*
    New River Crayfish
    USA

I   *Cambarus extraneus*
    Chickamanga Crayfish
    USA

I   *Cambarus obeyensis*
    Obey Crayfish
    USA

E   *Cambarus zophonastes*
    Hell Creek Crayfish
    USA

I   *Orconectes jeffersoni*
    Louisville Crayfish
    USA

E   *Orconectes shoupi*
    Nashville Crayfish
    USA

I   *Procambarus acherontis*
    Orlando Cave Crayfish
    USA

I   *Procambarus connus*
Corrollton Crayfish
USA

I   *Procambarus lepidodactylus*
Pee Dee Iotic Crayfish
USA

Family ASTACIDAE

V   *Astacus astacus*
Noble Crayfish
Austria; Belarus; Belgium; Bulgaria; Czech Republic?; Denmark; Estonia?; Finland; France; Germany; Hungary; Latvia?; Lithuania; Moldova?; Netherlands; Norway; Poland; Romania?; Russia; Slovakia; Sweden; Ukraine; Yugoslavia
[Cyprus; Italy; Switzerland]

R   *Austropotamobius pallipes*
White-clawed Crayfish
Austria; Czech Republic?; France; Germany; Hungary?; Ireland; Italy; Portugal; Slovakia; Spain; Switzerland; United Kingdom; Yugoslavia

K   *Austropotamobius torrentium*
Stone Crayfish
Austria; Czech Republic?; France; Germany; Hungary; Slovakia; Switzerland; Yugoslavia

E   *Pacifastacus fortis*
Shasta Crayfish
USA

Family PARASTACIDAE

I   *Astacoides madagascariensis*
Madagascar Freshwater Crayfish
Madagascar

I   *Astacopsis gouldi*
Giant Tasmanian Lobster
Australia: Tasmania

I   *Cherax tenuimanus*
Marron
Australia: Western Australia

R   *Engaeus australis*
Lilly Pilly Burrowing Crayfish
Australia: Victoria

K   *Engaeus mallacoota*
Mallacoota Burrowing Crayfish
Australia: Victoria

R   *Engaeus martigener*
Furneaux Burrowing Crayfish
Australia: Flinders Island

K   *Engaeus orramakunna*
Mount Arthur Burrowing Crayfish
Australia: Tasmania

R   *Engaeus phyllocercus*
Narracan Burrowing Crayfish
Australia: Victoria

R   *Engaeus rostrogaleatus*
Strzelecki Burrowing Crayfish
Australia: Victoria

V   *Engaeus spinicaudatus*
Scottsdale Burrowing Crayfish
Australia: Tasmania

V   *Engaeus sternalis*
Warragul Burrowing Crayfish
Australia: Victoria

E   *Engaewa similis*
Australia

I   *Euastacus armatus*
Murray River Cray
Australia

R   *Euastacus bindal*
Australia: Queensland

I   *Euastacus bispinosus*
Glenelg River Cray
Australia: Victoria

R   *Euastacus eungella*
Australia: Queensland

R   *Euastacus fleckeri*
Australia: Queensland

R   *Euastacus hystricosus*
Australia: Queensland

R   *Euastacus jagara*
Australia: Queensland

R   *Euastacus maidae*
Australia: Queensland

R   *Euastacus monteithorum*
Australia: Queensland

R   *Euastacus robertsi*
Australia: Queensland

R   *Euastacus setosus*
Australia: Queensland

R   *Euastacus urospinosus*
Australia: Queensland

Family COENOBITIDAE

R   *Birgus latro*
Coconut Crab
(Indo-Pacific)

Family PINNOTHERIDAE

K   *Parapinnixa affinis*
    Californian Bay Pea Crab
    USA

Class INSECTA

Order THYSANURA

Family MACHILIDAE

I   *Machiloides heteropus*
    Hawaiian Long-palp Bristletail
    USA: Hawaiian Islands

I   *Machiloides perkinsi*
    Perkin's Club-palp Bristletail
    USA: Hawaiian Islands

Order COLLEMBOLA

Family NEANURIDAE

I   *Acanthanura dendyi*
    Australia: Tasmania

I   *Acanthanura* sp.
    Australia: Tasmania

I   *Megalanura tasmaniae*
    Australia: Tasmania

I   *Womersleymeria bicornis*
    Australia: Tasmania

I   *Womersleymeria* sp.1
    Australia: Tasmania

I   *Womersleymeria* sp.2
    Australia: Tasmania

Order EPHEMEROPTERA

Family SIPHLONURIDAE

I   *Ameletus falsus*
    False Mayfly
    USA

I   *Isonychia diversa*
    Diverse Mayfly
    USA

R   *Tasmanophlebia lacus-coerulei*
    Large Blue Lake Mayfly
    Australia

Family BAETIDAE

I   *Heterocleon berneri*
    Berner's Two-winged Mayfly
    USA

Family OLIGONEURIIDAE

I   *Homoeoneuria cahabensis*
    Cahaba Sand-filtering Mayfly
    USA

I   *Homoeoneuria dolani*
    Blackwater Sand-filtering Mayfly
    USA

Family HEPTAGENIIDAE

I   *Pseudirion meridionalis*
    Meridion Blackwater Mayfly
    USA

Family BEHNINGIIDAE

I   *Dolania americana*
    American Sand-burrowing Mayfly
    USA

Family EPHEMERIDAE

I   *Ephemera compar*
    Colorado Burrowing Mayfly
    USA

I   *Ephemera triplex*
    West Virginia Burrowing Mayfly
    USA

Family EPHEMERELLIDAE

I   *Ceratella frisoni*
    Frison's Mayfly
    USA

I   *Ceratella spiculosa*
    Spicluose Mayfly
    USA

I   *Ephemerella argo*
    Argo Mayfly
    USA

Family CAENIDAE

I   *Brachycercus flavus*
    Yellow Mayfly
    USA

Order ODONATA

Family AMPHIPTERYGIDAE

I   *Amphipteryx agrioides*
    Belize; El Salvador; Guatemala; Honduras;
    Mexico

Family CHLOROCYPHIDAE

I   *Rhinocypha hageni*
    Philippines: Jolo

I **Rhinocypha latimaculata**
Philippines: Tawi Tawi

R **Rhinocypha ogasawarensis**
Japan: Ogasawara

R **Rhinocypha uenoi**
Japan: Iriomote

Family CALOPTERYGIDAE

R **Calopteryx angustipennis**
USA

E **Calopteryx syriaca**
Jordan; Syria; Turkey

I **Hetaerina rudis**
Guatemala; Mexico

Family SYNLESTIDAE

R **Chlorolestes apricans**
South Africa: eastern Cape

R **Chlorolestes draconicus**
South Africa

R **Ecchlorolestes nylephtha**
South Africa

R **Ecchlorolestes peringueyi**
South Africa

V **Phylolestes ethelae**
Dominican Republic

Family LESTIDAE

R **Indolestes boninensis**
Japan: Ogasawara

Family MEGAPODAGRIONIDAE

E **Amanipodagrion gilliesi**
Tanzania

I **Heteragrion eboratum**
Guatemala; Honduras

I **Heteragrion tricellulare**
Guatemala; Mexico

I **Hypolestes clara**
Jamaica

I **Hypolestes trinitatis**
Cuba

I **Paraphlebia zoe**
Mexico

R **Rhipidolestes okinawanus**
Japan: Okinawa

I **Thaumatoneura inopinata**
Costa Rica; Panama

Family HEMIPHLEBIIDAE

R **Hemiphlebia mirabilis**
Australia

Family COENAGRIONIDAE

I **Aciagrion rarum**
Angola

I **Argiagrion leoninum**
Sierra Leone

E **Argiocnemis solitaria**
Mauritius

I **Argiocnemis umbargae**
Cameroon

R **Boninagrion ezoin**
Japan: Ogasawara

I **Ceriagrion mourae**
Mozambique

V **Coenagrion mercuriale**
Southern Damselfly
?Albania; Algeria; Austria; Belgium; Bulgaria?; Czech Republic?; France; Germany; Hungary?; Italy; Liechtenstein; Luxembourg; Moldova?; Morocco; Netherlands; Portugal; Romania?; Slovakia?; Spain; Switzerland; Tunisia; Ukraine?; United Kingdom; Yugoslavia?

I **Enallagma camerunense**
Cameroon

I **Enallagma polychromaticum**
South Africa

V **Enallagma recurvatum**
Barrens Bluet Damselfly
USA

E **Ischnura gemina**
San Francisco Forktail Damselfly
USA

I **Megalagrion adytum**
Adytum Damselfly
USA: Hawaiian Islands

I **Megalagrion leptodemas**
Leptodemas Damselfly
USA: Hawaiian Islands

I **Megalagrion nigrohamatum**
Nigrohamatum Damselfly
USA: Hawaiian Islands

I **Megalagrion nigrolineatum**
Black-lined Damselfly
USA: Hawaiian Islands (Oahu)

I **Megalagrion oahuense**
Oahu Damselfly
USA: Hawaiian Islands (Oahu)

I **Megalagrion oceanicum**
Oceanic Damselfly
USA: Hawaiian Islands (Oahu)

E **Megalagrion pacificum**
Pacific Damselfly
USA: Hawaiian Islands

I **Megalagrion xanthomelas**
Orange-black Damselfly
USA: Hawaiian Islands

E **Mortonagrion hirosei**
Japan

V **Nehalennia pallidula**
USA

K **Pseudagrion quadrioculatum**
Zaire

Family PLATYCNEMIDIDAE

I **Metacnemis angusta**
South Africa

E **Platycnemis mauriciana**
Mauritius

Family PLATYSTICTIDAE

I **Palaemnema chiriquita**
Costa Rica

I **Palaemnema gigantula**
Costa Rica

I **Palaemnema melanota**
Costa Rica

I **Palaemnema paulicoba**
Mexico

I **Palaemnema reventazoni**
Costa Rica

Family PSEUDOSTIGMATIDAE

V **Mecistogaster asticta**
Brazil

E **Mecistogaster pronoti**
Brazil

Family EPIOPHLEBIIDAE

V **Epiophlebia laidlawi**
Relict Himalayan Dragonfly
India; Nepal

Family AESHNIDAE

K **Acanthaeshna victoria**
Australia

R **Aeshna meruensis**
Tanzania

R **Aeshna persephone**
USA

I **Aeshna viridis**
Austria; Czech Republic?; Denmark; Estonia?; Finland; Germany; Hungary; Latvia?; Lithuania?; Netherlands; Poland; Russia; Slovakia?; Sweden; Yugoslavia?

I **Aeshna williamsoniana**
Mexico

V **Cephalaeschna acutifrons**
India

R **Oligoaeschna kunigamiensis**
Japan: Okinawa

Family GOMPHIDAE

R **Asiagomphus yayeyamensis**
Japan: Yayeyama

V **Burmagomphus sivalikensis**
India

I **Cornigomphus guineensis**
Equatorial Guinea

I **Diaphlebia pallidistylus**
Costa Rica

I **Epigomphus camelus**
Costa Rica

I **Epigomphus clavatus**
Guatemala

I **Epigomphus crepidus**
Mexico

I **Epigomphus paulsoni**
Mexico

I **Epigomphus subsimilis**
Costa Rica

I **Epigomphus verticornis**
Costa Rica

K **Erpetogomphus lampropeltis**
USA

R **Gomphurus consanguis**
Cherokee Clubtail Dragonfly
USA

R **Gomphurus lynnae**
USA

R **Gomphurus modestus**
Gulf Clubtail
USA

R **Gomphus diminutus**
Diminutive Clubtail
USA

R **Gomphus graslini**
France; Spain

R **Gomphus hodgesi**
Hodges' Clubtail
USA

I **Gomphus sandrius**
Tennessee Clubtail Dragonfly
USA

R **Gomphus septima**
Septima's Clubtail Dragonfly
USA

R **Hylogomphus geminatus**
Twin-Striped Clubtail
USA

R **Hylogomphus parvidens**
USA

I **Isomma hieroglyphicum**
Madagascar

R **Leptogomphus yayeyamensis**
Japan: Ishigaki, Iriomote

R **Onychogomphus assimilis**
Armenia; Azerbaijan; Georgia; Turkey

E **Onychogomphus macrodon**
Israel; Jordan; Turkey

R **Ophiogomphus acuminatus**
USA

V **Ophiogomphus anomalus**
Canada; USA

E **Ophiogomphus cecilia**
Austria; Belarus?; Bulgaria; China; Czech
Republic; Denmark; Estonia?; Finland; France;
Germany; Hungary; Italy; Latvia?; Lithuania?;
Luxembourg; Moldova?; Portugal; Romania;
Russia; Slovakia; Sweden; Switzerland;
Turkey?; Ukraine?

V **Ophiogomphus howei**
Howe's Midget Snaketail Dragonfly
USA

R **Ophiogomphus incurvatus**
USA

R **Paragomphus sinaiticus**
Egypt; Niger; Oman; Saudi Arabia; Sudan

R **Progomphus bellei**
Belle's Sand Clubtail
USA

I **Progomphus risi**
Mexico

V **Stylurus potulentus**
Yellow-sided Clubtail
USA

R **Stylurus townesi**
Bronze Clubtail Dragonfly
USA

Family PETALURIDAE

K **Petalura pulcherrima**
Australia

Family CORDULEGASTERIDAE

E **Cordulegaster mzymtae**
Armenia; Azerbaijan; Georgia; Russia?;
Turkey

R **Chlorogomphus iriomotensis**
Japan: Iriomote

E **Zoraena sayi**
Florida Spiketail Dragonfly
USA

Family CORDULIIDAE

I **Antipodochlora braueri**
New Zealand

V **Austrocordulia leonardi**
Australia

R **Hemicordulia ogasawarensis**
Japan: Ogasawara

R **Hemicordulia okinawensis**
Japan: Okinawa, Amami

I **Libellulosoma minuta**
Madagascar

R **Macromia ishidai**
Japan: Yayeyama

R **Macromia kubokaiya**
Japan: Okinawa

R **Macromia margarita**
USA

R **Macromia splendens**
Shining Macromia Dragonfly
France; Portugal; Spain

R **Macromia urania**
Japan: Yayeyama

V   *Oxygastra curtisii*
    Orange-spotted Emerald
        Belgium; France; Germany; Italy; Morocco;
        Netherlands; Portugal; Spain; Switzerland;
        United Kingdom

R   *Somatochlora brevicincta*
    Canada

R   *Somatochlora calverti*
    Calverts' Emerald
    USA

E   *Somatochlora hineana*
    Ohio Emerald Dragonfly
    USA

R   *Somatochlora incurvata*
    Canada; USA

R   *Somatochlora margarita*
    Big Thicket Emerald Dragonfly
    USA

R   *Somatochlora ozarkensis*
    USA

V   *Williamsonia lintneri*
    Banded Bog Skimmer Dragonfly
    USA

Family LIBELLULIDAE

K   *Aethiothemis watuliki*
    Congo

K   *Allorhizucha campioni*
    Sierra Leone

K   *Anectothemis apicalis*
    Zaire

R   *Boninthemis insularis*
    Japan: Ogasawara

E   *Brachythemis fuscopalliata*
    Iraq; Israel; Turkey

I   *Brachythemis liberiensis*
    Guinea-Bissau; Liberia

K   *Congothemis longistyla*
    Zaire

I   *Leucorrhinia albifrons*
        Austria; Belarus?; Estonia?; Finland; France;
        Germany; Kazakhstan?; Latvia?; Lithuania?;
        Netherlands; Norway; Poland; Russia; Sweden;
        Switzerland; Ukraine?

I   *Leucorrhinia caudalis*
        Austria; Belarus?; Belgium; Czech Republic?;
        Estonia?; Finland; France; Germany; Hungary;
        Latvia?; Lithuania?; Netherlands; Norway;
        Poland; Russia; Sweden; Ukraine?;
        Yugoslavia?

E   *Libellula angelina*
    Japan

K   *Libellula jesseana*
    Purple Chaser
    USA

R   *Lyriothemis tricolor*
    Japan: Iriomote

V   *Monardithemis flava*
    Angola; Zambia

V   *Orthetrum rubens*
    South Africa

I   *Palpopleura albifrons*
    Gabon

I   *Trithemis hartwigi*
    Equatorial Guinea

I   *Trithemis nigra*
    São Tomé and Príncipe: Príncipe

V   *Urothemis luciana*
    South Africa

K   *Urothemis thomasi*
    Ethiopia; Oman; Saudi Arabia; Somalia

Order BLATTARIA

Family BLATTIDAE

I   *Aspiduchus cavernicola*
    Tuna Cave Roach
    Puerto Rico

Order MANTODEA

Family MANTIDAE

E   *Apteromantis aptera*
    Spain

Order GRYLLOBLATTARIA

Family GRYLLOBLATTIDAE

V   *Grylloblatta chirurgica*
    Mount St. Helens' Grylloblattid
    USA

Order ORTHOPTERA

Family STENOPELMATIDAE

I   *Ammopelmatus kelsoensis*
    Kelso Jerusalem Cricket
    USA

I   *Ammopelmatus muwu*
    Port Conception Jerusalem Cricket
    USA

V   *Deinacrida carinata*
    Herekopare Island Weta
    New Zealand

V   *Deinacrida fallai*
    Poor Knights Weta
    New Zealand

V   *Deinacrida heteracantha*
    Wetapunga
    New Zealand

V   *Deinacrida parva*
    Kaikoura Weta
    New Zealand

V   *Deinacrida rugosa*
    Stephens Island Weta
    New Zealand

V   *Deinacrida* sp.
    Mahoenui Giant Weta
    New Zealand

I   *Deinacrida tibiospina*
    Nelson Alpine Weta
    New Zealand

E   *Hemiandrus* sp.
    Tusked Weta
    New Zealand

E   *Hemidaina ricta*
    Banks Peninsula Weta
    New Zealand

I   *Stenopelmatus cahuilaensis*
    Coachella Valley Jerusalem Cricket
    USA

I   *Stenopelmatus navajo*
    Navajo Jerusalem Cricket
    USA

Family RHAPHIDOPHORIDAE

I   *Daihinibaenetes arizonensis*
    Arizona Giant Sand Treader Cricket
    USA

I   *Macrobaenetes kelsoensis*
    Kelso Giant Sand Treader Cricket
    USA

I   *Macrobaenetes valgum*
    Coachelia Giant Sand Treader Cricket
    USA

I   *Pristoceuthophilus* sp.
    Samwell Cave Cricket
    USA

I   *Tasmanoplectron isolatum*
    Australia: Tasmania

I   *Utabaenetes tanneri*
    Tanner's Black Camel Cricket
    USA

Family TETTIGONIIDAE

R   *Austrosaga spinifer*
    Australia: Western Australia

V   *Baetica ustulata*
    Spain

I   *Banza nihoae*
    Nihoa Banza Conehead Katydid
    USA: Hawaiian Islands

I   *Belocephalus micanopy*
    Big Pine Key Conehead Katydid
    USA

I   *Belocephalus sleighti*
    Keys Short-winged Conehead Katydid
    USA

I   *Conocephaloides remotus*
    Remote Conehead Katydid
    USA: Hawaiian Islands

R   *Hemisaga elongata*
    Australia: Northern Territory

R   *Hemisaga lucifer*
    Australia: Western Australia

R   *Hemisaga vepreculae*
    Australia: Western Australia

I   *Idiostatus middlekaufi*
    Middlekauf's Shieldback Katydid
    USA

R   *Isophya harzi*
    Carpathian Basin

R   *Ixalodectes flectocercus*
    Australia: Western Australia

R   *Kawanphila pachomai*
    Australia: Western Australia

R   *Metrioptera domogledi*
    Carpathian Basin

R   *Nanodectes bulbicercus*
    Australia: South Australia

I   *Neduba longipennis*
Santa Monica Shieldback Katydid
USA

E   *Onconotus servillei*
Carpathian Basin

R   *Pachysaga munggai*
Australia: Western Australia

R   *Pachysaga strobila*
Australia: Western Australia

R   *Phasmodes jeeba*
Australia: Western Australia

R   *Psacadonotus insulanus*
Australia: Kangaroo Island

R   *Psacadonotus seriatus*
Australia: Western Australia

V   *Saga pedo*
Predatory Bush Cricket
?Armenia; Austria; Azerbaijan?; Bulgaria; China?; Czech Republic; France; Georgia; Germany?; Hungary; Italy; Kazakhstan; Kyrgyzstan; Romania; Russia; Slovakia; Spain; Switzerland; Tajikistan; Turkmenia; Ukraine; Uzbekistan; Yugoslavia

R   *Throscodectes xederoides*
Australia: Western Australia

R   *Throscodectes xiphos*
Australia: Western Australia

R   *Windbalea viride*
Australia: Western Australia

R   *Zaprochilus ninae*
Australia: New South Wales

Family GRYLLOTALPIDAE

I   *Gryllotalpa major*
Prairie Mole Cricket
USA

Family GRYLLIDAE

I   *Caconemobius howarthi*
Howarth's Cave Cricket
USA: Hawaiian Islands

I   *Caconemobius schauinslandi*
Schauinsland's Bush Cricket
USA: Hawaiian Islands

I   *Caconemobius varius*
Kaumana Cave Cricket
USA: Hawaiian Islands

I   *Cycloptilum irregularis*
Keys Scaly Cricket
USA

I   *Leptogryllus deceptor*
Oahu Deceptor Bush Cricket
USA: Hawaiian Islands

I   *Oecanthus laricis*
Laricis Tree Cricket
USA

I   *Thaumatogryllus cavicola*
Volcanoes Cave Cricket
USA: Hawaiian Islands

I   *Thaumatogryllus variegatus*
Kauai Thin-footed Bush Cricket
USA: Hawaiian Islands

Family EUMASTACIDAE

I   *Eumorsea pinaleno*
Pinaleno Monkey Grasshopper
USA

I   *Psychomastatix deserticola*
Desert Monkey Grasshopper
USA

Family ACRIDIDAE

I   *Acrolophitus pulchellus*
Idaho Point-headed Grasshopper
USA

I   *Appalachia arcena*
Michigan Bog Grasshopper
USA

I   *Chloaeltis aspasma*
Siskiyou Chloealtis Grasshopper
USA

R   *Chortippus acroleucus*
Carpathian Basin

R   *Miramella irena*
Carpathian Basin

R   *Odontopodisma montana*
Carpathian Basin

R   *Odontopodisma rubripes*
Hungary

R   *Podismopsis transsylvanica*
Carpathian Basin

I   *Schayera baiulus*
(*Calliptamus baiulus*)
Australia: Tasmania

I   *Spharagemon superbum*
USA

R   *Stenobothrodes eurasius*
Carpathian Basin

R   *Zubovskia banatica*
Carpathian Basin

Family TETRIGIDAE

R   *Bienkotetrix transsylvanicus*
Carpathian Basin

I   *Tetrix sierrana*
Sierra Pygmy Grasshopper
USA

I   *Tettigidea empedonepia*
Torreya Pygmy Grasshopper
USA

Order DERMAPTERA

Family LABIDURIDAE

E   *Labidura herculeana*
Saint Helena Earwig
Saint Helena

Order PLECOPTERA

Family NEMOURIDAE

I   *Lednia tumana*
Meltwater Stonefly
USA

I   *Nemours wahkeena*
Wahkeena Falls Flightless Stonefly
USA

Family NOTONEMOURIDAE

I   *Kimminsoperla biloba*
Australia: Tasmania

I   *Kimminsoperla williamsi*
Australia: Tasmania

Family CAPNIIDAE

I   *Capnia lacustra*
Lake Tahoe Benthic Stonefly
USA

Family LEUCTRIDAE

I   *Leuctra szczytkoi*
Schoolhouse Springs Stonefly
USA

Family TAENIOPTERYGIDAE

I   *Taeniopteryx starki*
Leon River Stonefly
USA

Family PERLIDAE

I   *Beloneuria georgiana*
Georgia Stonefly
USA

I   *Beloneuria jamesae*
Cheaha Stonefly
USA

I   *Hansonoperla appalachia*
Hanson's Appalachian Stonefly
USA

Family PELTOPERLIDAE

I   *Soliperla fenderi*
Fender's Stonefly
USA

Family EUSTHENIIDAE

E   *Eusthenia nothofagi*
Otway Stonefly
Australia

I   *Eusthenia reticulata*
Australia: Tasmania

Family GRIPOPTERYGIDAE

R   *Leptoperla cacuminis*
Mount Kosciusko Wingless Stonefly
Australia

R   *Riekoperla darlingtoni*
Mount Donna Buang Wingless Stonefly
Australia

Order ZORAPTERA

Family ZOROTYPIDAE

I   *Zorotypus swezeyi*
Swezey's Zoroapteran
USA: Hawaiian Islands

Order ANOPLURA

Family HAEMATOPINIDAE

E   *Haematopinus oliveri*
Pygmy Hog Sucking Louse
India

Order HEMIPTERA

Family BELOSTOMATIDAE

I   *Belostoma saratogae*
Saratoga Springs Bug
USA

Family NAUCORIDAE

E **Ambrysus amargosus**
   Ash Meadows Bug
   USA

I **Pelocoris shoshone**
   Amargosa Bug
   USA

Family MESOVELIIDAE

I **Cavaticovelia aaa**
   Aaa Water Treader Bug
   USA

Family MACROVELIIDAE

I **Oravelia pege**
   Dry Creek Cliff Strider Bug
   USA

Family MIRIDAE

I **Cyrtopeltis phyllostegiae**
   Mirid Leaf Bug
   USA: Hawaiian Islands

I **Kalania hawaiiensis**
   Lanai Leaf Bug
   USA: Hawaiian Islands

Family REDUVIIDAE

I **Empicoris pulchrus**
   Pulchrus Thread Bug
   USA: Hawaiian Islands

I **Nesidiolestes ana**
   Ana Wingless Thread Bug
   USA: Hawaiian Islands

I **Nesidiolestes insularis**
   Mount Tantalus Wingless Thread Bug
   USA: Hawaiian Islands

I **Nesidiolestes roberti**
   Robert's Wingless Thread Bug
   USA: Hawaiian Islands

I **Nesidiolestes selium**
   Selium Wingless Thread Bug
   USA: Hawaiian Islands

I **Siacella smithi**
   Smith's Reduviid Bug
   USA: Hawaiian Islands

Family LYGAEIDAE

I **Metrarga obscura**
   Mauna Loa Seed Bug
   USA: Hawaiian Islands

I **Neseis alternatus**
   Kauai Band-legged Seed Bug
   USA: Hawaiian Islands

I **Neseis haleakalae**
   Mount Haleakala Seed Bug
   USA: Hawaiian Islands

I **Nesocryptias villosa**
   Villosan Flightless Seed Bug
   USA: Hawaiian Islands

I **Nysius frigatensis**
   French Frigate Shoal Seed Bug
   USA: Hawaiian Islands

I **Nysius neckerensis**
   Necker Goosefoot Seed Bug
   USA: Hawaiian Islands

I **Nysius nihoae**
   Nihoae Seed Bug
   USA: Hawaiian Islands

I **Nysius sulfusus**
   Necker Bunchgrass Seed Bug
   USA: Hawaiian Islands

I **Oceanides bryani**
   Bryan's Seed Bug
   USA: Hawaiian Islands

I **Oceanides perkensi**
   Perkin's Oceanides Seed Bug
   USA: Hawaiian Islands

I **Oceanides rugosiceps**
   Rough-headed Seed Bug
   USA: Hawaiian Islands

Family RHOPALIDAE

I **Ithamar annectans**
   Annectans Bug
   USA: Hawaiian Islands

I **Ithamar hawaiiensis**
   Hawaiian Bug
   USA: Hawaiian Islands

Order HOMOPTERA

Family CIXIIDAE

I **Oliarus consimilis**
   Kauai Parti-coloured Planthopper
   USA: Hawaiian Islands

I **Oliarus discrepans**
   Wild Cotton Planthopper
   USA: Hawaiian Islands

I **Oliarus lanaiensis**
   Lanai Planthopper
   USA: Hawaiian Islands

I **Oliarus lihue**
Lihue Planthopper
USA: Hawaiian Islands

I **Oliarus myoporicola**
Barber's Point Planthopper
USA: Hawaiian Islands

Family DELPHACIDAE

I **Nesorestias filicicola**
Mt Tantalus Shortwing Fern Planthopper
USA: Hawaiian Islands

I **Nesosydne acuta**
Iao Valley Planthopper
USA: Hawaiian Islands

I **Nesosydne bridwelli**
Bridewell's Planthopper
USA: Hawaiian Islands

I **Nesosydne cyrtandrae**
Nahiku Planthopper
USA: Hawaiian Islands

I **Nesosydne cyrtandricola**
Glenwood Planthopper
USA: Hawaiian Islands

I **Nesosydne kuschei**
Kusche's Planthopper
USA: Hawaiian Islands

I **Nesosydne leahi**
Diamond Head Planthopper
USA: Hawaiian Islands

I **Nesosydne longipes**
Long-footed Planthopper
USA: Hawaiian Islands

I **Nesosydne sulcata**
Keanae Planthopper
USA: Hawaiian Islands

Family CICADIDAE

V **Magicicada cassini**
Cassini Periodical Cicada
USA

V **Magicicada septendecim**
Decim Periodical Cicada
Canada

V **Magicicada septendecula**
Decula Periodical Cicada
USA

I **Maoricicada myersi**
Myers' Cicada
New Zealand

Family TETTIGARCTIDAE

I **Tettigarcta tormentosa**
Australia: Tasmania

Family CICADELLIDAE

I **Felexamia rubranura**
Red-veined Prairie Leafhopper
USA

Family APHIDIDAE

I **Ceriferella leucopogonis**
Australia: Tasmania

Order NEUROPTERA

Family ITHONIDAE

I **Oliarces clara**
USA: California, Hawaiian Islands

Family HEMEROBIIDAE

I **Nesothauma halakalae**
Haleakala Spongillafly
USA: Hawaiian Islands

I **Pseudopsectra cookeorum**
Cooke's Spongillafly
USA: Hawaiian Islands

I **Pseudopsectra lobipennis**
Lobe-wing Spongillafly
USA: Hawaiian Islands

I **Pseudopsectra swezeyi**
Swezey's Spongillafly
USA: Hawaiian Islands

I **Pseudopsectra usingeri**
Usinger's Spongillafly
USA: Hawaiian Islands

Family MYRMELEONTIDAE

I **Eidoleon perjurus**
Molokai Antlion
USA: Hawaiian Islands

Order COLEOPTERA

Family CARABIDAE

I **Agonum belleri**
Beller's Ground Beetle
USA

E **Aplothorax burchelli**
Saint Helena

V **Carabus intricatus**
Blue Ground Beetle
Albania; Belgium; Bulgaria; Czech Republic;
Denmark; France; Germany; Greece; Hungary;
Italy: including Sicily; Netherlands; Poland;
Romania; Slovakia?; Sweden; Switzerland;
United Kingdom; Yugoslavia

E **Carabus olympiae**
France; Italy

V **Elaphrus viridis**
Delta Green Ground Beetle
USA

V **Mormolyce phyllodes**
Ghost Walker Beetle
Malaysia

E **Rhadine persephone**
Tooth Cave Ground Beetle
USA

Family CICINDELIDAE

I **Cicindela arenicola**
Idaho Dunes Tiger Beetle
USA

I **Cicindela cazieri**
Cazier's Tiger Beetle
USA

E **Cicindela columbica**
Columbia River Tiger Beetle
USA

I **Cicindela marginata**
Tiger Beetle
USA

I **Cicindela marginipennis**
Cobblestone Tiger Beetle
USA

I **Cicindela puritana**
Puritan Tiger Beetle
USA

Family HALIPLIDAE

I **Brychius hungerfordi**
Hungerford's Crawling Water Beetle
USA

I **Haliplus nitens**
Disjunct Crawling Water Beetle
USA

Family DYTISCIDAE

I **Acilius duvergeri**
Algeria; Italy; Morocco; Portugal; Spain

I **Agabus clypealis**
Denmark; Germany; Poland; Russia; Sweden

E **Agabus discicollis**
Ethiopia

E **Agabus hozgargantae**
Spain: Andalucia

I **Agabus rumppi**
Death Valley Agabus Diving Beetle
USA

I **Aglymbus bimaculatus**
Brazil

I **Aglymbus bromeliarum**
Trinidad and Tobago

I **Colymbetes piceus**
Egypt; Iran; Iraq; Saudi Arabia

E **Deronectes aljibensis**
Spain: Andalucia

I **Deronectes costipennis**
Portugal; Spain

I **Deronectes depressicollis**
Spain: Andalucia

I **Deronectes ferrugineus**
Portugal

I **Deronectes wewalkai**
Spain

I **Desmopachria conchramis**
Fig Seed Diving Beetle
USA

R **Dytiscus latissimus**
Denmark; Finland; Germany; Poland; Siberia;
Sweden

R **Graptodytes delectus**
Spain: Canary Islands

I **Haideoporus texanus**
Texas Cave Beetle
USA

I **Hydaticus decorus**
Egypt; Saudi Arabia; Sudan; Yemen

I **Hydaticus okalehubyi**
Indonesia: Irian Jaya

I **Hydroporus elusivus**
Elusive Diving Beetle
USA

I **Hydroporus folkertsi**
Folkert's Diving Beetle
USA

I **Hydroporus hirsutus**
Woolly Diving Beetle
USA

I **Hydroporus humilis**
Egypt: Sinai

I **Hydroporus leechi**
Leech's Skyline Diving Beetle
USA

I **Hydroporus mariannae**
Israel

I **Hydroporus oasis**
Egypt

I **Hydroporus productus**
Algeria; Spain

I **Hydroporus spangleri**
Spangler's Diving Beetle
USA

I **Hydroporus sulphurius**
Sulphur Springs Diving beetle
USA

I **Hydroporus utahensis**
Utah Diving Beetle
USA

E **Hydrotarsus compunctus**
Spain: Canary Islands

V **Hydrotarsus pilosus**
Spain: Canary Islands

I **Hygrotus curvipes**
Curved-foot Diving Beetle
USA

I **Hygrotus diversipes**
Narrow-foot Diving Beetle
USA

I **Hygrotus fontinalis**
Travertine Band-thigh Diving Beetle
USA

I **Hygrotus sylvanus**
Sylvan Diving Beetle
USA

I **Hyphydrus dani**
Indonesia: Irian Jaya

I **Lacconectus birmanicus**
Myanmar

I **Lacconectus corayi**
Singapore

I **Lacconectus heinertzi**
Thailand

I **Lacconectus javanicus**
Indonesia: Java

I **Lacconectus laccophiloides**
Philippines

I **Lacconectus minutus**
Indonesia: Sumatra

I **Lacconectus muluensis**
Malaysia: Sarawak

I **Lacconectus oceanicus**
Indonesia: Mentawai Islands

I **Lacconectus pulcher**
Malaysia: Sabah

I **Lacconectus punctatus**
Viet Nam

I **Lacconectus punctipennis**
Indonesia: Bali, Java

I **Lacconectus ritsemae**
Indonesia: Java

I **Lacconectus sabahensis**
Malaysia: Sabah

E **Meladema imbricata**
Spain: Canary Islands

I **Meladema lanio**
Portugal: Madeira

I **Platynectes buruensis**
Indonesia: Buru

I **Platynectes decastigma**
Indonesia: Irian Jaya, Moluccas; Philippines?

I **Pleurodytes dineutoides**
Indonesia; Malaysia

R **Potamonectes canariensis**
Spain: Canary Islands

R **Potamonectes cazorlensis**
Spain: Andalucia

I **Potamonectes insignis**
Egypt; Saudi Arabia

I **Potamonectes lanceolatus**
Egypt; Saudi Arabia

I **Potamonectes walkeri**
Egypt

I **Rhantus crypticus**
Ecuador

E **Rhantus limbatus**
Argentina; Brazil; Uruguay

R **Rhithrodytes agnus**
Portugal

I **Sandracottus baeri**
Malaysia: Sabah; Philippines: Balabac

I **Sandracottus bizonatus**
Malaysia: Sabah

I **Sandracottus chevrolati**
Indonesia: Sumbawa, Timor

I **Sandracottus maculatus**
Indonesia: Java; Malaysia: Penang

I **Sandracottus rotundatus**
Indonesia: Sulawesi

Family GYRINIDAE

I **Spanglerogyrus albiventris**
Red Hills Unique Whirligig Beetle
USA

Family HYDRAENIDAE

I **Gymnochthebius maureenae**
Maureen's Minute Moss Beetle
USA

I **Hydraena maureenae**
Maureen's Moss Beetle
USA

I **Limnebius aridus**
Animas Minute Moss Beetle
USA

I **Limnebius texanus**
Texas Minute Moss Beetle
USA

I **Limnebius utahensis**
Utah Minute Moss Beetle
USA

I **Ochthebius crassalus**
Wing-shoulder Minute Moss Beetle
USA

I **Ochthebius putnamensis**
Indiana Minute Moss Beetle
USA

I **Ochthebius recticulus**
Wilbur Springs Minute Moss Beetle
USA

Family LEIODIDAE

I **Glacicavicola bathysciodes**
Blind Cave Beetle
USA

Family SILPHIDAE

E **Nicrophorus americanus**
American Burying Beetle
Canada; USA

Family HYDROPHILIDAE

I **Chaetarthria leechi**
Leech's Water Scavenger Beetle
USA

I **Chaetarthria utahensis**
Utah Water Scavenger Beetle
USA

I **Cymbiodyta arizonica**
Arizona Water Scavenger Beetle
USA

I **Hydrochara rickseckeri**
Ricksecker's Water Scavenger Beetle
USA

I **Paracymus seclusus**
Seclusive Water Scavenger Beetle
USA

Family LUCANIDAE

E **Apterocychus honoluluensis**
Kauai Flightless Stag Beetle
USA: Hawaiian Islands

V **Dorcus auriculatus**
New Zealand

V **Dorcus ithaginis**
New Zealand

Family TROGIDAE

V **Trox howelli**
Caracara Commensal Scarab Beetle
USA

Family GEOTRUPIDAE

V **Typhaeus hiostius**
Italy: Sardinia

Family SCARABAEIDAE

I **Aegialia concinna**
Ciervo Scarab Beetle
USA

I **Aegialia crescenta**
Cresent Dune Scarab Beetle
USA

I **Aegialia haroyi**
Hardy's Scarab Beetle
USA

I   *Aegialia magnifica*
Large Scarab Beetle
USA

I   *Anomala exigua*
Exiguous Scarab Beetle
USA

I   *Anomala eximia*
Archbold Scarab Beetle
USA

I   *Anomala tibialis*
Tibial Scarab Beetle
USA

I   *Aphodius fordi*
Ford's Beetle
USA

I   *Aphodius troglodytes*
Tortoise Commensal Scarab Beetle
USA

V   *Ataenius superficialis*
Big Pine Key Dung Beetle
USA

E   *Ataenius woodruffi*
Woodruff's Dung Beetle
USA

I   *Copris gopheri*
Tortoise Commensal Scarab Beetle
USA

I   *Cyclocephala miamiensis*
Miami Roundhead Scarab Beetle
USA

I   *Glaresis arenata*
Kelso Dune Scarab Beetle
USA

I   *Gronocarus multispinosus*
Spiny Florida Sandhill Scarab Beetle
USA

I   *Lichnanthe albopilosa*
White Sand Bear Scarab Beetle
USA

I   *Lichnanthe ursina*
Pacific Sand Bear Scarab Beetle
USA

I   *Mycotrupes pedester*
Scrub Island Burrowing Scarab Beetle
USA

I   *Onthophagus polyphemi*
Tortoise Commensal Scarab Beetle
USA

K   *Oryctes chevrolati*
Réunion

E   *Osmoderma eremita*
Hermit Beetle
Austria; Belarus?; Belgium; Czech Republic;
Denmark; Estonia?; Finland; France; Germany;
Greece; Hungary; Italy; Latvia; Liechtenstein;
Lithuania?; Moldova?; Netherlands; Norway;
Poland; Russia; Slovakia; Spain; Sweden;
Switzerland; Ukraine; Yugoslavia

I   *Peltotrupes youngi*
Ocala Burrowing Scarab Beetle
USA

I   *Polylamina pubescens*
Woody Gulf Dune Scarab Beetle
USA

I   *Polyphylla anteronivea*
Saline Valley Snow-front Scarab
USA

I   *Polyphylla avittata*
Spotted Warner Valley Dunes Scarab
USA

I   *Polyphylla barbata*
Barbate Scarab Beetle
USA

I   *Polyphylla nubila*
Atascodera Scarab Beetle
USA

V   *Prodontria lewisi*
Cromwell Chafer
New Zealand

I   *Pseudocotalpa giulianii*
Giuliani's Dune Scarab Beetle
USA

I   *Serica frosti*
Frost's Spring Scarab Beetle
USA

I   *Serica tantula*
Tantula Scarab Beetle
USA

I   *Trigonopelastes floridana*
Scrub Palmetto Flower Scarab Beetle
USA

Family BUPRESTIDAE

E   *Buprestis splendens*
Goldstreifiger
Albania; Austria; Belarus?; Denmark?;
Finland; Greece; Poland?; Russia?; Spain;
Sweden?; Yugoslavia?

Family ELMINTHIDAE

I **Atractelmis wawona**
Wawawona Riffle Beetle
USA

I **Cylloepus parkeri**
Parker's Riffle Beetle
USA

I **Dubiraphia brunnescens**
Brownish Riffle Beetle
USA

I **Dubiraphia giulianii**
Giuliani's Riffle Beetle
USA

I **Dubiraphia parva**
Little Riffle Beetle
USA

I **Dubiraphia robusta**
Robust Riffle Beetle
USA

I **Heterelmis stephani**
Stephan's Riffle Beetle
USA

I **Microcylloepus browni**
Brown's Riffle Beetle
USA

I **Optioservus browni**
Brown's Riffle Beetle
USA

I **Optioservus canus**
Pinnacles Riffle Beetle
USA

I **Optioservus phaeus**
Scott Riffle Beetle
USA

I **Stenelmis douglasensis**
Douglas Riffle Beetle
USA

I **Stenelmis gammoni**
Gammon's Riffle Beetle
USA

I **Zaitzeva thermae**
Warm Spring Riffle Beetle
USA

Family PSEPHENIDAE

I **Acneus beeri**
Beer's False Water Penny Beetle
USA

I **Acneus burnelli**
Burnell's False Water Penny Beetle
USA

I **Alabamaubria starki**
Stark's False Water Penny Beetle
USA

I **Dicranopselaphus variegatus**
Variegated False Water Penny Beetle
USA

I **Psephenus arizonensis**
Arizona Water Penny Beetle
USA

I **Psephenus montanus**
White Mountains Water Penny Beetle
USA

Family ELATERIDAE

V **Amychus candezei**
Chatham Island Amychus
New Zealand: Chatham Island

V **Amychus granulatus**
Cook Strait Amychus
New Zealand

I **Eanus hatchi**
Hatch's Click Beetle
Canada; USA

Family EUCNEMIDAE

I **Paleoxenus dohmi**
Dohrn's Elegant Eucnemid Beetle
USA

Family LAMPYRIDAE

I **Micronaspis floridana**
Florida Intertidal Firefly
USA

Family ANOBIIDAE

I **Holcobius pikoensis**
Piko Anobiid Beetle
USA: Hawaiian Islands

Family CUCUJIDAE

E **Cucujus cinnaberinus**
Austria; Czech Republic?; Estonia?; Finland;
Germany; Hungary; Latvia?; Lithuania;
Norway; Poland; Romania; Russia; Slovakia;
Sweden; Yugoslavia

Family TENEBRIONIDAE

I **Coelus globosus**
Globose Dune Beetle
Mexico; USA

I   *Coelus gracilis*
San Joaquin Dune Beetle
USA

R   *Polposipus herculeanus*
Frigate Island Giant Tenebrionid Beetle
Seychelles

Family MELOIDAE

I   *Lytta hoppingi*
Hopping's Blister Beetle
USA

I   *Lytta inseperata*
Mojave Desert Blister Beetle
USA

I   *Lytta mirifica*
Anthony Blister Beetle
Mexico; USA

I   *Lytta moesta*
Moestan Blister Beetle
USA

I   *Lytta molesta*
Molestan Blister Beetle
USA

I   *Lytta morrisoni*
Morrison's Blister Beetle
USA

Family ANTHICIDAE

I   *Anthicus antiochensis*
Antioch Dunes Beetle
USA

I   *Anthicus sacramento*
Sacramento Beetle
USA

Family CERAMBYCIDAE

E   *Aeschrithmysus dubautianus*
USA: Hawaiian Islands

E   *Aeschrithmysus swezeyi*
USA: Hawaiian Islands

E   *Aeschrithmysus terryi*
USA: Hawaiian Islands

E   *Cerambyx cerdo*
Cerambyx Longicorn
Algeria; Armenia?; Austria; Azerbaijan?;
Czech Republic; France; Germany; Georgia?;
Hungary; Iran; Moldova?; Morocco; Poland;
Spain; Sweden; Switzerland; Tunisia; Turkey?;
Ukraine; United Kingdom?

I   *Dryobius sexnotatus*
Six-banded Longhorn Beetle
USA

K   *Macrodontia cervicornis*
Brazil; Peru

E   *Morimus funereus*
?Belgium; Czech Republic?; Germany?;
Hungary; Moldova; Romania; Slovakia?;
Ukraine; Yugoslavia

I   *Necydalis rudei*
Rude's Longhorn Beetle
USA: Hawaiian Islands

E   *Nesithmysus bridwelli*
USA: Hawaiian Islands

E   *Nesithmysus frobesi*
USA: Hawaiian Islands

E   *Nesithmysus haasi*
USA: Hawaiian Islands

E   *Nesithmysus swezeyi*
USA: Hawaiian Islands

E   *Rosalia alpina*
Rosalia Longicorn
Algeria; Armenia; Austria; Azerbaijan;
Belgium?; Bulgaria; Czech Republic;
Denmark?; France; Georgia; Germany; Greece;
Hungary; Italy; Iran?; Israel; Jordan?;
Lebanon?; Liechtenstein; Morocco;
Netherlands; Poland; Portugal; Romania;
Russia?; Spain; Sweden; Switzerland; Syria;
Tunisia; Ukraine; Yugoslavia

Family CHRYSOMELIDAE

I   *Donacia idola*
Bog Idol Leaf Beetle
USA

Family CURCULIONIDAE

V   *Anagotus fairburni*
Flax Weevil
New Zealand

V   *Anagotus stephenensis*
Stephen's Island Weevil
New Zealand

V   *Anagotus turbotti*
Turbott's Weevil
New Zealand

E   *Deinocossonus nesiotes*
Oahu Nesiotes Weevil
USA: Hawaiian Islands

I **Dysticheus rotundicollis**
Antioch Dune Weevil
USA

V **Gymnopholus lichenifer**
Lichen Weevil
Papua New Guinea

V **Hadramphus spinipennis**
Coxella Weevil
New Zealand: Chatham Is

V **Hadramphus stilbocarpae**
Knobbled Weevil
New Zealand

E **Heteramphus filicum**
USA: Hawaiian Islands

V **Heterexis seticostatus**
New Zealand

V **Karocolens pittospori**
New Zealand

V **Lyperobius huttoni**
Wellington Speargrass Weevil
New Zealand

V **Megacolabus sculpturatus**
New Zealand

R **Microcryptorhynchus orientissimus**
Pitcairn Islands: Henderson Island

I **Miloderes nelsoni**
Nelson's Weevil
USA

I **Miloderes rulieni**
Rulien's Weevil
USA

I **Nesotocus giffordi**
Gifford's Weevil
USA: Hawaiian Islands

I **Nesotocus kauaiensis**
Kauai Weevil
USA: Hawaiian Islands

I **Nesotocus munroi**
Munro's Weevil
USA: Hawaiian Islands

E **Nothaldonis peaci**
New Zealand

V **Oclandius laeviusculus**
New Zealand

I **Onchobarus langei**
Lange's El Segundo Dune Weevil
USA

I **Pentarthrum obscura**
Obscure Weevil
USA: Hawaiian Islands

E **Pentarthrum pritchardias**
USA: Hawaiian Islands

R **Rhyncogonus hendersoni**
Pitcairn Islands: Henderson Island

I **Stenotrupis pritchardiae**
Nihoa Weevil
USA: Hawaiian Islands

I **Trigonoscuta brunnotesselata**
Brown-tassel Weevil
USA

I **Trigonoscuta doyeni**
Doyen's Dune Weevil
USA

V **Unas piceus**
New Zealand

Order MECOPTERA

Family APTEROPANORPIDAE

I **Apteropanorpa tasmanica**
Australia: Tasmania

Order DIPTERA

Family PSYCHODIDAE

I **Nemapalpus nearcticus**
Sugarfoot Moth fly
USA

Family MYCETOPHILIDAE

I **Arachnocampa tasmaniensis**
Australia: Tasmania

Family BLEPHAROCERIDAE

E **Edwardsina gigantea**
Giant Torrent Midge
Australia

E **Edwardsina tasmaniensis**
Tasmanian Torrent Midge
Australia: Tasmania

Family TABANIDAE

I **Apatalestea rossi**
Ross's Apatalestes Tabanid Fly
USA

I **Asaphomyia floridensis**
Florida Asaphomyian Tabanid Fly
USA

I **Asaphomyia texanus**
Texas Asaphomyian Tabanid Fly
USA

E **Brennania belkini**
Belkin's Dune Tabanid Fly
Mexico; USA

I **Merycomyia brunnea**
Brown Merycomyian Tabanid Fly
USA

Family ACROCERIDAE

I **Eulonchus marialiciae**
Mary Alice's Small-headed Fly
USA

Family ASILIDAE

I **Cophura hurdi**
Antioch Robberfly
USA

I **Efferia antiochi**
Antioch Robberfly
USA

I **Metapogon hurdi**
Hurd's Robberfly
USA

Family APIOCERIDAE

I **Raphiomydas triochilus**
Valley Mydas Fly
USA

Family EMPIDIDAE

I **Chersodromia hawaiiensis**
Hawaiian Dance Fly
USA: Hawaiian Islands

Family SYRPHIDAE

I **Mixogaster delongi**
Delong's Flower Fly
USA

Family ASTEIIDAE

I **Bryania bipunctata**
Nihoa Two-spotted Asterid Fly
USA: Hawaiian Islands

Family EPHYDRIDAE

I **Paracoenia calida**
Wilber Springs Shore Fly
USA

Order TRICHOPTERA

Family RHYACOPHILIDAE

I **Rhyacophila alexandra**
Alexander's Caddisfly
USA

I **Rhyacophila colonus**
Obrien Caddisfly
USA

I **Rhyacophila fenderi**
Fender's Caddisfly
USA

I **Rhyacophila haddocki**
Haddock's Caddisfly
USA

I **Rhyacophila lineata**
Castle Crags Caddisfly
USA

I **Rhyacophila mosana**
Bilobed Caddisfly
USA

I **Rhyacophila spinata**
Spiny Caddisfly
USA

I **Rhyacophila unipunctata**
One-spot Caddisfly
USA

Family GLOSSOSOMATIDAE

I **Agapetus artesus**
Artesian Caddisfly
USA

I **Agapetus denningi**
Denning's Caddisfly
USA

I **Agapetus medicus**
Arkansas Caddisfly
USA

I **Protoptila arca**
San Marcos Caddisfly
USA

Family HYDROPTILIDAE

I **Hydroptila decia**
Knoxville Micro Caddisfly
USA

I   *Neotrichia kitae*
    Kite's Micro Caddisfly
    USA

I   *Ochrotrichia alsea*
    Alsea Micro Caddisfly
    USA

I   *Ochrotrichia contorta*
    Contorted Micro Caddisfly
    USA

I   *Ochrotrichia phenosa*
    Deschutes Micro Caddisfly
    USA

I   *Ochrotrichia provosti*
    Provost's Micro Caddisfly
    USA

I   *Ochrotrichia vertreesi*
    Vertree's Micro Caddisfly
    USA

I   *Oxyethira florida*
    Florida Micro Caddisfly
    USA

Family PHILOPOTAMIDAE

I   *Dolophilodes oregona*
    Oregon Caddisfly
    USA

Family STENOPSYCHIDAE

I   *Stenopsychodes lineata*
    Australia: Tasmania

Family POLYCENTROPODIDAE

I   *Tasmanoplegas spilota*
    Australia: Tasmania

Family LIMNEPHILIDAE

I   *Apatania tavala*
    Cascades Caddisfly
    USA

I   *Archaeophylax vernalis*
    Australia: Tasmania

I   *Cryptochia excella*
    Kings Canyon Caddisfly
    USA

I   *Cryptochia neosa*
    Blue Mountains Caddisfly
    USA

I   *Ecclisomyia bilera*
    King's Creek Caddisfly
    USA

I   *Farula davisi*
    Green Springs Mountain Caddisfly
    USA

I   *Farula jewetti*
    Mount Hood Caddisfly
    USA

I   *Farula reaperi*
    Tombstone Prairie Caddisfly
    USA

I   *Glyphopsyche missouri*
    Missouri Caddisfly
    USA

I   *Limnephilus alconura*
    Kiamath Caddisfly
    USA

I   *Limnephilus atercus*
    Fort Dick Caddisfly
    USA

I   *Neothramma andersoni*
    Colombian Gorge Caddisfly
    USA

I   *Oligophlebodes mostbento*
    Tombstone Prairie Oligophlebodes
    USA

I   *Philocasca oron*
    Clatsop Caddisfly
    USA

Family LEPIDOSTOMATIDAE

I   *Lepidostoma fischeri*
    Fischer's Caddisfly
    USA

I   *Lepidostoma goedeni*
    Goeden's Caddisfly
    USA

Family KOKIRIIDAE

I   *Taskiria mccubbini*
    Australia: Tasmania

I   *Taskropsyche lacustris*
    Australia: Tasmania

Family PLECTROTARSIDAE

I   *Nanoplectrus truchnasi*
    Australia: Tasmania

Family SERICOSTOMATIDAE

I   *Agarodes ziczac*
    Zigzag Blackwater Caddisfly
    USA

Family ODONTOCERIDAE

I   *Psilotreta hansoni*
    USA

Family PHILORHEITHRIDAE

I   *Ramiheithrus kocinus*
    Australia: Tasmania

Family LEPTOCERIDAE

I   *Ceraclea floridana*
    Florida Longhorn Caddisfly
    USA

I   *Ceraclea vertreesi*
    Vertree's Caddisfly
    USA

I   *Oecetis parva*
    Little Longhorn Caddisfly
    USA

I   *Westriplectes pedderensis*
    Australia: Tasmania

Order LEPIDOPTERA

Family HEPIALIDAE

V   *Leto venus*
    Silver Spotted Ghost Moth
    South Africa

V   *Zelotypia stacyi*
    Bent Wing Swift Moth
    Australia

Family GRACILLARIIDAE

I   *Petrochroa neckerensis*
    Necker Leaf-miner Moth
    USA: Hawaiian Islands

E   *Phildoria wilkesiella*
    USA: Hawaiian Islands

Family GELECHIIDAE

V   *Kiwaia jeanae*
    New Zealand

Family CARPOSINIDAE

I   *Heterocrossa viridis*
    Green Carposinid Moth
    USA: Hawaiian Islands

Family SESIIDAE

I   *Synanthedon castaneae*
    Chestnut Clearwing Moth
    USA

Family TORTRICIDAE

R   *Grapholitha edwardsiana*
    San Francisco Tree Lupine
    USA

I   *Spheterista oheoheana*
    Ohe Ohe Leaf-roller Moth
    USA: Hawaiian Islands

I   *Spheterista pterotropiana*
    Green-Banded Ohe Ohe Leaf-roller Moth
    USA: Hawaiian Islands

I   *Spheterista reynoldsiana*
    Wallupe Leaf-Roller Moth
    USA: Hawaiian Islands

Family COCHYLIDAE

I   *Carolella busckana*
    Busk's Gall Moth
    USA

Family HESPERIIDAE

R   *Dalla octomaculata*
    Eight-Spotted Skipper
    Costa Rica; Panama

R   *Epargyreus antaeus*
    Jamaica

R   *Epargyreus spana*
    Dominican Republic

K   *Euscheman rafflesia*
    Australia

E   *Hesperia dacotae*
    Dakota Skipper
    Canada; USA

V   *Kedestes chaca*
    South Africa

V   *Metisella syrinx*
    Bamboo Sylph
    South Africa

V   *Panoquina errans*
    Wandering Skipper
    Mexico; USA

I   *Problema bulenta*
    Rare Skipper
    USA

I   *Syrichtus cribrellum*
    Spinose Skipper
    Georgia; Moldavia?; Romania; Russia; Ukraine

K *Syrichtus tessellum*
Tessellated Skipper
?Armenia; Azerbaijan?; Bulgaria; Georgia?;
Greece; Iran; Romania?; Russia; Turkey;
Ukraine; Yugoslavia

V *Tsitana dicksoni*
Dickson's Sylph
South Africa

Family MEGATHYMIDAE

I *Stallingsia maculosus*
Manfreda Giant Skipper
Mexico; USA

Family PAPILIONIDAE

R *Archon apollinaris*
Armenia; Bulgaria; Greece; Iran; Iraq; Israel;
Jordan; Lebanon; Romania; Syria; Turkey;
Turkmenistan

I *Atrophaneura atropos*
Philippines: Palawan

V *Atrophaneura jophon*
Sri Lankan Rose
Sri Lanka

R *Atrophaneura luchti*
Indonesia: Java

K *Atrophaneura palu*
Indonesia: Sulawesi

V *Atrophaneura schadenbergi*
Philippines: Luzon

R *Baronia brevicornis*
Short-horned Baronia
Mexico

V *Battus zetides*
Zetides Swallowtail
Dominican Republic; Haiti

K *Bhutanitis ludlowi*
Ludlow's Bhutan Swallowtail
Bhutan: Tashiyangsi Valley

R *Bhutanitis mansfieldi*
Mansfield's Three-tailed Swallowtail
China: Sichuan, Yunnan

R *Bhutanitis thaidina*
Chinese Three-tailed Swallowtail
China

V *Eurytides iphitas*
Yellow Kite Swallowtail
Brazil

V *Eurytides marcellinus*
Jamaican Kite
Jamaica

K *Graphium aurivilliusi*
Zaire

K *Graphium epaminondas*
Andamans Swordtail
India: Andaman Islands

R *Graphium idaeoides*
Philippines

V *Graphium levassori*
Comoro Islands

R *Graphium meeki*
Meek's Graphium
Papua New Guinea: Bougainville; Solomon
Islands

I *Graphium megaera*
Philippines: Palawan

R *Graphium mendana*
Papua New Guinea: Bougainville; Solomon
Islands

I *Graphium procles*
Malaysia: Sabah

V *Graphium sandawanum*
Philippines: Mindanao

R *Graphium stresemanni*
Indonesia: Moluccas

K *Luehdorfia chinensis*
Chinese Luehdorfia
China

I *Luehdorfia japonica*
Japanese Luehdorfia
Japan; Taiwan

I *Ornithoptera aesacus*
Indonesia: Obi

E *Ornithoptera alexandrae*
Queen Alexandra's Birdwing
Papua New Guinea: Popondetta in Northern
Province of New Guinea

I *Ornithoptera chimaera*
Chimaera Birdwing
Indonesia: Irian Jaya; Papua New Guinea: New
Guinea

V *Ornithoptera croesus*
Indonesia: Moluccas

V *Ornithoptera meridionalis*
Indonesia: Irian Jaya; Papua New Guinea: New
Guinea

I   *Ornithoptera paradisea*
Paradise Birdwing
     Indonesia: Irian Jaya; Papua New Guinea: New
Guinea

I   *Ornithoptera rothschildi*
Rothschild's Birdwing
     Indonesia: Arfak Mountains in Irian Jaya

K   *Ornithoptera tithonus*
     Indonesia: Irian Jaya

R   *Papilio acheron*
     Malaysia: Sabah, Sarawak

R   *Papilio antimachus*
African Giant Swallowtail
     Angola; Benin?; Cameroon; Central African
Republic; Congo; Côte d'Ivoire; Equatorial
Guinea; Gabon; Ghana; Guinea; Liberia;
Nigeria; Rwanda; Sierra Leone; Togo?;
Uganda; Zaire

I   *Papilio aristophontes*
     Comoro Islands

I   *Papilio aristor*
Scarce Haitian Swallowtail
     Dominican Republic; Haiti

V   *Papilio benguetanus*
     Philippines: Luzon

I   *Papilio caiguanabus*
Poey's Black Swallowtail
     Cuba

V   *Papilio carolinensis*
     Philippines: Mindanao

E   *Papilio chikae*
     Philippines: Luzon

V   *Papilio esperanza*
     Mexico

K   *Papilio garleppi*
     Bolivia; Brazil; French Guiana; Guyana; Peru;
Suriname

R   *Papilio grosesmithi*
     Madagascar

V   *Papilio himeros*
     Argentina; Brazil

E   *Papilio homerus*
Homerus Swallowtail
     Jamaica

E   *Papilio hospiton*
Corsican Swallowtail
     France: Corsica; Italy: Sardinia

R   *Papilio jordani*
Jordan's Swallowtail
     Indonesia: Sulawesi

V   *Papilio leucotaenia*
Cream-banded Swallowtail
     Burundi; Rwanda; Uganda

R   *Papilio mangoura*
     Madagascar

I   *Papilio manlius*
     Mauritius

V   *Papilio maraho*
     Taiwan

K   *Papilio maroni*
     French Guiana

V   *Papilio moerneri*
     Papua New Guinea: Bismarck Archipelago

V   *Papilio morondavana*
Madagascan Emperor Swallowtail
     Madagascar

V   *Papilio neumoegeni*
     Indonesia: Lesser Sunda Islands

V   *Papilio osmana*
     Philippines

V   *Papilio phorbanta*
Papillon La Pature
     Réunion

R   *Papilio sjoestedti*
Kilimanjaro Swallowtail
     Tanzania

R   *Papilio toboroi*
     Papua New Guinea: Bougainville; Solomon
Islands

R   *Papilio weymeri*
     Papua New Guinea: Bismarck Archipelago

V   *Parides ascanius*
Fluminense Swallowtail
     Brazil

V   *Parides burchellanus*
     Brazil

K   *Parides coelus*
     French Guiana

R   *Parides hahneli*
Hahnel's Amazonian Swallowtail
     Brazil

K   *Parides klagesi*
     Venezuela

K   *Parides pizarro*
Brazil; Peru

K   *Parides steinbachi*
Bolivia

R   *Parnassius apollo*
Apollo
Albania; Andorra; Armenia; Austria; Azerbaijan?; Bulgaria; China: Xinjiang Uygur; Czechoslovakia; Finland; France; Georgia; Germany; Greece; Hungary?; Italy: including Sicily; Iraq; Iran; Kazakhstan; Kyrgyzstan; Liechtenstein; Mongolia; Netherlands?; Norway; Poland; Romania; Russia; Spain; Sweden; Switzerland; Syria; Turkey; Ukraine; Yugoslavia

R   *Parnassius autocrator*
Afghanistan; Tajikistan

K   *Teinopalpus aureus*
Golden Kaiser-I-Hind
China: Guangdong; Viet Nam?

R   *Teinopalpus imperialis*
Kaiser-I-Hind
Bhutan; China: Hubei, Sichuan; India; Myanmar; Nepal

I   *Troides andromache*
Malaysia: Sabah, Sarawak; Indonesia?: Kalimantan

V   *Troides dohertyi*
Talaud Black Birdwing
Indonesia: Talaud Islands

I   *Troides prattorum*
Indonesia: Buru

Family PIERIDAE

I   *Artogeia virginiensis*
West Virginia White
Canada; USA

E   *Belenois orgygia*
South Africa

R   *Mylothris carcassoni*
Zimbabwe

Family LYCAENIDAE

R   *Acrodipsas illidgei*
Illidge's Ant-Blue
Australia

V   *Agriades zullichi*
Spain

V   *Alaena margaritacea*
South Africa

R   *Aloeides caledoni*
South Africa

R   *Aloeides carolynnae*
South Africa

R   *Aloeides dentatis*
Lesotho; South Africa

R   *Aloeides egerides*
South Africa

I   *Aloeides kaplani*
South Africa

R   *Aloeides lutescens*
South Africa

R   *Aloeides merces*
South Africa

I   *Aloeides nollothi*
South Africa

R   *Aloeides nubilus*
South Africa

I   *Aloeides pringlei*
South Africa

R   *Aloeides rossouwi*
South Africa

V   *Arawacus aethesa*
Brazil

R   *Aslauga australis*
South Africa

R   *Capys penningtoni*
South Africa

E   *Chrysoritis cotrelli*
South Africa

R   *Chrysoritis oreas*
Drakensburg Copper
South Africa

V   *Cyanophrys bertha*
Brazil

I   *Cyclyrius mandersi*
Mauritius

V   *Erikssonia acraeina*
South Africa

R   *Iolaus aphnaeoides*
(*Epamera aphnaeoides*)
South Africa

R   *Iolaus lulua*
(*Pseudiolaus lulua*)
White Spotted Sapphire
South Africa

E   *Joiceya praeclarus*
    Brazil

R   *Lepidochrysops bacchus*
    Wineland Blue
    South Africa

R   *Lepidochrysops badhami*
    South Africa

R   *Lepidochrysops balli*
    South Africa

R   *Lepidochrysops jefferyi*
    South Africa

R   *Lepidochrysops littoralis*
    South Africa

R   *Lepidochrysops loewensteini*
    South Africa

V   *Lepidochrysops lotana*
    South Africa

R   *Lepidochrysops oosthuizen*
    South Africa

R   *Lepidochrysops outeniqua*
    South Africa

R   *Lepidochrysops penningtoni*
    South Africa

R   *Lepidochrysops pephredo*
    South Africa

I   *Lepidochrysops poseidon*
    South Africa

R   *Lepidochrysops pringlei*
    South Africa

R   *Lepidochrysops quickelbergei*
    South Africa

R   *Lepidochrysops swanepoeli*
    South Africa

I   *Lepidochrysops titei*
    South Africa

R   *Lepidochrysops victori*
    South Africa

I   *Lepidochrysops wykehami*
    South Africa

E   *Lycaena dispar*
    Large Copper
    Armenia?; Austria; Azerbaijan?; Belarus?;
    Belgium; Bulgaria; Czech Republic; Estonia;
    Finland?; France; Georgia?; Germany; Greece;
    Hungary; Italy; Kazakhstan?; Latvia?;
    Lithuania; Luxembourg; Moldova?; Mongolia?;
    Netherlands; Poland; Romania; Russia;
    Slovakia; Switzerland; Turkey?; Ukraine;
    Yugoslavia;

R   *Lycaena hermes*
    Hermes Copper
    Mexico; USA

E   *Maculinea alcon*
    (including *M. rebeli*)
    Alcon Large Blue
    Albania?; Austria; Belarus?; Belgium;
    Bulgaria?; Czech Republic?; Denmark; France;
    Germany; Greece; Hungary; Italy;
    Kazakhstan?; Lithuania; Moldova?;
    Netherlands; Poland?; Romania; Russia;
    Slovakia?; Spain; Sweden; Switzerland;
    Turkey; Ukraine; Yugoslavia

E   *Maculinea arion*
    Large Blue
    Albania?; Armenia?; Austria; Azerbaijan?;
    Belarus?; Belgium; Bulgaria?; China; Czech
    Republic; Denmark; Estonia?; Finland; France:
    including Corsica; Georgia?; Germany; Greece;
    Hungary?; Iran?; Italy; Japan?; Kazakhstan?;
    Latvia?; Lithuania?; Moldova?; Poland;
    Romania?; Russia; Slovakia; Spain; Sweden;
    Switzerland; Turkey; Ukraine; Yugoslavia

V   *Maculinea arionides*
    Greater Large Blue
    China; Japan; former USSR

E   *Maculinea nausithous*
    Dusky Large Blue
    Armenia?; Austria; Bulgaria; Azerbaijan?;
    Belarus?; Czech Republic?; France; Georgia;
    Germany; Hungary; Kazakhstan?; Moldova?;
    Poland; Romania?; Russia; Spain; Switzerland;
    Ukraine; Yugoslavia

E   *Maculinea teleius*
    Scarce Large Blue
    Austria; Belgium; Czech Republic?; France;
    Georgia?; Germany; Hungary; Italy; Japan;
    Kazakhstan?; Mongolia?; Poland; Russia;
    Spain?; Switzerland; Ukraine; Yugoslavia

R   *Notarthrinus binghami*
    India

V   *Nirodia belphegor*
    Brazil

R   *Orachrysops ariadne*
    (*Lepidochrysops ariadne*)
    South Africa

V   *Orachrysops niobe*
    South Africa

R **Oreolyce dohertyi**
Naga Hedge Blue
India

V **Oxychaeta dicksoni**
Dickson's Copper
South Africa

E **Paralucia spinifera**
Bathurst Copper
Australia

R **Phasis pringlei**
South Africa

I **Plebejus emigdionis**
San Emigdio Blue
USA

R **Poecilmitis adonis**
South Africa

R **Poecilmitis aureus**
South Africa

R **Poecilmitis azurius**
South Africa

R **Poecilmitis balli**
South Africa

R **Poecilmitis daphne**
South Africa

R **Poecilmitis endymion**
South Africa

R **Poecilmitis henningi**
South Africa

R **Poecilmitis hyperion**
South Africa

R **Poecilmitis irene**
South Africa

R **Poecilmitis kaplani**
South Africa

R **Poecilmitis lyncurium**
Tsomo River Copper
South Africa

I **Poecilmitis lyndseyae**
South Africa

I **Poecilmitis orientalis**
South Africa

I **Poecilmitis pan**
South Africa

R **Poecilmitis penningtoni**
South Africa

R **Poecilmitis pyramus**
South Africa

R **Poecilmitis rileyi**
South Africa

R **Poecilmitis stepheni**
South Africa

R **Poecilmitis swanepoeli**
South Africa

I **Poecilmitis trimeni**
South Africa

R **Poecilmitis wykehami**
South Africa

V **Polyommatus humedasae**
Piedmont Anomalous Blue
Italy

R **Polyommatus galloi**
Higgin's Anomalous Blue
Italy

V **Polyommatus golgus**
(*Plebicula golgus*)
Sierra Nevada Blue
Spain

V **Spindasis collinsi**
Tanzania

K **Strymon avalona**
Avalon Hairstreak
USA

V **Styx infernalis**
Peru

I **Thestor brachycerus**
South Africa

I **Thestor compassbergae**
South Africa

I **Thestor dryburghi**
South Africa

R **Thestor kaplani**
Kaplan's Thestor
South Africa

R **Thestor pringlei**
South Africa

I **Thestor rossouwi**
South Africa

I **Thestor stepheni**
South Africa

R **Thestor strutti**
South Africa

I   *Thestor swanepoeli*
      South Africa

R   *Thestor tempe*
      South Africa

R   *Thestor yildizae*
      South Africa

R   *Trimenia wallengrenii*
      Wallengren's Copper
      South Africa

V   *Uranothauma usambarae*
      Tanzania

Family DANAIDAE

R   *Amauris comorana*
      Comoro Islands

R   *Amauris nossima*
      Comoro Islands; Madagascar

R   *Amauris phoedon*
      Mauritius

R   *Anetia briarea*
      Cuba; Dominican Republic; Haiti

R   *Anetia cubana*
      Cuba

R   *Anetia jaegeri*
      Dominican Republic; Haiti

R   *Anetia pantheratus*
      Cuba; Dominican Republic; Haiti

K   *Danaus cleophile*
      Dominican Republic; Haiti; Jamaica

R   *Euploea albicosta*
      Indonesia: Irian Jaya

R   *Euploea blossomae*
      Philippines

R   *Euploea caespes*
      Indonesia

R   *Euploea configurata*
      Indonesia: Sulawesi

R   *Euploea cordelia*
      Indonesia: Sulawesi

R   *Euploea dentiplaga*
      Indonesia

R   *Euploea doretta*
      Papua New Guinea: Bismarck Archipelago

R   *Euploea eboraci*
      Papua New Guinea: Bismarck Archipelago

R   *Euploea eupator*
      Indonesia: Sulawesi

R   *Euploea euphon*
      Mauritius; Réunion; Rodrigues

R   *Euploea gamelia*
      Indonesia: Java

R   *Euploea lacon*
      Papua New Guinea: Bismarck Archipelago

R   *Euploea latifasciata*
      Indonesia: Sulawesi

R   *Euploea magou*
      Indonesia: Sulawesi

R   *Euploea martinii*
      Indonesia: Sumatra

R   *Euploea mitra*
      Seychelles

R   *Euploea tobleri*
      Philippines

R   *Euploea tripunctata*
      Indonesia: Irian Jaya

R   *Idea electra*
      Philippines

R   *Idea iasonia*
      Sri Lanka

R   *Idea malabarica*
      India

K   *Idea tambusisiana*
      Sulawesi Tree Nymph
      Indonesia: Sulawesi

R   *Ideopsis hewitsonii*
      Indonesia: Irian Jaya

R   *Ideopsis klassika*
      Indonesia

R   *Ideopsis oberthurii*
      Indonesia

R   *Parantica albata*
      Indonesia: Java, Sumatra

R   *Parantica clinias*
      Papua New Guinea: Bismarck Archipelago

R   *Parantica crowleyi*
      Brunei?; Indonesia: Kalimantan; Malaysia:
      Sabah, Sarawak

R   *Parantica dannatti*
      Philippines

E   *Parantica davidi*
      Philippines

R   *Parantica garamantis*
   Papua New Guinea: Bougainville; Solomon
   Islands

K   *Parantica kirbyi*
   Indonesia: Irian Jaya; Papua New Guinea: New
   Guinea

R   *Parantica kuekenthali*
   Indonesia: Sulawesi

R   *Parantica marcia*
   Indonesia: Irian Jaya

R   *Parantica menadensis*
   Indonesia: Sulawesi

R   *Parantica milagros*
   Philippines

R   *Parantica nilgiriensis*
   India

R   *Parantica philo*
   Indonesia

R   *Parantica phyle*
   Philippines

R   *Parantica pseudomelaneus*
   Indonesia: Java

R   *Parantica pumila*
   New Caledonia

R   *Parantica rotundata*
   Papua New Guinea: Bismarck Archipelago

R   *Parantica schoenigi*
   Philippines

R   *Parantica sulewattan*
   Indonesia: Sulawesi

R   *Parantica taprobana*
   Sri Lanka

R   *Parantica tityoides*
   Indonesia: Sumatra

R   *Parantica toxopei*
   Indonesia: Sulawesi

R   *Parantica wegneri*
   Indonesia

R   *Parantica weiskei*
   Indonesia: Irian Jaya; Papua New Guinea: New
   Guinea

R   *Protoploea apatela*
   Indonesia: Irian Jaya; Papua New Guinea: New
   Guinea

R   *Tiradelphe schneideri*
   Solomon Islands

R   *Tirumala euploeomorpha*
   Solomon Islands

R   *Tirumala gautama*
   China: Hainan; India: Nicobar Islands;
   Malaysia: Langkawi Islands; Myanmar;
   Thailand; Viet Nam

Family SATYRIDAE

E   *Coenonympha oedippus*
   False Ringlet
   Austria; Belgium; France; Germany; Hungary;
   Italy; Japan; Kazakhstan?; Liechtenstein;
   Mongolia?; Poland; Russia; Slovakia; Spain;
   Switzerland; Ukraine

V   *Erebia christi*
   Raetzer's Ringlet
   Italy; Switzerland

I   *Erebia gorgone*
   Gavarnie Ringlet
   France; Spain

R   *Erebia ottomana*
   Ottoman Brassy Ringlet
   Albania; Bulgaria; France; Greece; Italy;
   Turkey; Yugoslavia

R   *Erebia scipio*
   Larche Ringlet
   France; Italy

R   *Erebia sthennyo*
   False Dewy Ringlet
   France; Spain

V   *Erebia sudetica*
   Sudeten Ringlet
   Austria; Czech Republic?; France; Hungary;
   Italy; Poland; Romania; Slovakia?; Switzerland

R   *Lethe distans*
   Scarce Red Forester
   India; Myanmar

R   *Lethe margaritae*
   Bhutan; India

R   *Lethe ramadeva*
   Bhutan; India; Myanmar

R   *Lethe satyavati*
   India

V   *Stygionympha dicksoni*
   Dickson's Brown
   South Africa

Family NYMPHALIDAE

I   *Anaea floridalis*
Florida Leafwing
USA

I   *Antanartia borbonica*
Madagascar; Mauritius; Réunion

R   *Apaturopsis kilusa*
Madagascar

R   *Apaturopsis pauliani*
Madagascar

E   *Boloria acrocnema*
Uncompahgre Fritillary Butterfly
USA

R   *Charaxes cowani*
Madagascar

V   *Charaxes marieps*
South Africa

V   *Charaxes usambarae*
Tanzania

V   *Cymothoe amaniensis*
Tanzania

R   *Cymothoe aurivillii*
Tanzania

V   *Cymothoe magambae*
Tanzania

R   *Cymothoe melanjae*
Malawi

V   *Cymothoe teita*
Kenya

I   *Euryphura achlys*
Mottled Green
Kenya; Malawi; Mozambique; South Africa;
Tanzania; Zimbabwe

I   *Euthalia malapana*
Taiwan

R   *Euxanthe madagascariensis*
Madagascar

V   *Fabriciana elisa*
Corsican Fritillary
France: Corsica; Italy: Sardinia

E   *Heliconius nattereri*
Natterer's Longwing
Brazil

E   *Hypodryas maturna*
Scarce Fritillary
Austria; Belgium; Czech Republic?; France;
Germany; Greece; Hungary; Kazakhstan?;
Lithuania; Luxemburg; Poland; Romania;
Russia; Sweden; Yugoslavia

V   *Hypolimnas antevorta*
Tanzania

R   *Neptis manasa*
Pale Hockeystick Sailer
China; India

R   *Neptis nycteas*
India: Sikkim

E   *Phalanta philiberti*
Seychelles

E   *Phyciodes batesi*
Tawny Crescent Butterfly
USA

I   *Salamis angustina*
Salamis Retrecie
Madagascar; Mauritius; Réunion

I   *Sasakia charonda*
Japan; Taiwan

R   *Smerina manoro*
Madagascar

I   *Speyeria idalia*
Regal Fritillary
Canada; USA

Family ACRAEIDAE

R   *Acraea hova*
Madagascar

R   *Acraea sambavae*
Madagascar

Family PYRALIDAE

V   *Kupea electilis*
New Zealand

I   *Margaronia cyanomichla*
Blue Margaronian
USA: Hawaiian Islands

I   *Margaronia exaula*
Green Margaronian
USA: Hawaiian Islands

I   *Oeoblia dryadopa*
Ohenaupaka Oeobian Moth
USA: Hawaiian Islands

Family GEOMETRIDAE

I   *Acalyphes philorites*
     Australia: Tasmania

I   *Dirce aesiodora*
     Australia: Tasmania

I   *Dirce lunaris*
     Australia: Tasmania

I   *Dirce oriplancta*
     Australia: Tasmania

I   *Dirce solaris*
     Australia: Tasmania

I   *Fletcherana ioxantha*
     Ioxantha Looper Moth
       USA: Hawaiian Islands

Family LASIOCAMPIDAE

E   *Eriogaster catax*
       Austria; Belgium; Bulgaria; Czech Republic;
       Germany; Hungary; Italy; Netherlands;
       Slovakia; Spain; Yugoslavia

V   *Phyllodesma ilicifolia*
     Small Lappet Moth
       ?Austria; Belarus?; Belgium; China; Czech
       Republic?; Denmark; Estonia?; Finland;
       France; Germany; Italy?; Japan; Kazakhstan?;
       Latvia?; Lithuania?; Mongolia?; Norway?;
       Poland; Romania; Russia; Slovakia?; Spain?;
       Sweden; Switzerland?; Ukraine?

Family SATURNIIDAE

V   *Graellsia isabelae*
     Spanish Moon Moth
       France; Spain

Family SPHINGIDAE

V   *Euproserpinus euterpe*
     Kern Primrose Sphinx Moth
       USA

E   *Euproserpinus wiesti*
     Prairie Sphinx Moth
       USA

V   *Hyles hippophaes*
       ?Afghanistan; Armenia?; Azerbaijan?; China:
       Xinjiang; France; Georgia?; Germany; Greece;
       Iran; Iraq?; Kazakhstan?; Kyrgyzstan?;
       Mongolia; Pakistan?; Romania; Spain;
       Switzerland; Syria; Tajikistan?; Turkey;
       Turkmenistan?; Uzbekistan?; Yugoslavia

E   *Manduca blackburni*
     Blackburn's Sphinx Moth
       USA: Hawaiian Islands (Maui)

V   *Proserpinus proserpina*
     Willowherb Hawkmoth
       ?Armenia; Austria; Azerbaijan?; Belgium;
       Bulgaria; France; Germany; Greece; Hungary;
       Iran; Iraq?; Italy; Lebanon; Kazakhstan?;
       Morocco; Portugal; Spain; Switzerland; Syria?;
       Turkey; Turkmenistan?; Uzbekistan

Family NOCTUIDAE

I   *Catocala marmorata*
     Marbled Underwing Moth
       USA

I   *Catocala pretiosa*
     Precious Underwing Moth
       USA

I   *Erythroecia hebardi*
     Hebard's Noctuid Moth
       USA

I   *Lithophane lemmeri*
     Lemmer's Noctuid Moth
       USA

I   *Pyreferra ceromatica*
     Ceromatic Noctuid Moth
       Canada; USA

Order HYMENOPTERA

Family EUPELMIDAE

I   *Eupelmus nihoaensis*
     Nihoa Eupelmus Wasp
       USA: Hawaiian Islands

Family BETHYLIDAE

I   *Sclerodermus nihoaensis*
     Nihoa Sclerodermus Wasp
       USA: Hawaiian Islands

Family MUTILLIDAE

I   *Myrmosula pacifica*
     Antioch Mutillid Wasp
       USA

Family FORMICIDAE

K   *Aneuretus simoni*
     Sri Lankan Relict Ant
       Sri Lanka

V   *Formica aquilonia*
     European Red Wood Ant
       Austria; Belarus; Bulgaria; Finland; France;
       Germany; Italy; Latvia; Norway; Russia;
       Sweden; Switzerland; United Kingdom;
       Yugoslavia

V   *Formica lugubris*
     European Red Wood Ant
        Austria; Bulgaria; Finland; France; Germany;
        Hungary; Ireland; Italy; Norway; Romania;
        Russia; Slovakia; Spain; Sweden; Switzerland;
        United Kingdom; Yugoslavia

V   *Formica polyctena*
     European Red Wood Ant
        Austria; Belgium; Bulgaria; Czech Republic;
        Finland; France; Germany; Hungary; Italy;
        Latvia; Lithuania; Netherlands; Norway;
        Poland; Romania; Russia; Slovakia; Spain;
        Sweden; Switzerland; Ukraine; Yugoslavia

V   *Formica pratensis/nigricans*
     European Red Wood Ant
        Austria; Belgium; Bulgaria; Czech Republic;
        Estonia; Finland; France; Georgia; Germany;
        Hungary; Italy; Latvia; Lithuania;
        Luxembourg; Moldova; Netherlands; Norway;
        Poland; Romania; Russia; Slovakia; Spain;
        Sweden; Switzerland; Turkey; Ukraine; United
        Kingdom; Yugoslavia

V   *Formica rufa*
     European Red Wood Ant
        Austria; Belarus; Belgium; Bulgaria; Czech
        Republic; Denmark; Estonia; Finland; France;
        Germany; Hungary; Italy; Latvia; Lithuania;
        Luxembourg; Moldova; Netherlands; Norway;
        Poland; Romania; Russia; Slovakia; Spain;
        Sweden; Switzerland; Turkey; Ukraine; United
        Kingdom; Yugoslavia

I   *Formica uralensis*
     European Red Wood Ant
        Belarus, Denmark, Estonia, Finland, France,
        Germany; Kazakhstan, Latvia, Lithuania,
        Norway, Poland, Russia, Sweden, Switzerland,
        Ukraine

K   *Nothomyrmecia macrops*
     Australian Ant
     Australia

Family VESPIDAE

E   *Odynerus niihauensis*
     Niihau Vespid Wasp
        USA: Hawaiian Islands

E   *Odynerus soror*
     Soror Vespid Wasp
        USA: Hawaiian Islands

Family SPHECIDAE

E   *Deinomimesa hawaiiensis*
     Hawaiian Sphecid Wasp
        USA: Hawaiian Islands

E   *Deinomimesa punae*
     Puna Sphecid Wasp
        USA: Hawaiian Islands

E   *Ectemnius curtipes*
     Short-foot Sphecid Wasp
        USA: Hawaiian Islands

E   *Ectemnius fulvicrus*
     Brown Cross Sphecid Wasp
        USA: Hawaiian Islands

E   *Ectemnius giffardi*
     Giffard's Sphecid Wasp
        USA: Hawaiian Islands

E   *Ectemnius haleakalae*
     Haleakala Sphecid Wasp
        USA: Hawaiian Islands

I   *Eucerceris ruficeps*
     Redheaded Sphecid Wasp
        USA

E   *Nesomimesa kauaiensis*
     Kauai Sphecid Wasp
        USA: Hawaiian Islands

E   *Nesomimesa perkins*
        USA: Hawaiian Islands

E   *Nesomimesa sciopteryx*
     Shade-winged Sphecid Wasp
        USA: Hawaiian Islands

I   *Philanthus nasalis*
     Antioch Sphecid Wasp
        USA

Family MEGACHILIDAE

K   *Chalicodoma pluto*
     Wallace's Giant Bee
        Indonesia: Moluccas

Phylum ONYCHOPHORA

Family PERIPATIDAE

R   *Macroperipatus insularis*
     Jamaica

V   *Mesoperipatus tholloni*
     Congo

R   *Plicatoperipatus jamaicensis*
     Jamaica

V   *Speleoperipatus spelaeus*
     Jamaica

Family PERIPATOPSIDAE

V   *Opisthopatus roseus*
South Africa

V   *Peripatoides indigo*
New Zealand

R   *Peripatoides suteri*
New Zealand

V   *Peripatopsis alba*
South Africa

R   *Peripatopsis clavigera*
South Africa

E   *Peripatopsis leonina*
South Africa: Signal Hill near Capetown

V   *Tasmanipatus barretti*
Australia: Tasmania

V   *Tasmanipatus anophthalmus*
Australia: Tasmania

Phylum ECHINODERMATA

Class ECHINOIDEA

Order ECHINOIDA

Family ECHINIDAE

K   *Echinus esculentus*
European Edible Sea Urchin
(North-east Atlantic)

List 2

EXTINCT SPECIES

Class MAMMALIA

Order DASYUROMORPHIA

Family THYLACINIDAE

Ex **Thylacinus cynocephalus**
Thylacine
Australia: Tasmania (1934)

Order PERAMELEMORPHIA

Family PERAMELIDAE

Ex **Chaeropus ecaudatus**
Pig-footed Bandicoot
Australia (1907)

Ex **Macrotis leucura**
Lesser Bilby
Australia (1931)

Ex **Perameles eremiana**
Desert Bandicoot
Australia (1935)

Order DIPROTODONTIA

Family POTOROIDAE

Ex **Caloprymnus campestris**
Desert Rat-kangaroo
Australia (1935)

Ex **Potorous platyops**
Broad-faced Potoroo
Australia (1875)

Family MACROPODIDAE

Ex **Lagorchestes asomatus**
Central Hare-wallaby
Australia (1931)

Ex **Lagorchestes leporides**
Eastern Hare-wallaby
Australia (1890)

Ex **Macropus greyi**
Toolache Wallaby
Australia (1927)

Ex **Onychogalea lunata**
Crescent Nailtail Wallaby
Australia (1964)

Order INSECTIVORA

Family NESOPHONTIDAE

Nesophontes hypomicrus
Atalaye Nesophontes
Dominican Republic; Haiti

Nesophontes micrus
Western Cuban Nesophontes
Cuba

Nesophontes paramicrus
Saint Michel Nesophontes
Dominican Republic; Haiti

Nesophontes zamicrus
Haitian Nesophontes
Dominican Republic; Haiti

Nesophontes sp.
Cayman Islands

Order CHIROPTERA

Family PTEROPODIDAE

Ex **Acerodon lucifer**
Panay Giant Fruit Bat
Philippines: Panay (1888)

Ex? **Dobsonia chapmani**
Philippine Bare-backed Fruit Bat
Philippines: Cebu, Negros (1964)

Ex **Nyctimene sanctacrucis**
Solomon Islands: Santa Cruz Islands

Ex? **Pteropus brunneus**
Australia: Percy Island

Ex **Pteropus loochoensis**
(*Pteropus mariannus loochoensis*)
Okinawa Flying-fox
Japan: Nansei-shoto (Okinawa)

Ex **Pteropus pilosus**
Palau Flying-fox
Palau (19th C)

Ex **Pteropus subniger**
Mauritius; Réunion

Ex? **Pteropus tokudae**
Guam Flying-fox
Guam (1968)

Family PHYLLOSTOMIDAE

Ex **Phyllonycteris major**
Puerto Rican Flower Bat
Puerto Rico

Family VESPERTILIONIDAE

Ex? **Kerivoula africana**
Tanzanian Woolly Bat
Tanzania

Ex **Pipistrellus sturdeei**
Bonin Pipistrelle
Japan: Ogasawara-shoto

Family MYSTACINIDAE

Ex   *Mystacina robusta*
New Zealand Greater Short-tailed Bat
New Zealand: Big South Cape Island,
Solomon Island (1960s)

Order CARNIVORA

Family CANIDAE

Ex   *Dusicyon australis*
Falkland Island Wolf
Falkland Islands (1876)

Family PHOCIDAE

Ex   *Monachus tropicalis*
Caribbean Monk Seal
Bahamas; Colombia: Isla de Providencia;
Cuba; Guadeloupe; Haiti: Alta Vela; Honduras;
Jamaica: Pedro Cays; Mexico; USA (1962)

Family PROCYONIDAE

Ex?   *Procyon gloveralleni*
(*Procyon lotor gloveralleni*)
Barbados Raccoon
Barbados

Order SIRENIA

Family DUGONGIDAE

Ex   *Hydrodamalis gigas*
Steller's Sea Cow
(Bering Sea; North Pacific Ocean)
Russia; USA? (1768)

Order PERISSODACTYLA

Family EQUIDAE

Ex   *Equus quagga*
(*Equus burchellii quagga*)
Quagga
South Africa (1883)

Order ARTIODACTYLA

Family SUIDAE

Ex?   *Sus bucculentus*
(*Sus verrucosus bucculentus*)
Vietnam Warty Pig
Viet Nam

Family CERVIDAE

Cervus schomburgki
(*Cervus duvaucelli schomburgki*)
Schomburgk's Deer
Thailand (1932)

Family BOVIDAE

Ex   *Gazella rufina*
Red Gazelle
Algeria (19th C)

Ex   *Hippotragus leucophaeus*
Bluebuck
South Africa (1800)

Order RODENTIA

Family MURIDAE

Ex   *Conilurus albipes*
Rabbit-eared Tree-rat
Australia (1875)

Ex?   *Crateromys paulus*
Ilin Island Cloud Rat
Philippines: Ilin Island

Ex?   *Leimacomys buettneri*
Togo

Ex   *Leporillus apicalis*
Lesser Stick-nest Rat
Australia (1933)

Megalomys desmarestii
Martinique Rice Rat
Martinique (1902)

Megalomys luciae
Saint Lucia Rice Rat
Saint Lucia (19th C)

Nesoryzomys darwini
Santa Cruz Rice Rat
Ecuador: Galapagos Islands

Ex   *Notomys amplus*
Short-tailed Hopping-mouse
Australia (1894)

Ex   *Notomys longicaudatus*
Long-tailed Hopping-mouse
Australia (1901)

Ex   *Notomys macrotis*
(includes *N. megalotis*)
Big-eared Hopping-mouse
Australia (pre 1850)

Ex   *Notomys mordax*
Darling Downs Hopping-mouse
Australia (pre 1846)

Oligoryzomys victus
Saint Vincent Rice Rat
Saint Vincent (1897)

Ex? ***Oryzomys nelsoni***
Nelson's Rice Rat
Mexico

Ex ***Peromyscus pembertoni***
Pemberton's Deer Mouse
Mexico: San Pedro Nolasco Island

Ex ***Pitymys bavaricus***
Bavarian Pine Vole
Germany

Ex ***Pseudomys fieldi***
Alice Springs Mouse
Australia (1895)

Ex ***Pseudomys gouldii***
Gould's Mouse
Australia (1930)

Rattus macleari
Maclear's Rat
Christmas Island (1908)

Rattus nativitatis
Bulldog Rat
Christmas Island (1908)

Family ECHIMYIDAE

Boromys offella
Cuba

Boromys torrei
Cuba

Brotomys contractus
Dominican Republic; Haiti

Brotomys voratus
Dominican Republic; Haiti

Family CAPROMYIDAE

Capromys sp.
Cayman Islands

Geocapromys columbianus
Cuba

Geocapromys sp.
Cayman Islands

Isolobodon portoricensis
Dominican Republic; Haiti
[Puerto Rico] (20th C)

Plagiodontia velozi
Dominican Republic; Haiti

Order LAGOMORPHA

Family OCHOTONIDAE

Ex ***Prolagus sardus***
Sardinian Pika
Italy: Sardinia; France: Corsica (18th C)

Class AVES

Order STRUTHIONIFORMES

Family DROMAIIDAE

Dromaius ater
King Island Emu
Australia: King Island

Dromaius baudinianus
(***Dromaius diemenianus***)
Kangaroo Island Emu
Australia: Kangaroo Island (1803)

Family AEPYORNITHIDAE

Aepyornis maximus
Great Elephantbird
Madagascar (1650)

Family ANOMALOPTERYGIDAE

Dinornis torosus
Brawny Great Moa
New Zealand (1670)

Eurapteryx gravis
Burly Lesser Moa
New Zealand (1640)

Megalaperyx didinus
South Island Tokoweka
New Zealand (1785)

Order PODICIPEDIFORMES

Family PODICIPEDIDAE

Ex ***Podilymbus gigas***
Atitlan Grebe
Guatemala (1980-1986/7)

Order PROCELLARIIFORMES

Family PROCELLARIIDAE

Pterodroma sp.
Mauritius: Rodrigues (1726)

Order PELICANIFORMES

Family PHALACROCORACIDAE

Phalacrocorax perspicillatus
Pallas's Cormorant
Russia: Bering Straits (1852)

Order CICONIIFORMES

Family ARDEIDAE

Ixobrychus novaezelandiae
Black-backed Bittern
New Zealand (1900)

Nycticorax mauritianus
Mauritius Night-heron
Mauritius (by 1700)

Nycticorax megacephalus
Rodrigues Night-heron
Mauritius: Rodrigues (1761)

Nycticorax sp.
Réunion (by 1700)

Family CICONIIDAE

Ciconia sp.
Réunion (1674)

Family THRESKIORNITHIDAE

Borbonibis latipes
Réunion Flightless Ibis
Réunion (1773)

Order ANSERIFORMES

Family ANATIDAE

Alopochen mauritianus
Mauritian Shelduck
Mauritius (1698)

Anas theodori
Mauritian Duck
Mauritius; ?Réunion (1696)

Camptorhynchus labradorius
Labrador Duck
Canada; USA (1878)

Cygnus sumnerensis
Chatham Island Swan
New Zealand: Chatham Island (1590-1690)

Mergus australis
Auckland Islands Merganser
New Zealand (1905)

Ex **Rhodonessa caryophyllacea**
Pink-headed Duck
India; Myanmar; Nepal (1935)

Order FALCONIFORMES

Family FALCONIDAE

Falco sp.
Réunion (1674)

Ex **Polyborus lutosus**
Guadalupe Caracara
Mexico: Guadalupe Island (1900)

Order GALLIFORMES

Family PHASIANIDAE

Coturnix novaezelandiae
New Zealand Quail
New Zealand (1875)

Ex **Ophrysia superciliosa**
Himalayan Quail
India (1868)

Order GRUIFORMES

Family RALLIDAE

Aphanapteryx bonasia
Red Rail
Mauritius (1700)

Aphanapteryx leguati
Rodrigues Rail
Mauritius: Rodrigues (1761)

Atlantisia elpenor
Ascension Flightless Crake
United Kingdom: Ascension Island (1656)

Fulica newtoni
Mascarene Coot
Mauritius; Réunion (1693)

Gallinula pacifica
Samoan Moorhen
Western Samoa: Savaii (1908-1926)

Gallirallus dieffenbachii
Dieffenbach's Rail
New Zealand: Chatham Island (1840)

Gallirallus lafresnayanus
New Caledonian Rail
New Caledonia (1904)

Gallirallus modestus
Chatham Islands Rail
New Zealand: Chatham Island (1900)

Gallirallus pacificus
Tahiti Rail
French Polynesia (1773-4)

Gallirallus wakensis
Wake Island Rail
USA: Wake Island (1945)

Ex **Nesoclopeus woodfordi**
Woodford's Rail
Papua New Guinea; ?Solomon Islands: Guadalcanal, Santa Isabel (1936)

Porphyrio albus
(*Notornis alba*)
Lord Howe Swamphen
   Australia: Lord Howe Island (1834)

Porzana monasa
Kosrae Crake
   Federated States of Micronesia (1827)

Porzana palmeri
Laysan Crake
   USA: Hawaiian Islands (Laysan) (1944)

Porzana sandwichensis
Hawaiian Crake
   USA: Hawaiian Islands (1898)

Order CHARADRIIFORMES

Family SCOLOPACIDAE

Prosobonia leucoptera
Tahitian Sandpiper
   French Polynesia: Moorea, Tahiti (1773)

Family CHARADRIIDAE

Haematopus meadewaldoi
Canary Islands Oystercatcher
   Spain: Canary Islands (1913)

Family LARIDAE

Alca impennis
Great Auk
   Canada; Denmark: Faeroe Islands; Greenland;
   Iceland; Russia; United Kingdom (1844)

Order COLUMBIFORMES

Family RAPHIDAE

Pezophaps solitaria
Rodrigues Solitaire
   Mauritius: Rodrigues (1765)

Raphus cucullatus
Dodo
   Mauritius (1665)

Raphus solitarius
Réunion Solitaire
   Réunion (1710-1715)

Family COLUMBIDAE

Alectroenas nitidissima
Mauritius Blue Pigeon
   Mauritius (1835)

'*Alectroenas*' *rodericana*
Rodrigues Pigeon
   Mauritius: Rodrigues (1726)

Columba jouyi
Ryukyu Pigeon
   Japan: Nansei-shoto (1936)

Columba versicolor
Bonin Wood Pigeon
   Japan: Ogasawara-shoto (1889)

Ectopistes migratorius
Passenger Pigeon
   USA (1914)

Ex *Microgoura meeki*
Choiseul Pigeon
   Solomon Islands: Choiseul (1904)

Ex *Ptilinopus mercierii*
Red-moustached Fruit-Dove
   French Polynesia: ?Fatuhiva, Hivaoa, ?Tahuata
   (1922)

Order PSITTACIFORMES

Family LORIIDAE

Charmosyna diadema
New Caledonian Lorikeet
   New Caledonia (1860)

Family PSITTACIDAE

Ara tricolor
Cuban Red Macaw
   Cuba (1885)

Conuropsis carolinensis
Carolina Parakeet
   USA (1914)

Cyanoramphus ulietanus
Raiatea Parakeet
   French Polynesia: Raiatea (1773)

Cyanoramphus zealandicus
Black-fronted Parakeet
   French Polynesia: Tahiti (1844)

'*Lophopsittacus*' *bensoni*
Mauritius Grey Parrot
   Mauritius (1765)

Lophopsittacus mauritianus
Mauritius Parrot
   Mauritius (1675)

Mascarinus mascarinus
Mascarene Parrot
   Réunion (1775 in wild, 1834 in captivity)

'*Necropsittacus*' *rodericanus*
Rodrigues Parrot
   Mauritius: Rodrigues (1761)

Ex **Nestor productus**
Norfolk Island Kaka
Norfolk Island (1851)

Psephotus pulcherrimus
Paradise Parrot
Australia (1927)

Ex **Psittacula exsul**
Newton's Parakeet
Mauritius: Rodrigues (1876)

Psittacula wardi
Seychelles Parrot
Seychelles (1870)

Order CUCULIFORMES

Family CUCULIDAE

Ex **Coua delalandei**
Snail-eating Coua
Madagascar (1930)

Order STRIGIFORMES

Family STRIGIDAE

'Athene' murivora
Rodrigues Little Owl
Mauritius: Rodrigues (1726)

?Sauzieri sp.
Mauritian Owl
Mauritius

Ex **Sceloglaux albifacies**
Laughing Owl
New Zealand (1914)

'Scops' commersoni
Mauritian Owl
Mauritius (1836)

Family AEGOTHELIDAE

Aegotheles savesi
New Caledonian Owlet-nightjar
New Caledonia (1880)

Order APODIFORMES

Family TROCHILIDAE

Chlorostilbon bracei
Grace's Emerald
Bahamas (1877)

Order PASSERIFORMES

Family XENICIDAE

Xenicus lyalli
Stephens Island Wren
New Zealand: Stephens Island (1874)

Family PYCNONOTIDAE

Hypsipetes sp.
Mauritius: Rodrigues (1600s?)

Family MUSCICAPIDAE

Ex **Eutrichomyias rowleyi**
Cerulean Paradise-Flycatcher
Indonesia: Sangihe (1978)

Gerygone insularis
Lord Howe Gerygone
Australia: Lord Howe Island

Turnagra capensis
Piopio
New Zealand (1955)

Turdus ravidus
Grand Cayman Thrush
Cayman Islands (1938)

Zoothera terrestris
Bonin Thrush
Japan: Ogasawara-shoto (1928)

Family ZOSTEROPIDAE

Zosterops strenuus
Robust White-eye
Australia: Lord Howe Island (1928)

Family MELIPHAGIDAE

Chaetoptila angustipluma
Kioea
USA: Hawaiian Islands (1860)

Moho apicalis
Oahu Oo
USA: Hawaiian Islands (Oahu) (1837)

Moho nobilis
Hawaii Oo
USA: Hawaiian Islands (Hawaii) (1934)

Family DREPANIDAE

Chloridops kona
Kona Grosbeak
USA: Hawaiian Islands (1894)

Ciridops anna
Ula-ai-hawane
USA: Hawaiian Islands (1892)

Drepanis funerea
Black Mamo
USA: Hawaiian Islands (1907)

Drepanis pacifica
Hawaii Mamo
USA: Hawaiian Islands (1899)

Ex   ***Paroreomyza flammea***
Molokai Creeper
  USA: Hawaiian Islands (Molokai) (1963)

Rhodacanthis flaviceps
Lesser Koa-finch
  USA: Hawaiian Islands (1891)

Rhodacanthis palmeri
Greater Koa-finch
  USA: Hawaiian Islands (1896)

Viridonia sagittirostris
Greater Amakihi
  USA: Hawaiian Islands (1900)

Family ICTERIDAE

Quiscalus palustris
Slender-billed Grackle
  Mexico (1910)

Family FRINGILLIDAE

Chaunoproctus ferreorostris
Bonin Grosbeak
  Japan: Ogasawara-shoto (1890)

Spiza townsendi
Townsend's Finch
  USA (1833)

Family PLOCEIDAE

Foudia sp.
Reunion Fody
  Réunion (1671)

Family STURNIDAE

Aplonis corvina
Kosrae Mountain Starling
  Federated States of Micronesia: Kosrae (1828)

Aplonis fusca
Tasman Starling
  Australia: Lord Howe Island, Norfolk Island

Aplonis mavornata
Mysterious Starling
  Unknown (1825)

Ex   ***Aplonis pelzelni***
Pohnpei Starling
  Federated States of Micronesia: Pohnpei
  (1956)

Fregilupus varius
Réunion Starling
  Réunion (1854)

Necrospar rodericanus
Rodrigues Starling
  Mauritius: Rodrigues (1726)

Family CALLAEIDAE

Heteralocha acutirostris
Huia
  New Zealand (1907)

Class REPTILIA

Order TESTUDINES

Family TESTUDINIDAE

Cylindraspis borbonica
  Réunion (1800)

Cylindraspis indica
  Réunion (1800)

Cylindraspis inepta
  Mauritius (early 18th C)

Cylindraspis peltastes
  Mauritius: Rodrigues (1800)

Cylindraspis triserrata
  Mauritius (early 18th C)

Cylindraspis vosmaeri
  Mauritius: Rodrigues (1800)

Order SAURIA

Family GEKKONIDAE

Hoplodactylus delcourti
  New Zealand (mid 19th C)

Ex   ***Phelsuma gigas***
(includes *P. edwardnewtonii* and *P. newtonii*)
Rodrigues Day Gecko
  Mauritius: Rodrigues

Family IGUANIDAE

Leiocephalus eremitus
  USA: Navassa Island (1900)

Leiocephalus herminieri
  Martinique (1830s)

Family TEIIDAE

Ameiva cineracea
  Guadeloupe (early 20th C)

Ameiva major
Martinique Giant Ameiva
  Martinique

Family SCINCIDAE

Leiolopisma mauritiana
  Mauritius (1600)

Ex?   ***Macroscincus coctei***
Cape Verde Giant Skink
  Cape Verde: Branco, Razo (early 20th C)

Ex? ***Tachygia microlepis***
Tonga Ground Skink
Tonga: Tongatapu

Ex? ***Tetradactylus eastwoodae***
Eastwood's Longtailed Seps
South Africa

Family ANGUIDAE

Ex? ***Celestus occiduus***
Jamaica Giant Galliwasp
Jamaica (1840)

Order SERPENTES

Family TYPHLOPIDAE

Typhlops cariei
Mauritius (17th C)

Family BOIDAE

Ex? ***Bolyeria multocarinata***
Round Island Boa
Mauritius: Round Island (1975)

Family COLUBRIDAE

Alsophis sancticrucis
Saint Croix Racer
Virgin Islands of the United States (20th C)

Class AMPHIBIA

Order ANURA

Family DISCOGLOSSIDAE

Ex? ***Discoglossus nigriventer***
Israel Painted Frog
Israel: Lake Huleh (1940)

Family RANIDAE

Ex? ***Arthroleptides dutoiti***
Kenya: Mt. Elgon

Ex? ***Rana fisheri***
(*Rana onca, Rana pipiens fisheri*)
Vegas Valley Leopard Frog
USA (1960)

Ex? ***Rana tlaloci***
Mexico

Class CEPHALASPIDOMORPHI

Order PETROMYZONTIFORMES

Family PETROMYZONTIDAE

Ex ***Lampetra minima***
Miller Lake Lamprey
USA (1953)

Class ACTINOPTERYGII

Order CYPRINIFORMES

Family CYPRINIDAE

Ex? ***Acanthobrama hulensis***
Israel: Lake Huleh

Ex? ***Cyprinus yilongensis***
China: Yunnan Province

Ex ***Evarra bustamantei***
Mexican Dace
Mexico (1970)

Ex ***Evarra eigenmanni***
Mexican Dace
Mexico (1970)

Ex ***Evarra tlahuacensis***
Mexican Dace
Mexico (1970)

Ex ***Gila crassicauda***
Thicktail Chub
USA (1957)

Ex ***Lepidomeda altivelis***
Pahranagat Spinedace
USA (1940)

Ex ***Notropis amecae***
Ameca Shiner
Mexico (1970)

Ex ***Notropis aulidion***
Durango Shiner
Mexico (1965)

Ex ***Notropis orca***
Phantom Shiner
Mexico; USA (1975)

Ex ***Pogonichthys ciscoides***
Clear Lake Splittail
USA (1970)

Ex ***Rhinichthys deaconi***
Las Vegas Dace
USA (1955)

Ex ***Stypodon signifer***
Stumptooth Minnow
Mexico (1930)

Family CATOSTOMIDAE

Ex ***Chasmistes muriei***
Snake River Sucker
USA (1928)

Ex ***Lagochila lacera***
Harelip Sucker
USA (1910)

Order SILURIFORMES

Family TRICHOMYCTERIDAE

Ex   ***Rhizosomichthys totae***
        Colombia: Lake Tota

Order SALMONIFORMES

Family RETROPINNIDAE

Ex   ***Prototroctes oxyrhynchus***
        New Zealand Grayling
        New Zealand (1920s)

Family SALMONIDAE

Ex   ***Coregonus alpenae***
        Longjaw Cisco
        (Great Lakes)
        Canada; USA (1978)

Ex   ***Coregonus johannae***
        Deepwater Cisco
        (Great Lakes)
        Canada; USA (1955)

Ex   ***Salvelinus agassizi***
        Silver Trout
        USA (1930)

Order ATHERINIFORMES

Family MELANOTAENIIDAE

Ex?   ***Melanotaenia eachamensis***
        (possibly a form of *M. splendida*)
        Lake Eacham Rainbowfish
        Australia

Order CYPRINODONTIFORMES

Family CYPRINODONTIDAE

Ex   ***Cyprinodon latifasciatus***
        Perrito de Parras
        Mexico (1930)

Ex?   ***Cyprinodon* spp.**
        Perritos de Sandia
        Mexico

Ex   ***Fundulus albolineatus***
        Whiteline Topminnow
        USA (1900)

Family GOODEIDAE

Ex   ***Characodon garmani***
        Parras Characodon
        Mexico (1900)

Ex   ***Empetrichthys merriami***
        Ash Meadows Killifish
        USA (1953)

Family POECILIIDAE

Ex   ***Gambusia amistadensis***
        Amistad Gambusia
        USA (1973)

Ex   ***Gambusia georgei***
        San Marcos Gambusia
        USA (1983)

Ex   ***Priapella bonita***
        Guayacon Ojiazul
        Mexico

Order SYNGNATHIFORMES

Family SYNGNATHIDAE

Ex   ***Syngnathus watermayeri***
        River Pipefish
        South Africa

Order SCORPAENIFORMES

Family COTTIDAE

Ex   ***Cottus echinatus***
        Utah Lake Sculpin
        USA (1928)

Order PERCIFORMES

Family PERCIDAE

Ex?   ***Etheostoma sellare***
        Maryland Darter
        USA

Phylum PLATYHELMINTHES

Class TURBELLARIA

Order TRICLADIDA

Family KENKIIDAE

Ex?   ***Romankenkius pedderensis***
        Lake Pedder Planarian
        Australia: Tasmania

Phylum MOLLUSCA

Class GASTROPODA

Order ARCHEOGASTROPODA

Family LOTTIIDAE

Ex   ***Lottia alveus***
        Eelgrass Limpet
        USA

Family HELICINIDAE

Ex   *Ogasawarana chichijimana*
       Japan: Ogasawara

Ex   *Ogasawarana habei*
       Japan: Ogasawara

Ex   *Ogasawarana hirasei*
       Japan: Ogasawara

Ex   *Ogasawarana metamorpha*
       Japan: Ogasawara

Ex   *Ogasawarana rex*
       Japan: Ogasawara

Ex   *Ogasawarana yoshiwarana*
       Japan: Ogasawara

Order MESOGASTROPODA

Family CYCLOPHORIDAE

Ex   *Cyclosurus mariei*
       Mayotte

Ex   *Cyclophorus horridulum*
       Mayotte

Family POMATIASIDAE

Ex   *Tropidophora carinata*
       Mauritius; Réunion (1881)

Ex   *Tropidophora desmazuresi*
       Mauritius: Rodrigues

Ex   *Tropidophora semilirata*
       Mayotte

Family ACICULIDAE

Ex?   *Renea bourguignatiana*
       France; Italy

Family HYDROBIIDAE

Ex   *Bythinella intermedia*
       Austria

Ex   *Bythiospeum pfeifferi*
       Austria

Ex?   *Bythiospeum tschapecki*
       Austria

Ex?   *Iglica gratulabunda*
       Austria

Ex   *Lithoglyphus umbilicata*
       (*Clappia umbilicata*)
       Umbilicate Pebblesnail
       USA

Ex   *Ohridohauffenia drimica*
       Yugoslavia (1980s)

Ex?   *Posticobia norfolkensis*
       Australia: Norfolk Island

Family ASSIMINEIDAE

Ex   *Conacmella vagans*
       Japan: Ogasawara

Ex   *Omphalotropis plicosa*
       Mauritius

Family PLEUROCERIDAE

Ex   *Anculopsis anthonyix*
       (*Leptoxis anthonyix*)
       Anthony's River Snail
       USA

Ex   *Anculosa clipeata*
       (*Leptoxis clipeata*)
       Agate Rocksnail
       USA

Ex   *Anculosa formanii*
       (*Leptoxis formanii*)
       Interrupted Rocksnail
       USA

Ex   *Anculosa ligata*
       (*Leptoxis ligata*)
       Rotund Rocksnail
       USA

Ex   *Anculosa lirata*
       (*Leptoxis lirata*)
       Lyrate Rocksnail
       USA

Ex   *Anculosa occulata*
       (*Leptoxis occulata*)
       Bigmouth Rocksnail
       USA

Ex   *Aculopsis praerosa*
       (*Leptoxis praerosa*)
       Onyx Rocksnail
       USA

Ex   *Anculosa showalteri*
       (*Leptoxis showalteri*)
       Coosa Rocksnail
       USA

Ex   *Anculosa vittata*
       (*Leptoxis vittata*)
       Striped Rocksnail
       USA

Ex   *Goniobasis alabamensis*
       (*Elimia alabamensis*)
       Mud Elimia
       USA

Ex *Goniobasis clausa*
(*Elimia clausa*)
Closed Elimia
USA

Ex *Goniobasis fusiformis*
(*Elimia fusiformis*)
Fusiform Elimia
USA

Ex *Goniobasis hartmanniana*
(*Elimia hartmanniana*)
High-spired Elimia
USA

Ex *Goniobasis impressa*
(*Elimia impressa*)
Constricted Elimia
USA

Ex *Goniobasis jonesi*
(*Elimia jonesi*)
Hearty Elimia
USA

Ex *Goniobasis laeta*
(*Elimia laeta*)
Ribbed Elimia
USA

Ex *Goniobasis pilsbryi*
(*Elimia pilsbryi*)
Rough-lined Elimia
USA

Ex *Goniobasis pupaeformis*
(*Elimia pupaeformis*)
Pupa Elimia
USA

Ex *Goniobasis pygmaea*
(*Elimia pygmaea*)
Pygmy Elimia
USA

Ex *Goniobasis varians*
(*Elimia varians*)
Puzzle Elimia
USA

Ex *Gyrotoma excisa*
Excised Slitshell
USA (1924)

Ex *Gyrotoma lewisii*
Striate Slitshell
USA (1924)

Ex *Gyrotoma pagoda*
Pagoda Slitshell
USA (1924)

Ex *Gyrotoma pumila*
Ribbed Slitshell
USA (1924)

Ex *Gyrotoma pyramidata*
Pyramid Slitshell
USA (1924)

Ex *Gyrotoma walkeri*
Round Slitshell
USA (1924)

Order STYLOMMATOPHORA

Family ACHATINELLIDAE

Ex? *Achatinella abbreviata*
USA: Hawaiian Islands (Oahu) (1963)

Ex *Achatinella buddii*
USA: Hawaiian Islands (Oahu) (early 1900s)

Ex *Achatinella caesia*
USA: Hawaiian Islands (Oahu) (early 1900s)

Ex *Achatinella casta*
USA: Hawaiian Islands (Oahu)

Ex *Achatinella decora*
USA: Hawaiian Islands (Oahu) (early 1900s)

Ex? *Achatinella dimorpha*
USA: Hawaiian Islands (Oahu)

Ex? *Achatinella elegans*
USA: Hawaiian Islands (Oahu) (1952)

Ex? *Achatinella juddii*
USA: Hawaiian Islands (Oahu) (1958)

Ex? *Achatinella juncea*
USA: Hawaiian Islands (Oahu)

Ex *Achatinella lehuiensis*
USA: Hawaiian Islands (Oahu) (1922)

Ex *Achatinella livida*
USA: Hawaiian Islands (Oahu)

Ex *Achatinella papyracea*
USA: Hawaiian Islands (Oahu) (1945)

Ex? *Achatinella rosea*
USA: Hawaiian Islands (Oahu) (1949)

Ex *Achatinella spaldingi*
USA: Hawaiian Islands (Oahu) (1938)

Ex *Achatinella thaanumi*
USA: Hawaiian Islands (Oahu) (1900s)

Ex *Achatinella valida*
USA: Hawaiian Islands (Oahu) (1951)

Ex *Achatinella vittata*
USA: Hawaiian Islands (Oahu) (1953)

Ex   *Auriculella expansa*
   USA: Hawaiian Islands (Maui)

Ex   *Auriculella uniplicata*
   USA: Hawaiian Islands (Maui)

Ex   *Lamellidea monodonta*
   Japan: Ogasawara

Ex   *Lamellidea nakadai*
   Japan: Ogasawara

Ex   *Newcombia philippiana*
   USA: Hawaiian Islands (Molokai)

Ex   *Partulina crassa*
   USA: Hawaiian Islands (Lanai) (1914)

Ex   *Partulina montagui*
   USA: Hawaiian Islands (Oahu) (1913)

Ex   *Perdicella fulgurans*
   USA: Hawaiian Islands (Maui)

Ex   *Perdicella maniensis*
   USA: Hawaiian Islands (Maui)

Ex   *Perdicella zebra*
   USA: Hawaiian Islands (Maui)

Ex? *Perdicella zebrina*
   USA: Hawaiian Islands (Maui)

Family AMASTRIDAE

Ex   *Amastra albolabris*
   USA: Hawaiian Islands (Oahu)

Ex   *Amastra cornea*
   USA: Hawaiian Islands (Oahu)

Ex   *Amastra crassilabrum*
   USA: Hawaiian Islands (Oahu)

Ex? *Amastra elongata*
   USA: Hawaiian Islands

Ex? *Amastra forbesi*
   USA: Hawaiian Islands (Oahu)

Ex   *Amastra pellucida*
   USA: Hawaiian Islands (Oahu)

Ex   *Amastra porcus*
   USA: Hawaiian Islands (Oahu)

Ex   *Amastra reticulata*
   USA: Hawaiian Islands (Oahu)

Ex   *Amastra subrostrata*
   USA: Hawaiian Islands (Oahu)

Ex   *Amastra subsoror*
   USA: Hawaiian Islands (Maui)

Ex   *Amastra tenuispira*
   USA: Hawaiian Islands (Oahu)

Ex? *Amastra umbilicata*
   USA: Hawaiian Islands (Molokai)

Ex   *Carelia anceophila*
   USA: Hawaiian Islands (Kauai) (1930)

Ex   *Carelia bicolor*
   USA: Hawaiian Islands (Kauai) (1970)

Ex   *Carelia cochlea*
   USA: Hawaiian Islands (Kauai)

Ex   *Carelia cumingiana*
   USA: Hawaiian Islands (Kauai) (1930)

Ex   *Carelia dolei*
   USA: Hawaiian Islands (Kauai)

Ex   *Carelia evelynae*
   USA: Hawaiian Islands (Kauai)

Ex   *Carelia glossema*
   USA: Hawaiian Islands (Kauai) (1930)

Ex   *Carelia hyattiana*
   USA: Hawaiian Islands (Kauai)

Ex   *Carelia kalalauensis*
   USA: Hawaiian Islands (Kauai) (1945/47)

Ex   *Carelia knudseni*
   USA: Hawaiian Islands (Kauai) (1930)

Ex   *Carelia lirata*
   USA: Hawaiian Islands (Kauai)

Ex   *Carelia lymani*
   USA: Hawaiian Islands (Kauai)

Ex   *Carelia mirabilis*
   USA: Hawaiian Islands (Kauai)

Ex   *Carelia necra*
   USA: Hawaiian Islands (Kauai)

Ex   *Carelia olivacea*
   USA: Hawaiian Islands (Kauai) (1930)

Ex   *Carelia paradoxa*
   USA: Hawaiian Islands (Kauai) (1930)

Ex   *Carelia periscelis*
   USA: Hawaiian Islands (Kauai) (1930)

Ex   *Carelia pilsbryi*
   USA: Hawaiian Islands (Kauai)

Ex   *Carelia* sp.
   USA: Hawaiian Islands (Kauai)

Ex   *Carelia sinclairi*
   USA: Hawaiian Islands (Niihau)

Ex   *Carelia tenebrosa*
   USA: Hawaiian Islands (Kauai) (1930)

Ex *Carelia turricula*
 USA: Hawaiian Islands (Kauai) (1930)

Family PUPILLIDAE

Ex? *Leiostyla abbreviata*
 Portugal: Madeira (1870s)

Ex? *Leiostyla cassida*
 Portugal: Madeira (1870s)

Ex? *Leiostyla gibba*
 Portugal: Madeira (1870s)

Ex? *Leiostyla heterodon*
 Portugal: Madeira

Ex? *Leiostyla lamellosa*
 Portugal: Madeira (1870s)

Ex? *Leiostyla simulator*
 Portugal: Madeira (1870s)

Ex *Pupilla obliquicosta*
 (*Pupa obliquicosta*)
 Saint Helena (1870s)

Family VERTIGINIDAE

Ex *Campolaemus perexilis*
 Saint Helena (1870s)

Ex *Gastrocopta chichijimana*
 Japan: Ogasawara

Ex *Gastrocopta ogasawarana*
 Japan: Ogasawara

Ex *Lyropupa perlonga*
 USA: Hawaiian Islands

Ex *Nesopupa turtoni*
 Saint Helena (1870s)

Family CERASTUIDAE

Ex *Rhachis comorensis*
 Mayotte

Ex *Rhachis sanguineus*
 Mauritius

Family PARTULIDAE

Ex *Partula affinis*
 French Polynesia: Tahiti

Ex *Partula approximata*
 French Polynesia: Raiatea

Ex *Partula atilis*
 French Polynesia: Raiatea

Ex *Partula attenuata*
 French Polynesia: Raiatea

Ex *Partula aurantia*
 French Polynesia: Moorea

Ex *Partula auriculata*
 French Polynesia: Raiatea

Ex *Partula candida*
 French Polynesia: Raiatea

Ex *Partula castanea*
 French Polynesia: Raiatea

Ex *Partula cedistia*
 French Polynesia: Raiatea

Ex *Partula citrina*
 French Polynesia: Raiatea

Ex *Partula clara*
 French Polynesia: Tahiti

Ex *Partula compacta*
 French Polynesia: Raiatea

Ex *Partula crassilabris*
 French Polynesia: Raiatea

Ex *Partula cuneata*
 French Polynesia: Raiatea

Ex *Partula dolichostoma*
 French Polynesia: Raiatea

Ex *Partula exigua*
 French Polynesia: Moorea (1977)

Ex *Partula filosa*
 French Polynesia: Tahiti

Ex *Partula formosa*
 French Polynesia: Raiatea

Ex *Partula fusea*
 French Polynesia: Raiatea

Ex *Partula garretti*
 French Polynesia: Raiatea

Ex *Partula hyalina*
 French Polynesia: Tahiti

Ex *Partula imperforata*
 French Polynesia: Raiatea

Ex *Partula leptochila*
 French Polynesia: Raiatea

Ex *Partula levilineata*
 French Polynesia: Raiatea

Ex *Partula levistriata*
 French Polynesia: Raiatea

Ex *Partula lutea*
 French Polynesia: BoraBora

Ex *Partula microstoma*
 French Polynesia: Raiatea

Ex   *Partula mirabilis*
   French Polynesia: Moorea

Ex   *Partula mooreana*
   French Polynesia: Moorea

Ex   *Partula nodosa*
   French Polynesia: Tahiti

Ex   *Partula otaheitana*
   French Polynesia: Tahiti

Ex   *Partula producta*
   French Polynesia: Tahiti

Ex   *Partula protea*
   French Polynesia: Raiatea

Ex   *Partula protracta*
   French Polynesia: Raiatea

Ex   *Partula radiata*
   French Polynesia: Raiatea

Ex   *Partula raiatensis*
   French Polynesia: Raiatea

Ex   *Partula remota*
   French Polynesia: Raiatea

Ex   *Partula rustica*
   French Polynesia: Raiatea

Ex   *Partula salifana*
   Mount Alifana Partula
   Guam

Ex   *Partula suturalis*
   Sutural Partula
   French Polynesia: Moorea

Ex   *Partula taeniata*
   French Polynesia: Moorea

Ex   *Partula thalia*
   French Polynesia: Raiatea

Ex   *Partula tohiveana*
   French Polynesia: Moorea

Ex   *Partula tristis*
   French Polynesia: Raiatea

Ex   *Partula turgida*
   French Polynesia: Raiatea

Ex   *Partula variabilis*
   French Polynesia: Raiatea

Ex   *Partula vittata*
   French Polynesia: Raiatea

Ex   *Samoana abbreviata*
   American Samoa (1940)

Family ORTHALICIDAE

Ex   *Aspastus loyaltiensis*
   (*Leuchocharis loyaltiensis*)
   New Caledonia (1900s)

Ex   *Aspastus porphyrocheila*
   (*Leuchocharis porphyrocheila*)
   New Caledonia (1900s)

Family FERUSSACIIDAE

Ex?   *Amphorella iridescens*
   Portugal: Madeira

Ex?   *Cecilioides eulima*
   Portugal: Madeira (1870s)

Family SUBULINIDAE

Ex   *Chilonopsis blofeldi*
   Saint Helena (1870s)

Ex   *Chilonopsis exulatus*
   Saint Helena (1870s)

Ex   *Chilonopsis helena*
   Saint Helena (1870s)

Ex?   *Chilonopsis melanoides*
   Saint Helena (1870s)

Ex   *Chilonopsis nonpareil*
   Saint Helena (1870s)

Ex   *Chilonopsis subplicatus*
   Saint Helena (1870s)

Ex   *Chilonopsis subtruncatus*
   Saint Helena (1870s)

Ex   *Chilonopsis turtoni*
   Saint Helena (1870s)

Family STREPTAXIDAE

Ex   *Edentulina thomasetti*
   Seychelles (1908)

Ex   *Gibbus lyonetianus*
   Mauritius (1905)

Ex   *Gonidomus newtoni*
   Mauritius (1867)

Ex   *Gonospira nevilli*
   Mauritius

Ex?   *Gulella antelmiana*
   Mauritius

Ex   *Gulella mayottensis*
   Mayotte

Family ENDODONTIDAE

Ex   *Hirasea biconcava*
   Japan: Ogasawara

Ex   *Hirasea eutheca*
     Japan: Ogasawara

Ex   *Hirasea goniobasis*
     Japan: Ogasawara

Ex   *Hirasea hypolia*
     Japan: Ogasawara

Ex   *Hirasea major*
     Japan: Ogasawara

Ex   *Hirasea nesiotica*
     Japan: Ogasawara

Ex   *Hirasea planulata*
     Japan: Ogasawara

Ex   *Hirasea sinuosa*
     Japan: Ogasawara

Ex   *Hirasea clara*
     (*Hirasiella clara*)
     Japan: Ogasawara

Ex   *Kondoconcha othnius*
     French Polynesia: Rapa (1934)

Ex   *Libera subcavernula*
     Cook Islands: Raratonga (1880s)

Ex   *Libera tumuloides*
     Cook Islands: Raratonga (1880s)

Ex   *Mautodontha acuticosta*
     French Polynesia: Raiatea (1880s)

Ex   *Mautodontha boraborensis*
     French Polynesia: Borabora (1880s)

Ex   *Mautodontha ceuthma*
     French Polynesia: Raivavae (1880s)

Ex   *Mautodontha consimilis*
     French Polynesia: Raiatea (1880s)

Ex   *Mautodontha consobrina*
     French Polynesia: Huahine (1880s)

Ex   *Mautodontha maupiensis*
     French Polynesia: Maupiti (1880s)

Ex   *Mautodontha parvidens*
     French Polynesia: Society Islands (1880s)

Ex   *Mautodontha punctiperforata*
     French Polynesia: Moorea (1880s)

Ex   *Mautodontha saintjohni*
     French Polynesia: Borabora (1880s)

Ex   *Mautodontha subtilis*
     French Polynesia: Huahine (1880s)

Ex   *Mautodontha unilamellata*
     Cook Islands: Raratonga (1880s)

Ex   *Mautodontha zebrina*
     Cook Islands: Raratonga (1880s)

Ex   *Opanara altiapica*
     French Polynesia: Rapa (1934)

Ex   *Opanara areaensis*
     French Polynesia: Rapa (1934)

Ex   *Opanara bitridentata*
     French Polynesia: Rapa (1934)

Ex   *Opanara caliculata*
     French Polynesia: Rapa (1934)

Ex   *Opanara depasoapicata*
     French Polynesia: Rapa (1934)

Ex   *Opanara duplicidentata*
     French Polynesia: Rapa (1934)

Ex   *Opanara fosbergi*
     French Polynesia: Rapa (1934)

Ex   *Opanara megomphala*
     French Polynesia: Rapa (1934)

Ex   *Opanara perahuensis*
     French Polynesia: Rapa (1934)

Ex   *Orangia cookei*
     French Polynesia: Rapa (1934)

Ex   *Orangia maituatensis*
     French Polynesia: Rapa (1934)

Ex   *Orangia sporadica*
     French Polynesia: Rapa (1934)

Ex   *Ptychodon dianae*
     (*Pseudohelenoconcha dianae*)
     Saint Helena (1870s)

Ex   *Ptychodon laetissima*
     (*Pseudohelenoconcha laetissima*)
     Saint Helena (1870s)

Ex   *Ptychodon persoluta*
     (*Pseudohelenoconcha persoluta*)
     Saint Helena (1870s)

Ex   *Ptychodon spurca*
     (*Pseudohelenoconcha spurca*)
     Saint Helena (1870s)

Ex   *Rhysoconcha atanuiensis*
     French Polynesia: Rapa (1934)

Ex   *Rhysoconcha variumbilicata*
     French Polynesia: Rapa (1934)

Ex   *Ruatara koarana*
     French Polynesia: Rapa (1934)

Ex   *Ruatara oparica*
     French Polynesia: Rapa (1934)

Ex *Taipidon anceyana*
  French Polynesia: Hiva Oa (1880s)

Ex *Taipidon marquesana*
  French Polynesia: Nuku Hiva (1880s)

Ex *Taipidon octolamellata*
  French Polynesia: Hiva Oa (1880s)

Ex *Thaumatodon multilamellata*
  Cook Islands: Rarotonga (1880s)

Family CHAROPIDAE

Ex *Helenoconcha leptalea*
  Saint Helena (1870s)

Ex *Helenoconcha minutissima*
  Saint Helena (1870s)

Ex *Helenoconcha polyodon*
  Saint Helena (1870s)

Ex *Helenoconcha pseustes*
  Saint Helena (1870s)

Ex *Helenoconcha sexdentata*
  Saint Helena (1870s)

Ex *Helenodiscus bilamellata*
  Saint Helena (1870s)

Ex *Helenodiscus vernoni*
  Saint Helena (1870s)

Ex *Sinployea canalis*
  Cook Islands: Rarotonga (1872)

Ex *Sinployea decorticata*
  Cook Islands: Rarotonga (1872)

Ex *Sinployea harveyensis*
  Cook Islands: Rarotonga (1872)

Ex *Sinployea otareae*
  Cook Islands: Rarotonga (1872)

Ex *Sinployea planospira*
  Cook Islands: Rarotonga (1872)

Ex *Sinployea proxima*
  Cook Islands: Rarotonga (1872)

Ex *Sinployea rudis*
  Cook Islands: Rarotonga (1872)

Ex *Sinployea tenuicostata*
  Cook Islands: Rarotonga (1872)

Ex *Sinployea youngi*
  Cook Islands: Rarotonga (1872)

Family DISCIDAE

Ex? *Discus guerinianus*
  Portugal: Madeira (1870s)

Family SUCCINEIDAE

Ex *Succinea guamensis*
  Guam

Family HELIXARIONIDAE

Ex? *Caldwellia philyrina*
  Mauritius

Ex *Ctenoglypta newtoni*
  Mauritius (1871)

Ex? *Erepta stylodon*
  Mauritius

Ex *Erepta nevilli*
  Mauritius

Ex *Harmogenanina linophora*
  Mauritius; Réunion

Ex *Harmogenanina subdetecta*
  Réunion

Ex *Pachystyla rufozonata*
  Mauritius (1869)

Family ARIOPHANTIDAE

Ex *Colparion madgei*
  Mauritius: Rodrigues (1938)

Ex *Vitrinula chaunax*
  Japan: Ogasawara

Ex *Vitrinula chichijimana*
  Japan: Ogasawara

Ex *Vitrinula hahajimana*
  Japan: Ogasawara

Family CAMAENIDAE

Ex *Mandarina luhuana*
  Japan: Ogasawara

Family HELICIDAE

Ex *Chilostoma ziegleri*
  Austria

Ex? *Discula lyelliana*
  Portugal: Madeira (1870s)

Ex? *Discula tetrica*
  Portugal: Madeira (1870s)

Ex? *Geomitra delphinuloides*
  Portugal: Madeira (1870s)

Ex? *Pseudocampylaea lowei*
  Portugal: Madeira (Porto Santo) (late 19th C)

Family ARIONIDAE

Ex *Arion simrothi*
  Germany

Class BIVALVIA

Order UNIONIDA

Family UNIONIDAE

Ex **Alasmidonta robusta**
Cardina Elktoe
USA

Ex? **Dysnomia arcaeformis?**
(*Epioblasma arcaeformis?*)
Sugarspoon
USA (1940s)

Ex **Dysnomia biemarginata**
(*Epioblasma biemarginata*)
Angled Riffleshell
USA (1960s)

Ex **Dysnomia flexuosa**
(*Epioblasma flexuosa*)
Leafshell
USA (1940s)

Ex **Dysnomia haysiana**
(*Epioblasma haysiana*)
Acornshell
USA

Ex **Dysnomia lefevrei**
(*Epioblasma lefevrei*)
USA

Ex **Dysnomia lenior**
(*Epioblasma lenior*)
Narrow Catspaw
USA (1965)

Ex? **Dysnomia lewisii?**
(*Epioblasma lewisii?*)
Forkshell
USA (1964)

Ex **Dysnomia personata**
(*Epioblasma personata*)
Round Combshell
USA (1930)

Ex **Dysnomia propinqua**
(*Epioblasma propinqua*)
Tennessee Riffleshell
USA (1930)

Ex **Dysnomia sampsoni**
(*Epioblasma sampsoni*)
Wabash Riffleshell
USA (1950s/60s)

Ex **Dysnomia stewardsoni**
(*Epioblasma stewardsoni*)
Cumberland Leafshell
USA (1930)

Phylum ARTHROPODA

Class CRUSTACEA

Order AMPHIPODA

Family PARAMELITIDAE

Ex? **Austrogammarus australis**
Australia: Melbourne, Victoria

Family CRANGONYCTIDAE

Ex **Stygobromus lucifugus**
Rubious Cave Amphipod
USA

Order DECAPODA

Family ATYIDAE

Syncaris pasadenas
Pasadena Freshwater Shrimp
USA (1933)

Family ASTACIDAE

Ex? **Pacifastacus nigrescens**
Sooty Crayfish
USA (1860s)

Class INSECTA

Order EPHEMEROPTERA

Family SIPHLONURIDAE

Ex **Acanthometropus pecatonica**
Pecatonica River Mayfly
USA (1927)

Family EPHEMERIDAE

Ex **Pantagenia robusta**
Robust Burrowing Mayfly
USA

Order ODONATA

Family COENAGRIONIDAE

Ex? **Megalagrion jugorum**
Jugorum Megalagrion Damselfly
USA: Hawaiian Islands

Family GOMPHIDAE

Ex? **Ophiogomphus edmundo**
Edmund's Snaketail Dragonfly
USA

Family LIBELLULIDAE

Ex? **Sympetrum dilatatum**
Saint Helena

Order ORTHOPTERA

Family TETTIGONIIDAE

Ex *Neduba extincta*
Antioch Dunes Shieldback Katydid
USA (1937)

Order PHASMATOPTERA

Family PHASMATIDAE

Ex? *Dryococelus australis*
Lord Howe Island Stick-insect
Australia: Lord Howe Island, Ball's Pyramid
(1970s)

Order PLECOPTERA

Family CHLOROPERLIDAE

Ex *Alloperla roberti*
Robert's Stonefly
USA

Order HOMOPTERA

Family PSEUDOCOCCIDAE

Ex *Clavicoccus erinaceus*
USA: Hawaiian Islands

Ex *Phyllococcus oahuensis*
USA: Hawaiian Islands

Order COLEOPTERA

Family CARABIDAE

Mecodema punctellum
New Zealand: Stephens Island

Family DYTISCIDAE

Ex? *Hygrotus artus*
Mono Lake Diving Beetle
USA

Ex? *Megadytes ducalis*
Brazil

Ex? *Rhantus alutaceus*
New Caledonia

Ex? *Rhantus novacaledoniae*
New Caledonia

Ex? *Rhantus orbignyi*
Argentina; Brazil

Ex? *Rhantus papuanus*
Papua New Guinea

Ex? *Siettitia balsetensis*
Perrin's Cave Beetle
France

Family CERAMBYCIDAE

Ex *Xylotoles costatus*
New Zealand: Chatham Island (1930s)

Family CURCULIONIDAE

Ex *Dryophthorus distinguendus*
USA: Hawaiian Islands

Ex *Dryotribus mimeticus*
USA: Hawaiian Islands

Ex? *Hadramphus tuberculatus*
New Zealand (1910)

Ex *Macrancylus linearis*
USA: Hawaiian Islands

Ex *Oedemasylus laysanensis*
USA: Hawaiian Islands

Ex? *Pentarthrum blackburni*
Blackburn's Weevil
USA: Hawaiian Islands

Rhyncogonus bryani
USA: Hawaiian Islands

Ex? *Trigonoscuta rossi*
Fort Ross Weevil
USA

Ex? *Trigonoscuta yorbalindae*
Yorba Linda Weevil
USA

Order DIPTERA

Family TABANIDAE

Ex *Stonemyia volutina*
Volutine Stoneyian Tabanid Fly
USA

Family DOLICHOPODIDAE

Ex *Campsicnemus mirabilis*
USA: Hawaiian Islands

Family DROSOPHILIDAE

Ex *Drosophila lanaiensis*
USA: Hawaiian Islands

Order TRICHOPTERA

Family RHYACOPHILIDAE

Ex *Rhyacophila amabilis*
Castle Lake Caddisfly
USA

Family HYDROPSYCHIDAE

Hydropsyche tobiasi
Tobias' Caddisfly
Germany (1920s)

Family LEPTOCERIDAE

Ex   *Triaenodes phalacris*
       Athens Caddisfly
       USA

Ex   *Triaenodes tridonata*
       Three-tooth Caddisfly
       USA

Order LEPIDOPTERA

Family NEPTICULIDAE

Ex?   *Ectodemia castaneae*
       American Chestnut Moth
       USA

Ex?   *Ectodemia phleophaga*
       Phleophagan Chestnut Moth
       USA

Family TISCHERIIDAE

Ex?   *Tischeria perplexa*
       Chestnut Clearwing Moth
       USA

Family COLEOPHORIDAE

Ex?   *Coleophora leucochrysella*
       USA

Family ARGYRESTHIIDAE

Ex?   *Argyresthia castaneela*
       Chestnut Ermine Moth
       USA

Family ZYGAENIDAE

       Levuana irridescens
       Levuana Moth
       USA: Hawaiian Islands (1929)

Family LYCAENIDAE

Ex   *Deloneura immaculata*
       South Africa

Ex   *Glaucopsyche xerces*
       Xerces Blue
       USA (early 1940s)

Ex   *Lepidochrysops hypopolia*
       South Africa

Family LIBYTHEIDAE

Ex   *Libythea cinyras*
       Mauritius (1865)

Family PYRALIDAE

       Genophantis leahi
       USA: Hawaiian Islands (Oahu) (early 1900s)

Hedylepta asaphrombra
USA: Hawaiian Islands (1970s)

Hedylepta continuatalis
USA: Hawaiian Islands (1958)

Hedylepta epicentra
USA: Hawaiian Islands (Oahu) (early 1900s)

Hedylepta euryprora
USA: Hawaiian Islands (Hawaii)

Hedylepta fullawayi
USA: Hawaiian Islands (Hawaii)

Hedylepta laysanensis
USA: Hawaiian Islands (Laysan)

Hedylepta meyricki
USA: Hawaiian Islands (Hawaii)

Hedylepta musicola
USA: Hawaiian Islands (Maui, Molokai)

Hedylepta telegrapha
USA: Hawaiian Islands (Hawaii)

Oeobia sp.
USA: Hawaiian Islands (Laysan) (1911)

Family GEOMETRIDAE

Ex?   *Scotorythra megalophylla*
       Kona Giant Looper Moth
       USA: Hawaiian Islands (Hawaii) (early 1900s)

Ex?   *Scotorythra nesiotes*
       Ko'olau Giant Looper Moth
       USA: Hawaiian Islands (Oahu) (early 1900s)

Ex?   *Scotorythra paratactis*
       Hawaiian Hopseed Looper Moth
       USA: Hawaiian Islands (Oahu) (early 1900s)

Ex?   *Tritocleis microphylla*
       Ola'a Peppered Looper Moth
       USA: Hawaiian Islands (Hawaii) (1890s)

Family SPHINGIDAE

Ex?   *Tinostoma smaragditis*
       Fabulous Green Sphinx of Kauai
       USA: Hawaiian Islands

Family NOCTUIDAE

Ex?   *Agrotis crinigera*
       Poko Noctuid Moth
       USA: Hawaiian Islands (1926)

Ex   *Agrotis fasciata*
       Midway Noctuid Moth
       USA: Hawaiian Islands (Midway)

Ex? *Agrotis kerri*
Kerr's Noctuid Moth
USA: Hawaiian Islands (French Frigate Shoals) (1923)

Ex *Agrotis laysanensis*
Laysan Noctuid Moth
USA: Hawaiian Islands (Laysan) (1911)

Ex *Agrotis photophila*
USA: Hawaiian Islands

Ex *Agrotis procellaris*
USA: Hawaiian Islands (pre 1900)

Ex? *Helicoverpa confusa*
Confused Moth
USA: Hawaiian Islands (post 1927)

Ex *Helicoverpa minuta*
Minute Noctuid Moth
USA: Hawaiian Islands (Lisianski) (pre 1911)

Ex *Hypena laysanensis*
Laysan Dropseed Noctuid Moth
USA: Hawaiian Islands (1911)

Ex? *Hypena newelli*
Hilo Noctuid Moth
USA: Hawaiian Islands (Hawaii)

Ex? *Hypena plagiota*
Lovegrass Noctuid Moth
USA: Hawaiian Islands (Kauai, Oahu)

Ex? *Hypena senicula*
Kaholuamano Noctuid Moth
USA: Hawaiian Islands (Kauai)

List 3

THREATENED GENERA (etc)

Class ACTINOPTERYGII

Order PERCIFORMES

Family CICHLIDAE

I   **Haplochromine spp.** (> 250 spp.)
     Lake Victoria cichlid fishes
        (Lake Victoria)
        Kenya; Tanzania; Uganda

I   **Tilapiine spp.** (2 spp.)
     Lake Victoria cichlid fishes
        (Lake Victoria)
        Kenya; Tanzania; Uganda

Phylum ANNELIDA

Class OLIGOCHAETA

Order HAPLOTAXIDA

Family MICROCHAETIDAE

V   *Microchaetus* (23 species)
     South African Giant Earthworms
     South Africa

V   *Proandricus* (17 species)
     South African Giant Earthworms
     South Africa

V   *Tritogenia* (approx. 13 species)
     South African Giant Earthworms
     South Africa

Family ACANTHODRILIDAE

V   *Chilota* (13 species)
     Southern African Acanthodriline Earthworms
     South Africa

V   *Diplotrema* (15 species)
     Southern African Acanthodriline Earthworms
     South Africa

V   *Microscolex* (3 species)
     Southern African Acanthodriline Earthworms
     Lesotho; South Africa

V   *Udeina* (59 species)
     Southern African Acanthodriline Earthworms
     Lesotho; South Africa

Phylum ARTHROPODA

Class INSECTA

Order COLEOPTERA

Family ELATERIDAE

E   *Eopenthes* (17 species)
     Hawaiian Click Beetles
        USA: Hawaiian Islands

I   *Itodacnus* spp.
     Necker Click Beetles
        USA: Hawaiian Islands

Family CERAMBYCIDAE

E   *Plagithmysus* (49 species)
        USA: Hawaiian Islands

Family AGLYCYDERIDAE

E   *Proterhinus* (72 species)
     Hawaiian Proterhinus Beetles
        USA: Hawaiian Islands

Family CURCULIONIDAE

I   *Oodemas* (whole genus)
     Windward Chain Weevils
        USA: Hawaiian Islands

E   *Rhyncogonus* (22 species)
     (at least one species extinct)
     Hawaiian Snout Beetles
        USA: Hawaiian Islands

Order LEPIDOPTERA

Family PYRALIDAE

I   *Hedylepta* (14 species)
     (some species listed in extinct section)
     Hedyleptan Moths
        USA: Hawaiian Islands

Order HYMENOPTERA

Family COLLETIDAE

I   *Hylaeus* (64 species)
     (*Nesoprosopis*)
     (some species probably extinct)
     Yellow-faced Bee
        USA: Hawaiian Islands

List 4

THREATENED AND EXTINCT SUBSPECIES

Class MAMMALIA

Order CHIROPTERA

Family PTEROPODIDAE

V *Pteropus seychellensis aldabrensis*
Aldabra Flying-fox
Seychelles: Aldabra Atoll

Family VESPERTILIONIDAE

I *Lasiurus cinereus semotus*
Hawaiian Hoary Bat
USA: Hawaiian Islands

K *Myotis formosus bartelsi*
(*M. bartelsi*)
Bartel's Myotis
Indonesia: Java

R *Myotis formosus hermani*
(*M. hermani*)
Herman's Myotis
Indonesia: Sumatra

Order PRIMATES

Family LEMURIDAE

E *Hapalemur griseus alaotrensis*
Alaotran Gentle Lemur
Madagascar

K *Hapalemur griseus griseus*
Grey Gentle Lemur
Madagascar

V *Hapalemur griseus occidentalis*
Western Gentle Lemur
Madagascar

R *Eulemur fulvus albifrons*
White-fronted Lemur
Madagascar

V *Eulemur fulvus albocollaris*
White-collared Lemur
Madagascar

V *Eulemur fulvus collaris*
Collared Lemur
Madagascar

R *Eulemur fulvus fulvus*
Brown Lemur
Madagascar

V *Eulemur fulvus mayottensis*
Mayotte Lemur
Mayotte

R *Eulemur fulvus rufus*
(*E. macaco rufus*)
Red-fronted Lemur
Madagascar

V *Eulemur fulvus sanfordi*
(*E. macaco sanfordi*)
Sanford's Lemur
Madagascar

E *Eulemur macaco flavifrons*
Sclater's Lemur
Madagascar

V *Eulemur macaco macaco*
Black Lemur
Madagascar

Family CALLITRICHIDAE

E *Callithrix argentata leucippe*
Golden-white Bare-ear Marmoset
Brazil

E *Saguinus bicolor bicolor*
Pied Tamarin
Brazil

V *Saguinus fuscicollis leucogenys*
Andean Saddle-back Tamarin
Peru

V *Saguinus imperator imperator*
Black-chinned Emperor Tamarin
Bolivia; Brazil; Peru

Family CEBIDAE

E *Alouatta fusca fusca*
Northern Brown Howling Monkey
Brazil

E *Aloutta belzebul ululata*
Red-handed Howling Monkey
Brazil

E *Aloutta palliata aequatorialis*
South Pacific Blackish Howling Monkey
Colombia; Ecuador; Panama?; Peru

V *Aotos lemurinus griseimembra*
Night Monkey
Colombia

E *Ateles belzebuth hybridus*
Hybrid Spider Monkey
Colombia; Venezuela

E *Ateles belzebuth marginatus*
White-whiskered Spider Monkey
Brazil

V *Callicebus cupreus ornatus*
Ornate Titi
Colombia

E *Callicebus personatus barbarabrownae*
Northern Bahian Blond Titi
Brazil

E *Callicebus personatus melanochir*
Southern Bahian Masked Titi
Brazil

E *Callicebus personatus nigrifrons*
Black-fronted Titi
Brazil

E *Callicebus personatus personatus*
Northern Masked Titi
Brazil

V *Callicebus torquatus lucifer*
Widow Monkey
Brazil; Colombia; Peru

V *Cebus albifrons cuscinus*
White-fronted Capuchin
Bolivia?; Peru

V *Cebus albifrons yuracus*
Andean White-fronted Capuchin
Ecuador; Peru

V *Cebus apella robustus*
Robust Tufted Capuchin
Brazil

E *Cebus apella xanthosternos*
Yellow-breasted Capuchin Monkey
Brazil

E *Chiropotes satanas satanas*
Black Saki
Brazil

V *Chiropotes satanas utahicki*
Uta Hick's Bearded Saki
Brazil

E *Lagothrix lagotricha lugens*
Colombian Woolly Monkey
Colombia

Family CERCOPITHECIDAE

K *Cercocebus albigena aterrimus*
(*C. aterrimus*)
Black Mangabey
Angola; Zaire

E *Cercocebus galeritus galeritus*
Tana River Mangabey
Kenya; Tanzania

E *Cercocebus galeritus 'sanjei'*
Sanje Mangabey
Tanzania

V *Cercocebus torquatus torquatus*
Collared Mangabey
Cameroon; Congo; Côte d'Ivoire;
Equatorial Guinea: Rio Muni; Gabon; Ghana;
Guinea; Liberia; Nigeria; Senegal; Sierra
Leone

E *Cercopithecus diana roloway*
Roloway Guenon
Côte d'Ivoire; Ghana; Togo

V *Macaca ochreata brunnescens*
(*M. brunnescens*)
Muna-Butung Macaque
Indonesia: Butung, Muna

E *Macaca fuscata yakui*
Yakushima Macaque
Japan

E *Macaca nemestrina pagensis*
(*M. pagensis*)
Mentawai Macaque
Indonesia: Mentawai Islands, Siberut, Sipora,
North and South Pagai Islands

V *Macaca tonkeana hecki*
(*M. hecki*)
Heck's Macaque
Indonesia: Sulawesi

K *Papio hamadryas papio*
(*P. papio*)
Guinea Baboon
Gambia; Guinea; Guinea-Bissau?; Liberia?;
Mali; Mauritania; Senegal; Sierra Leone

R *Procolobus badius temminckii*
(*Procolobus temminckii*)
(*Procolobus badius* has been included in the
genus *Colobus*)
Temminck's Red Colobus
Gambia; Guinea; Guinea-Bissau; Senegal

E *Procolobus badius waldroni*
Miss Waldron's Bay Colobus
Côte d'Ivoire; Ghana

E *Procolobus badius pennantii*
(*P. pennantii*)
Eastern Red Colobus
Equatorial Guinea: Fernando Po

E *Procolobus badius bouvieri*
(*P. pennantii bouvieri*)
Bouvier's Red Colobus
Congo

K   ***Procolobus badius ellioti***
(*P. rufomitratus ellioti*)
Elliot's Red Colobus
    Uganda (ex?); Zaire

K   ***Procolobus badius foai***
(*P. rufomitratus foai, P. pennantii foai*)
Foa Red Colobus
    Zaire

E   ***Procolobus badius gordonorum***
(*P. gordonorum, P. pennantii gordonorum*)
Uhehe Red Colobus
    Tanzania

E   ***Procolobus badius kirkii***
(*Procolobus kirkii, P. pennantii kirkii*)
Zanzibar Red Colobus
    Tanzania: Zanzibar
    Tanzania: [Pemba Island]

K   ***Procolobus badius oustaleti***
(*P. rufomitratus oustaleti, P. pennantii oustaleti*)
Oustalet's Red Colobus
    Central African Republic; Sudan?; Zaire

V   ***Procolobus badius tephrosceles***
(*P. rufomitratus tephrosceles, P. pennantii tephrosceles*)
Uganda Red Colobus
    Burundi; Rwanda; Tanzania; Uganda

K   ***Procolobus badius tholloni***
(*P. rufomitratus tholloni, P. pennantii tholloni*)
Thollon's Red Colobus
    Zaire

E   ***Procolobus badius preussi***
(*P. preussi, P. pennanti preussi*)
Preuss's Colobus
    Cameroon; Nigeria (ex?)

V   ***Procolobus badius rufomitratus***
(*P. rufomitratus, P. rufomitratus rufomitratus*)
Tana River Colobus
    Kenya

E   ***Pygathrix roxellana bieti***
(*Pygathrix bieti*, sometimes included in *Rhinopithecus*)
Yunnan Snub-nosed Monkey
    China

Family HOMINIDAE

E   ***Gorilla gorilla beringei***
Mountain Gorilla
    Burundi (ex?); Rwanda; Uganda; Zaire: Virunga Volcano region

E   ***Pan troglodytes verus***
West African Chimpanzee
    Côte d'Ivoire; Ghana; Guinea; Guinea-Bissau (ex?); Liberia; Mali; Senegal; Sierra Leone [Gambia]

Order CARNIVORA

Family FELIDAE

E   ***Acinonyx jubatus venaticus***
Asiatic Cheetah
    Iran

R   ***Caracal caracal michaelis***
(*Lynx caracal michaelis, Felis caracal michaelis*)
Turkmenian Caracal
    Kazakhstan; Tajikistan; Turkmenia; Uzbekistan

E   ***Felis margarita scheffeli***
Pakistan Sand Cat
    Pakistan

E   ***Prionailurus bengalensis iriomotensis***
(*Prionailurus iriomotensis*, sometimes included in *Felis*)
Iriomote Cat
    Japan: Iriomote Island

E   ***Panthera leo persica***
Asiatic Lion
    India

E   ***Panthera pardus orientalis***
Amur Leopard
    China; D.P.R. Korea; Korea Republic; Russia

E   ***Panthera pardus nimr***
South Arabian Leopard
    Oman; Saudi Arabia; Yemen

E   ***Panthera pardus kotiya***
Sri Lankan Leopard
    Sri Lanka

V   ***Panthera pardus japonensis***
North Chinese Leopard
    China

I   ***Panthera pardus saxicolor***
North Persian Leopard
    Afghanistan; Iran; Turkmenistan

I   ***Panthera pardus melas***
Javan Leopard
    Indonesia: Java

E   ***Puma concolor coryi***
(*Felis concolor coryi*)
Florida Cougar
    USA

E   **Puma concolor couguar**
     (*Felis concolor cougar*)
     Eastern Puma
         Canada; USA

Family HERPESTIDAE

E   **Bdeogale crassicauda omnivora**
     Sokoke Bushy-tailed Mongoose
         Kenya; Tanzania

Family HYAENIDAE

E   **Hyaena hyaena barbara**
     Barbary Hyaena
         Algeria; Morocco; Tunisia

Family MUSTELIDAE

Ex? **Conepatus mesoleucus telmalestes**
     Big Thicket Hog-nosed Skunk
         USA: Texas

E   **Eira barbara senex**
     Greyheaded Tayra
         Belize; Guatemala: Mexico

V   **Lutra longicaudis longicaudis**
     (*L. platensis*, also assigned to *Lontra*)
     La Plata Otter
         Argentina; Bolivia; Brazil; Paraguay?; Uruguay

V   **Lutra lutra lutra**
     European Otter
         Eurasia

E   **Martes flavigula robinsoni**
     Javan Yellow-throated Marten
         Indonesia: Java

R   **Martes melampus tsuensis**
     Tsushima Island Marten
         Japan

K   **Melogale personata orientalis**
     (*M. orientalis*)
     Javan Ferret-badger
         Indonesia: Java

I   **Martes zibellina brachyura**
     Japanese Sable
         Japan: Hokkaido

V   **Vormela peregusna peregusna**
     European Marbled Polecat
         Bulgaria; Greece; Romania; Turkey; Ukraine;
         Yugoslavia

Family ODOBENIDAE

K   **Odobenus rosmarus laptevi**
     Laptev Walrus
         Russia

Family OTARIIDAE

Ex   **Zalophus californianus japonicus**
     Japanese Sealion
         Japan; D.P.R. Korea; Korea Republic

Family PHOCIDAE

V   **Phoca hispida botnica**
     Baltic Ringed Seal
         Estonia?; Finland; Russia; Sweden

V   **Phoca hispida ladogensis**
     Ladoga Ringed Seal
         Russia: Lake Ladoga

E   **Phoca hispida saimensis**
     Saimaa Ringed Seal
         Finland: Lake Saimaa

K   **Phoca vitulina mellonae**
     Ungava Seal
         Canada; Greenland

V   **Phoca vitulina stejnegeri**
     Kuril Seal
         Kuril Sea

Family URSIDAE

E   **Selenarctos thibetanus gedrosianus**
     (*Ursus thibetanus gedrosianus*)
     Baluchistan Bear
         Iran; Pakistan

Ex   **Ursus arctos nelsoni**
     Mexican Grizzly Bear
         Mexico; USA

Family VIVERRIDAE

I   **Arctictis binturong whitei**
     Palawan Binturong
         Philippines: Palawan

E   **Arctogalidia trivirgata trilineata**
     Javan Small-toothed Palm Civet
         Indonesia: Java

I   **Crossarchus ansorgei ansorgei**
     Angolan Cusimanse
         Angola

R   **Genetta genetta isabelae**
     Ibiza Genet
         Spain: Ibiza

E   **Paradoxurus hermaphroditus lignicolor**
     (*P. lignicolor*)
     Mentawai Palm Civet
         Indonesia: Sumatra

I   **Poiana richardsoni liberiensis**
     Leighton's Linsang
         Liberia; Côte d'Ivoire; Sierra Leone

E   *Viverra megaspila civettina*
(*V. civettina*)
Malabar Large-spotted Civet
India: Kerala

Order PERISSODACTYLA

Family EQUIDAE

Ex?   *Equus ferus przewalskii*
(*E. caballus przewalskii, E. przewalskii*)
Przewalski's Horse
China; Mongolia

Ex?   *Equus hemionus hemionus*
North Mongolian Kulan
Mongolia

Ex   *Equus hemionus hemippus*
Syrian Wild Ass
Iran; Iraq; Israel; Saudi Arabia; Syria

E   *Equus hemionus khur*
Indian Wild Ass
India

E   *Equus hemionus kulan*
Kulan
Kazakhstan; Turkmenistan

I   *Equus hemionus luteus*
Gobi Kulan
China; Mongolia

E   *Equus hemionus onager*
Onager
Iran

V   *Equus kiang holderi*
Eastern Kiang
China

I   *Equus kiang kiang*
Western Kiang
India; Nepal

I   *Equus kiang polyodon*
Southern Kiang
China; India: Sikkim

E   *Equus zebra zebra*
Cape Mountain Zebra
South Africa

Family RHINOCEROTIDAE

E   *Ceratotherium simum cottoni*
Northern White Rhinoceros
Zaire

Order ARTIODACTYLA

Family SUIDAE

V   *Hylochoerus meinertzhageni ivoriensis*
Western Forest Hog
West Africa

Ex   *Phacochoerus aethiopicus aethiopicus*
Cape Warthog
South Africa: Cape Province

V   *Phacochoerus aethiopicus delameri*
Somali Warthog
Kenya; Somalia

I   *Phacochoerus africanus aeliani*
Eritrean Warthog
Djibouti; Eritrea

R   *Sus barbatus ahoenobarbus*
Palawan Bearded Pig
Philippines: Balabac, Palawan, Calamian Islands

V   *Sus barbatus oi*
Western Bearded Pig
Indonesia: Sumatra, Kundur, Ungar Islands; Malaysia

V   *Sus scrofa riukiuanus*
Ryukyu Islands Wild Pig
Japan: Ryukyu Islands

Family HIPPOPOTAMIDAE

Ex   *Hexaprotodon liberiensis heslopi*
Nigeria

Family TRAGULIDAE

V   *Tragulus napu nigricans*
Balabac Chevrotain
Philippines: Balabac Island

Family CERVIDAE

E   *Cervus elaphus yarkandensis*
Yarkand Deer
China

E   *Cervus eldii eldii*
Manipur Brow-antlered Deer
India

E   *Cervus eldii siamensis*
Thailand Brow-antlered Deer
Cambodia; China (ex?); Laos; Thailand; Viet Nam

Ex? *Cervus nippon grassianus*
Shansi Sika
China

E *Cervus nippon keramae*
Ryukyu Sika
Japan: Ryukyu Islands

E *Cervus nippon mandarinus*
North China Sika
China

E *Cervus nippon pseudaxis*
(*C. n. kopschi*)
South China Sika
China; Viet Nam

I *Cervus nippon sichanicus*
Sichuan Sika
China

E *Cervus nippon taiouanus*
Formosan Sika
Taiwan (ex?)
[Japan: Oshima Island]

R *Odocoileus hemionus cerrosensis*
Cedros Island Mule Deer
Mexico: Cedros Island

E *Odocoileus virginianus clavium*
Key Deer
USA: Florida Keys

E *Ozotoceros bezoarticus celer*
Argentinian Pampas Deer
Argentina

E *Rangifer tarandus pearyi*
Peary Caribou
Canada

Family ANTILOCAPRIDAE

E *Antilocapra americana peninsularis*
Baja California Pronghorn
Mexico

E *Antilocapra americana sonoriensis*
Sonoran Pronghorn
Mexico; USA

Family BOVIDAE

E *Aepyceros melampus petersi*
Black-faced Impala
Angola; Namibia

Ex *Alcelaphus buselaphus buselaphus*
Bubal Hartebeest
Algeria; Egypt; Morocco; Tunisia

E *Alcelaphus buselaphus swaynei*
Swayne's Hartebeest
Ethiopia

E *Alcelaphus buselaphus tora*
Tora Hartebeest
Eritrea?; Ethiopia; Sudan

Ex *Ammotragus lervia ornatus*
Egyptian Barbary Sheep
Egypt

E *Budorcas taxicolor bedfordi*
Golden Takin
China

I *Budorcas taxicolor taxicolor*
Mishmi Takin
Bhutan; China; India; Myanmar

K *Budorcas taxicolor tibetana*
Sichuan Takin
China

K *Budorcas taxicolor whitei*
Bhutan Takin
Bhutan; China; India

R *Capra aegagrus blythi*
Sind Ibex
Pakistan

E *Capra aegagrus chialtanensis*
Chiltan Goat
Pakistan

R *Capra aegagrus cretica*
Cretan Goat
Greece

R *Capra aegagrus turcmenica*
Turkman Wild Goat
Turkmenistan

E *Capra pyrenaica pyrenaica*
Pyrenean Ibex
Spain

R *Capra pyrenaica victoriae*
Gredos Ibex
Spain

E *Capricornis sumatraensis sumatraensis*
Sumatran Serow
Indonesia: Sumatra; Malaysia

R *Cephalophus ogilbyi crusalbum*
White-legged Duiker
Congo?; Gabon

E *Cephalophus nigrifrons rubidus*
Ruwenzori Black-fronted Duiker
Uganda; Zaire?

R *Damaliscus dorcas dorcas*
Bontebok
South Africa

V *Damaliscus lunatus korrigum*
Korrigum
Benin; Burkina Faso; Cameroon; Niger; Nigeria; Togo

Ex? *Gazella dorcas saudiya*
Saudi Gazelle
Iraq?; Kuwait?; Saudi Arabia?; United Arab Emirates?; Yemen?

E *Gazella gazella acaciae*
Acacia Gazelle
Israel; Jordan?

R *Gazella gazella farasani*
Farasan Gazelle
Saudi Arabia: Farasan Islands

E *Gazella gazella muscatensis*
Muscat Gazelle
Oman

E *Gazella subgutturosa marica*
Arabian Sand Gazelle
Iran?; Jordan; Oman; Saudi Arabia; Syria?; United Arab Emirates; Yemen?

E *Hippotragus niger variani*
Giant Sable Antelope
Angola

Ex *Kobus leche robertsi*
Roberts' Lechwe
Zambia

E *Nemorhaedus baileyi baileyi*
Tibetan Red Goral
China

K *Nemorhaedus baileyi cranbrooki*
Red Goral
India; Myanmar

V *Nemorhaedus caudatus evansi*
Evans' Long-tailed Goral
Thailand

E *Nemorhaedus goral bedfordi*
Western Himalayan Goral
Pakistan

E *Oreotragus oreotragus porteousi*
Western Klipspringer
Nigeria

V *Ourebia ourebi haggardi*
Haggard's Oribi
Kenya; Somalia

I *Ovis ammon ammon*
Altai Argali
China; Mongolia; Russia

E *Ovis ammon darwini*
Mongolian Argali, Gobi Argali
China; Mongolia

I *Ovis ammon hodgsoni*
Tibetan Argali
China; India; Nepal

E *Ovis ammon jubata*
Shansi Argali, Northern Chinese Argali
China

E *Ovis ammon karelini*
Tien Shan Argali
China; Kazakhstan

E *Ovis ammon nigrimontana*
Kara Tau Argali
Kazakhstan

I *Ovis ammon polii*
Marco Polo Argali, Pamir Argali
Afghanistan; China; Pakistan; Tadjikistan

V *Ovis canadensis cremnobates*
Peninsular Bighorn Sheep
Mexico; USA

V *Ovis canadensis mexicana*
Mexican Bighorn Sheep
Mexico; USA

V *Ovis canadensis weemsi*
Weems' Bighorn Sheep
Mexico

V *Ovis nivicola borealis*
Putorean Snow Sheep, Norilsk Snow Sheep
Russia

K *Ovis orientalis arkal*
Transcaspian Urial
Iran; Turkmenistan; Uzbekistan

V *Ovis orientalis blanfordi*
Blanford's Urial
Pakistan

E *Ovis orientalis bocharensis*
Bukhara Urial
Tajikistan; Uzbekistan

I *Ovis orientalis cycloceros*
Afghan Urial
Afghanistan; Pakistan; Turkmenistan

I *Ovis orientalis gmelini*
Armenian Mouflon
Armenia; Azerbaijan; Iran; Turkey

K *Ovis orientalis isphahanica*
Esfahan Mouflon
Iran

K *Ovis orientalis laristanica*
Laristan Mouflon
Iran

R *Ovis orientalis musimon*
European Mouflon
France: Corsica; Italy: Sardinia

V *Ovis orientalis ophion*
Cyprus Mouflon
Cyprus

K *Ovis orientalis orientalis*
Red Sheep
Iran

V *Ovis orientalis punjabiensis*
Punjab Urial
Pakistan

E *Ovis orientalis severtzovi*
Severtzov's Urial
Uzbekistan

E *Ovis orientalis vignei*
Ladahk Urial
India; Pakistan

E *Redunca fulvorufula adamauae*
Western Mountain Reedbuck
Cameroon; Nigeria

V *Redunca fulvorufula chanleri*
Chanler's Mountain Reedbuck
Ethiopia; Kenya; Sudan; Tanzania; Uganda

K *Rupicapra rupicapra asiatica*
Turkish Chamois
Turkey

I *Rupicapra rupicapra balcanica*
Balkan Chamois
Albania; Bulgaria; Greece; Yugoslavia

E *Rupicapra rupicapra cartusiana*
Chartreuse Chamois
France

R *Rupicapra rupicapra caucasica*
Caucasian Chamois
Georgia; Russia

V *Rupicapra rupicapra tatrica*
Tatra Chamois
Poland; Slovakia

V *Rupicapra pyrenaica ornata*
Apennine Chamois
Italy: Abruzzo National Park

E *Saiga tatarica mongolica*
Mongolian Saiga
Mongolia

E *Tragelaphus derbianus derbianus*
(*T. oryx derbianus*, also assigned to *Taurotragus*)
Western Giant Eland
Guinea?; Guinea-Bissau; Mali?; Senegal

V *Tragelaphus eurycerus isaaci*
Eastern Bongo
Kenya

Order RODENTIA

Family APLODONTIDAE

I *Aplodontia rufa nigra*
Point Arena Mountain Beaver
USA: California

I *Aplodontia rufa phaea*
Point Reyes Mountain Beaver
USA: California

Family SCIURIDAE

E *Glaucomys sabrinus coloratus*
Carolina Flying Squirrel
USA

E *Glaucomys sabrinus fuscus*
Virginia Flying Squirrel
USA

R *Glaucomys volans goldmani*
Mexican Flying Squirrel
Mexico

R *Glaucomys volans guerreroensis*
Guerrero Flying Squirrel
Mexico

R *Glaucomys volans oaxacensis*
Oaxaca Flying Squirrel
Mexico

E *Ratufa indica dealbata*
Dangs Giant Squirrel
India

E *Ratufa indica elphinstoni*
Maharashtra Giant Squirrel
India

E *Sciurus niger cinereus*
Delmarva Fox Squirrel
USA

E *Tamias minimus atristriatus*
(*Eutamias minimus atristriatus*)
New Mexico Least Chipmunk
USA: New Mexico

E **Tamias quadrivittatus australis**
(*Eutamias quadrivittatus australis*)
Organ Mountains Chipmunk
USA: New Mexico

E **Tamiasciurus hudsonicus grahamensis**
Mount Graham Red Squirrel
USA: Arizona

Family CASTORIDAE

E **Castor canadensis frondator**
Broad-tail Beaver
Mexico

E **Castor canadensis mexicanus**
Rio Grande Beaver
Mexico

E **Castor fiber birulai**
Mongolian Beaver
Mongolia

Family GEOMYIDAE

R **Thomomys umbrinus emotus**
Southern Pocket Gopher
USA: New Mexico

Family HETEROMYIDAE

E **Dipodomys heermanni morroensis**
Morro Bay Kangaroo-rat
USA

K **Dipodomys microps leucotis**
Houserock Chisel-toothed Kangaroo Rat
USA: Arizona

E **Dipodomys nitratoides exilis**
Fresno Kangaroo Rat
USA: California

E **Dipodomys nitratoides nitratoides**
Tipton Kangaroo Rat
USA: California

E **Perognathus inornatus psammophilus**
(*P. longimembris psammophilus*)
Salinas Pocket Mouse
USA: California

E **Perognathus longimembris brevinasus**
Los Angeles Little Pocket Mouse
USA: California

Family DIPODIDAE

E **Zapus hudsonius luteus**
(*Z. princeps luteus*)
Meadow Jumping Mouse
USA: New Mexico

I **Zapus trinotatus orarius**
Point Reyes Jumping Mouse
USA: California

Family MURIDAE

E **Microtus californicus scirpensis**
Amargosa Vole
USA: California

E **Microtus mexicanus hualpaiensis**
Hualapai Vole
USA: Arizona

I **Microtus mexicanus navaho**
USA: Arizona

E **Microtus pennsylvanicus chihuahuensis**
Chihuahua Vole
Mexico

E **Microtus pennsylvanicus dukecampbelli**
Florida Saltmarsh Vole
USA: Florida

E **Neotoma floridana smalli**
Key Largo Woodrat
USA

V **Neotoma fuscipes riparia**
San Joaquin Valley Woodrat
USA: California

I **Oryzomys palustris argentatus**
(*O. argentatus*)
Silver Rice Rat
USA

E **Peromyscus gossypinus allapaticola**
Key Largo Cotton Mouse
USA

E **Peromyscus polionotus allophrys**
Choctawhatchee Beach Mouse
USA

E **Peromyscus polionotus ammobates**
Alabama Beach Mouse
USA

I **Peromyscus polionotus niveiventris**
South-eastern Beach Mouse
USA

E **Peromyscus polionotus phasma**
Anastasia Island Beach Mouse
USA

E **Peromyscus polionotus trissyllepsis**
Perdido Key Beach Mouse
USA

V **Reithrodontomys megalotis limicola**
Southern Marsh Harvest Mouse
   USA: California

E **Sigmodon arizonae plenus**
(*S. hispidus plenus*)
Colorado River Cotton Rat
   USA: Arizona?, California

Order LAGOMORPHA

Family OCHOTONIDAE

V **Ochotona alpina argentata**
China

V **Ochotona alpina nitida**
Russia

V **Ochotona alpina ssp.**
Mongolia

E **Ochotona cansus sorrela**
China

V **Ochotona cansus morosa**
China

E **Ochotona pallasi hamica**
China; Mongolia

I **Ochotona pallasi sunidica**
China

E **Ochotona thibetana sikimaria**
India

I **Ochotona thibetana huangensis**
China

Family LEPORIDAE

E **Sylvilagus palustris hefneri**
Lower Keys Marsh Rabbit
   USA: Florida Keys

Order MACROSCELIDEA

Family MACROSCELIDIDAE

K **Petrodromus tetradactylus sangi**
Four-toed Elephant-shrew
   Kenya

K **Rhynchocyon cirnei cirnei**
Chequered Elephant-shrew
   Mozambique

R **Rhynchocyon cirnei hendersoni**
Henderson's Chequered Elephant-shrew
   Malawi

Class AVES

Order TINAMIFORMES

Family TINAMIDAE

E/Ex **Crypturellus erythropus saltuarius**
(*C. saltuarius*)
Magdalena Tinamou
   Colombia (ex?)

Order PROCELLARIIFORMES

Family PROCELLARIIDAE

E/Ex **Pterodroma hasitata caribbaea**
(*P. caribbaea*)
Jamaica Petrel
   Jamaica (ex?)

K **Puffinus auricularis newelli**
(*Puffinus newelli*)
Newell's Shearwater
   USA: Hawaiian Islands (Hawaii, Kauai)

Order CICONIIFORMES

Family THRESKIORNITHIDAE

I **Bostrychia olivacea bocagei**
(*B. bocagei*)
Dwarf Olive Ibis
   São Tomé and Principe: São Tomé

Order GRUIFORMES

Family RALLIDAE

R **Gallinula nesiotis comeri**
(*Gallinula comeri*)
Gough Moorhen
   Saint Helena: Gough Island

Order CHARADRIIFORMES

Family HAEMATOPODIDAE

E **Haematopus unicolor chathamensis**
(*H. chathamensis*)
Chatham Islands Oystercatcher
   New Zealand: Chatham Islands

Order PSITTACIFORMES

Family PSITTACIDAE

K **Aratinga holochlora brevipes**
(*A. brevipes*)
Socorro Parakeet
   Mexico: Socorro Island

Order STRIGIFORMES

Family STRIGIDAE

K   ***Otus magicus albiventris***
(*O. alfredi*)
Flores Scops-Owl
    Indonesia: Flores

R   ***Otus magicus insularis***
(*O. insularis*)
Seychelles Scops-Owl
    Seychelles: Mahe

K   ***Otus spilocephalus stresemanni***
(*O. stresemanni*)
Sumatran Scops-Owl
    Indonesia: Sumatra

Order APODIFORMES

Family APODIDAE

K   ***Apus barbatus sladeniae***
(*Apus sladeniae*)
Fernando Po Swift
    Angola; Cameroon; Equatorial Guinea: Bioko;
    Nigeria?

Order CORACIIFORMES

Family ALCEDINIDAE

Ex   ***Todirhamphus cinnamominus miyakoensis***
(*Halcyon miyakoensis*)
Ryukyu Kingfisher
    Japan: Nansei-shoto

Order PASSERIFORMES

Family FURNARIIDAE

V   ***Asthenes dorbignyi huancavelicae***
Pale-tailed Canastero
    Peru

E   ***Cinclodes excelsior aricomae***
(*Cinclodes aricomae*)
Royal Cinclodes
    Bolivia; Peru

Family COTINGIDAE

R   ***Laniisoma elegans elegans***
(*L. elegans*)
Shrike-like Cotinga
    Brazil

Family TYRANNIDAE

E   ***Onychorhynchus coronatus occidentalis***
Western Royal-Flycatcher
    Ecuador; Peru

Family PYCNONOTIDAE

K   ***Hypsipetes borbonicus olivaceus***
(*Hypsipetes olivaceus*)
Mauritius Bulbul
    Mauritius

Family MUSCICAPIDAE

K   ***Gerygone magnirostris hypoxantha***
(*G. hypoxantha*)
Biak Gerygone
    Indonesia: Biak

E   ***Turdus olivaceus helleri***
(*T. helleri*)
Teita Thrush
    Kenya

Family MELIPHAGIDAE

K   ***Manorina flavigula melanotis***
(*M. melanotis*)
Black-eared Miner
    Australia

Class REPTILIA

Order TESTUDINES

Family EMYDIDAE

V   ***Trachemys scripta callirostris***
(*Pseudemys scripta callirostris, Pseudemys ornata callirostris, Chrysemys ornata callirostris*)
Colombian Slider
    Colombia; Venezuela

R   ***Trachemys stejnegeri malonei***
(*Pseudemys malonei, Pseudemys terrapen malonei, Chrysemys malonei*)
Inagua Island Turtle
    Bahamas: Great Inagua Island

R   ***Trachemys terrapen felis***
(*Pseudemys felis*)
Cat Island Freshwater Turtle
    [Bahamas: Cat Island]

Family TESTUDINIDAE

V   ***Testudo graeca graeca***
(includes *Testudo whitei, T. flavominimaralis Furculachelys whitei, F. nabeulensis*)
Spur-thighed Tortoise
    Algeria; Egypt?; Libya; Morocco; Spain;
    Tunisia
    [France; Italy]

V   ***Testudo hermanni boettgeri***
(*Testudo hermanni hermanni*)
Eastern Hermann's Tortoise
    Albania; Bulgaria; Greece; Italy; Romania;
    Turkey; Yugoslavia
    [Malta]

E   ***Testudo hermanni hermanni***
(*Testudo hermanni robertmertensi*)
Western Hermann's Tortoise
    France; Italy; Spain: Balearic Islands,
    [mainland]

Order SAURIA

Family PYGOPODIDAE

V   ***Aprasia rostrata rostrata***
Hermite Island Worm-lizard
    Australia

Family AGAMIDAE

V   ***Tympanocryptis lineata pinguicolla***
South-eastern Lined Earless Dragon
    Australia

Family IGUANIDAE

K   ***Phrynosoma coronatum blainvillei***
San Diego Horned Lizard
    Mexico: Baja California; USA: California

Family LACERTIDAE

R   ***Podarcis filfolensis filfolensis***
(*Lacerta filfolensis filfolensis*)
Filfola Lizard
    Malta: Filfola Island

Family SCINCIDAE

V   ***Egernia pulchra longicauda***
Jurien Bay Rock-skink
    Australia

E   ***Eulamprus tympanum*** ssp.
Dreeite Water Skink
    Australia

R   ***Gongylomorphus bojerii fontenayi***
(*Scelotes bojeri*)
Macabe Forest Skink
    Mauritius: Macabe Forest

Family ANIELLIDAE

I   ***Aniella pulchra nigra***
Black Legless Lizard
    USA: California

Family VARANIDAE

V   ***Varanus griseus caspius***
Central Asian Desert Monitor
    Central Asia

Order SERPENTES

Family BOIDAE

R   ***Charina bottae umbratica***
Rubber Boa
    USA: California

R   ***Epicrates monensis monensis***
(*Epicrates gracilis monensis*)
Mona Island Boa
    Puerto Rico: Mona Island

R   ***Epicrates striatus fosteri***
Bahamas Boa
    Bahamas

V   ***Morelia spilota imbricata***
Western Australian Carpet Python
    Australia

Family COLUBRIDAE

V   ***Drymarchon corais couperi***
Eastern Indigo Snake
    USA

R   ***Masticophis flagellum ruddocki***
San Joaquin Coachwhip
    USA: San Joaquin Valley, California

R   ***Masticophis lateralis euryxanthus***
Almeda Striped Racer
    USA: California

V   ***Natrix natrix cetti***
Sardinian Grass Snake
    Italy: Sardinia

R   ***Nerodia fasciata taeniata***
Atlantic Saltmarsh Snake
    USA: Florida

V   ***Nerodia harteri paucimaculata***
Concho Water Snake
    USA: Colorado and Concho River system

K   ***Nerodia sipedon insularum***
Lake Erie Water Snake
    (Lake Erie)
    Canada; USA

E   ***Thamnophis sirtalis tetrataenia***
San Francisco Garter Snake
    USA: California

Family ELAPIDAE

V   *Notechis ater ater*
Krefft's Tiger Snake
Australia

Family VIPERIDAE

V   *Crotalus willardi obscurus*
New Mexican Ridge-nosed Rattlesnake
Mexico; USA

R   *Vipera ammodytes transcaucasiana*
Transcaucasian Long-nosed Viper
Armenia; Azerbaijan; Georgia; Russia; Turkey

E   *Vipera ursinii rakosiensis*
Orsini's Viper
Austria (ex?); Hungary; Romania

Class AMPHIBIA

Order ANURA

Family BUFONIDAE

I   *Bufo boreas nelsoni*
(alternatively treated as a full species *Bufo nelsoni*)
Amargosa Toad
USA: Nevada

Family HYLIDAE

I   *Pseudacris streckeri illinoensis*
Illinois Chorus Frog
USA

Family PELOBATIDAE

V   *Pelobates fuscus insubricus*
Italian Spadefoot Toad
Italy: plains of River Po; Switzerland: Ticino (ex?)

Order CAUDATA

Family AMBYSTOMATIDAE

R   *Ambystoma dumerilii dumerilii*
Lake Patzcuaro Salamander or Achoque
Mexico: Lake Patzcuaro

E   *Ambystoma macrodactylum croceum*
Santa Cruz Long-toed Salamander
USA: California

V   *Ambystoma tigrinum californiense*
(*Ambystoma californiense*)
California Tiger Salamander
USA: California

Class CEPHALASPIDOMORPHI

Order PETROMYZONTIFORMES

Family PETROMYZONTIDAE

R   *Lampetra tridentata* ssp.
Pacific Lamprey
USA

Class ACTINOPTERYGII

Order ACIPENSERIFORMES

Family ACIPENSERIDAE

V   *Acipenser oxyrhynchus* ssp.
Atlantic Sturgeon
Canada; USA

Order CYPRINIFORMES

Family CYPRINIDAE

V   *Dionda episcopa* ssp.
Roundnose Minnow
Mexico

V   *Gila bicolor* ssp.
Tui Chub
USA

V   *Gila robusta* ssp.
Roundtail Chub
Mexico; USA

V   *Lepidomeda mollispinis* ssp.
Virgin Spinedace
USA

E   *Pseudorasbora pumila* ssp.
Ushimotsugo
Japan: Honshu Island

E   *Rhodeus atremius suigensis*
Suigen Zenitanago
Japan: Honshu Island

E   *Rhodeus ocellatus smithi*
Nippon Baratanago
Japan: Yao city, Osaka

V   *Rhinichthys cataractae* ssp.
Longnose Dace
Canada; USA

V   *Rhinichthys osculus* ssp.
Speckled Dace
Canada; Mexico; USA

Family CATOSTOMIDAE

R   *Catostomus catostomus lacustris*
Jasper Longnose Sucker
Canada

E   *Catostomus clarki intermedius*
White River Sucker
USA

R   *Catostomus dicobolus yarrowi*
Zuni Bluehead Sucker
USA

R   *Catostomus occidentalis lacusanserinus*
Goose Lake Sucker
USA

Ex   *Chasmistes liorus liorus*
June Sucker
USA

E   *Chasmistes liorus mictus*
June Sucker
USA

R   *Catostomus rimiculus* ssp.
Jenny Creek Sucker
USA

Order CHARACIFORMES

Family CHARACIDAE

R   *Astyanax mexicanus jordani*
Sardina Ciega
Mexico

Order SALMONIFORMES

Family PLECOGLOSSIDAE

E   *Plecoglossus altivelis ryukyuensis*
Ryukyu Ayu-fish
Japan: Ryukyu Islands

Family SALMONIDAE

V   *Onchorhynchus clarki* ssp.
Cutthroat Trout
USA

V   *Stenodus leucichthys leucichthys*
Beloribitsa
Azerbaijan?; Khazakstan; Russia

Order CYPRINODONTIFORMES

Family GOODEIDAE

Ex   *Empetrichthys latos concavus*
Raycraft Ranch Poolfish
USA

E   *Empetrichthys latos latos*
Pahrump Poolfish
USA

Ex   *Empetrichthys latos pahrump*
Pahrump Ranch Poolfish
USA

Family CYPRINODONTIDAE

R   *Cyprinodon salinus milleri*
Cottonball Marsh Pupfish
USA

R   *Cyprinodon salinus salinus*
Salt Creek Pupfish
USA

V   *Cyprinodon eximius* ssp.
Conchos Pupfish
Mexico; USA

E   *Cyprinodon macularius* ssp.
Desert Pupfish
Mexico; USA

V   *Cyprinodon nevadensis* ssp.
Amargosa Pupfish
USA

Order GASTEROSTEIFORMES

Family GASTEROSTEIDAE

E   *Gasterosteus aculeatus santaeannae*
Santa Ana Stickleback
USA

E   *Gasterosteus aculeatus williamsoni*
Unarmored Threespine Stickleback
USA

Order PERCIFORMES

Family CENTRARCHIDAE

R   *Lepomis megalotis* ssp.
Mojarra de Cuatro Cienegas
Mexico

R   *Micropterus salmoides* ssp.
Robalo de Cuatro Cienegas
Mexico

Family CICHLIDAE

E   *Cichlasoma urophtalmus ericymba*
Mojarra de Bulha
Mexico

R   *Oreochromis alcalicus grahami*
Lake Magadi Tilapia
Kenya

Family EMBIOTOCIDAE

R   *Hysterocarpus traski pomo*
Russian River Tule Perch
USA

Phylum Mollusca

Class GASTROPODA

Order ARCHAEOGASTROPODA

Family HELICINIDAE

V *Pleuropoma zigzac ponapense*
    Federated States of Micronesia: Pohnpei

V *Pleuropoma zigzac zigzac*
    Federated States of Micronesia: Kosrae

Order MESOGASTROPODA

Family DIPLOMMATINIDAE

V *Palaina strigata kororensis*
    Palau: Koror

Order STYLOMMATOPHORA

Family CLAUSILIIDAE

R *Macrogastra lineolata euzieriana*
    France

Family DISCIDAE

V *Oreohelix idahoensis idahoensis*
    Idaho Banded Mountain Snail
    USA

R *Oreohelix strigosa goniogyra*
    Carinated Striate Banded Mountain Snail
    USA

Family POLYGYRIDAE

V *Mesodon clarki nantahala*
    Noonday Snail
    USA

I *Mesodon clausus trossulus*
    Banded Mesodon
    USA

I *Stenotrema leai cheatumi*
    USA

Family CAMAENIDAE

R *Glyptorhagada wilkawillina umbilicata*
    Australia: South Australia

Family HELMINTHOGLYPTIDAE

I *Eremarionta indioensis cathedralis*
    Cathedral Desert Snail
    USA

K *Eremarionta rowelli bakerensis*
    Baker Desert Snail
    USA

K *Eremarionta rowelli mccoiana*
    McCoy Desert Snail
    USA

K *Helminthoglypta arrosa pomoensis*
    USA

I *Helminthoglypta expansilabris mattolensis*
    Cape Shoulderband
    USA

K *Helminthoglypta nickliniana awania*
    Nicklin's Peninsula Snail
    USA

I *Helminthoglypta nickliniana bridgesi*
    USA

I *Helminthoglypta nickliniana contracosta*
    USA

E *Helminthoglypta sequoicola consors*
    USA

K *Helminthoglypta stiversiana miwoka*
    Dented Peninsula Snail
    USA

R *Helminthoglypta stiversiana williamsi*
    USA

K *Monadenia fidelis minor*
    USA

V *Monadenia fidelis pronotis*
    Rocky Coast Sideband
    USA

K *Monadenia yosemitensis yosemitensis*
    Indian Yosemite Snail
    USA

K *Monadenia mormonum buttoni*
    USA

V *Monadenia mormonum hirsuta*
    USA

Class BIVALVIA

Order UNIONOIDA

Family MARGARITIFERIDAE

I *Margaritifera margaritifera durrovensis*
    Ireland

Family UNIONIDAE

E *Dysnomia florentina curtisi*
    (*Epioblasma florentina*)
    Curtis Pearlymussel
    USA

E   *Dysnomia florentina florentina*
    (*Epioblasma florentina florentina*)
    Yellow-blossom
    USA

E   *Dysnomia florentina walkeri*
    (*Epioblasma florentina walkeri*)
    Tan Rifleshell
    USA

E   *Dysnomia obliquata obliquata*
    (*Epioblasma obliquata obliquata*)
    Catspaw
    USA

E   *Dysnomia obliquata perobliqua*
    (*Epioblasma obliquata perobliqua*)
    White Catspaw
    USA

E   *Dysnomia torulosa gubernaculum*
    (*Epioblasma torulosa gubernaculum*)
    Green-blossom
    USA

E   *Dysnomia torulosa rangiana*
    (*Epioblasma torulosa rangiana*)
    Northern Rifleshell
    Canada; USA

E   *Dysnomia torulosa torulosa*
    (*Epioblasma torulosa torulosa*)
    Tubercled-blossom
    Canada; USA

Phylum ARTHROPODA

Class INSECTA

Order ODONATA

Family CALOPTERYGIDAE

R   *Matrona basilaris japonica*
    Japan: Amami-oshima, Okinawa, Tokunoshima

Family COENAGRIONIDAE

E   *Coenagrion hylas freyi*
    Frey's Damselfly
    Austria; Germany; Switzerland

I   *Megalagrion amaurodytum fallax*
    Fallax Damselfly
    USA: Hawaiian Islands

I   *Megalagrion amaurodytum peles*
    Pele Damselfly
    USA: Hawaiian Islands

I   *Megalagrion amaurodytum waianaeanum*
    Waianae Damselfly
    USA: Hawaiian Islands

E   *Seychellibasis alluaudi alluaudi*
    Seychelles

Family EUPHAEIDAE

R   *Bayadera brevicauda ishigakiana*
    Japan: Iriomote, Ishigaki

Family PLATYCNEMIDAE

R   *Coeliccia flavicauda masakii*
    Japan: Yayeyama

R   *Coeliccia ryakyuensis amamii*
    Japan: Amami

R   *Coeliccia ryakyuensis ryukyuensis*
    Japan: Okinawa

Family AESHNIDAE

R   *Planaeschna ishigakiana ishigakiana*
    Japan: Yayeyama

R   *Planaeschna ishigakiana nagaminei*
    Japan: Amami

R   *Planaeschna risi sakishimana*
    Japan: Yayeyama

Family GOMPHIDAE

R   *Asiagomphus amamiensis amamiensis*
    Japan: Amami-oshima

R   *Asiagomphus amamiensis okinawanus*
    Japan: Okinawa

I   *Ophiogomphus incurvatus alleghaniensis*
    Alleghany Snaketail Dragonfly
    USA

R   *Stylogomphus ryukyuensis asatoi*
    Japan: Kerama, Okinawa

R   *Stylogomphus ryukyuensis watanabei*
    Japan: Iriomote

Family CORDULEGASTERIDAE

R   *Chlorogomphus brevistigmata okinawanus*
    Japan: Okinawa

R   *Chlorogomphus brunneus brunneus*
    Japan: Okinawa

R   *Chlorogomphus brunneus keramensis*
    Japan: Kerama

Family CORDULIIDAE

R   *Hemicordulia mindana nipponica*
    Japan: Nakanoshima, Tanegashima, Yayeyama

Family LIBELLULIDAE

K   *Eleuthemis beuttikoferi quadrigutta*
    Mozambique; Zimbabwe

R   *Leucorrhinia intermedia ijimai*
    Japan: Hokkaido

R   *Orthetrum poecilops miyajimaense*
    Japan

Order COLEOPTERA

Family CARABIDAE

I   *Sphaeroderus schaumi shenandoah*
    Schaum's Blue Ridge Ground Beetle
    USA

Family CICINDELIDAE

I   *Cicindela chlorocephala smythi*
    Smyth's Tiger Beetle
    USA

I   *Cicindela dorsalis dorsalis*
    North-eastern Beach Tiger Beetle
    USA

I   *Cicindela latesignata obliviosa*
    Oblivious Tiger Beetle
    USA

I   *Cicindela limbata albissima*
    Coral Pink Dunes Tiger Beetle
    USA

I   *Cicindela nevadica olmosa*
    Los Olmos Tiger Beetle
    USA

I   *Cicindela nigrocoerula subtropica*
    Subtropical Blue-Black Tiger Beetle
    USA

I   *Cicindela obsoleta neojuvenalis*
    Neojuvenile Tiger Beetle
    USA

I   *Cicindela tranquebarica viridissima*
    Greenest Tiger Beetle
    USA

Family DYTISCIDAE

Ex *Dytiscus lapponicus disjunctus*
    Italy: Alpes Maritime

Family SCARABAEIDAE

K   *Dynastes hercules glaseri*
    Trinidad and Tobago

V   *Dynastes hercules hercules*
    Hercules Beetle
      Dominica; Guadeloupe

V   *Dynastes hercules reidi*
    Hercules Beetle
      Martinique; Saint Lucia

Family ELMINTHIDAE

I   *Huleechius marroni carolus*
    Marron's San Carlos Riffle Beetle
    USA

I   *Stenelmis calida calida*
    Devil's Hole Warm Spring Riffle Beetle
    USA

I   *Stenelmis calida moapa*
    Moapa Warm Springs Riffle Beetle
    USA

Family LAMPYRIDAE

I   *Photuris brunnipennis floridana*
    Everglades Browing Firefly
    USA

Family CERAMBYCIDAE

E   *Crossidius mojavensis mojavensis*
    Mojave Rabbitbrush Longhorn Beetle
    USA

V   *Desmocerus californicus dimorphus*
    Valley Elderberry Longhorn Beetle
    USA

Family CURCULIONIDAE

I   *Trigonoscuta dorothea dorothea*
    Dorothy's El Segundo Dune Weevil
    USA

Order LEPIDOPTERA

Family HESPERIIDAE

I   *Antipodia chaostola leucophaea*
    Australia: Tasmania

E   *Hesperia leonard montana*
    (*Hesperia pawnee montana*)
    Pawnee Montane Skipper
    USA

I   *Hesperilla mastersi marakupa*
    Australia: Tasmania

V   *Kedestes barerae bunta*
    Barber's Ranger
    South Africa

I   *Oreisplanus munionga larana*
    Australia: Tasmania

V   *Panoquina panoquinoides errans*
    Salt Marsh Skipper
    Mexico; USA

I   *Pseudocopaeodes eunus eunus*
    Wandering Skipper
    USA

Family PAPILIONIDAE

E *Eurytides lysithous harrisianus*
Harris' Mimic Swallowtail
Brazil

R *Graphium alebion chungianus*
Taiwan

V *Graphium antiphates ceylonicus*
Sri Lankan Five-bar Swordtail
Sri Lanka

E *Papilio aristodemus ponceanus*
Schaus' Swallowtail
USA

E *Papilio desmondi teita*
Taita Blue-banded Papilio
Kenya

Ex *Papilio phorbanta nana*
Seychelles

E *Parnassius apollo vinningensis*
Germany

I *Parnassius clodius shepardii*
Shepard's Clodius Parnassian
USA

Ex *Parnassius clodius strohbeeni*
Strohbeen's Clodius Parnassian
USA

E *Troides aeacus kaguya*
Taiwan

Family PIERIDAE

I *Euchloe hyantis andrewsi*
Andrew's Marble Butterfly
USA

R *Pieris krueperi devta*
India

Family LYCAENIDAE

R *Aloeides dentatis dentatis*
South Africa

I *Aloeides dentatis maseruna*
Lesotho; South Africa

R *Aloeides trimeni southeyae*
South Africa

R *Argyrocupha malagrida cedrusmontana*
Lion's Head Copper
South Africa

V *Argyrocupha malagrida malagrida*
Lion's Head Copper
South Africa

V *Argyrocupha malagrida maryae*
Lion's Head Copper
South Africa

R *Argyrocupha malagrida paarlensis*
Lion's Head Copper
South Africa

R *Bowkeria phosphor borealis*
South Africa

R *Bowkeria phosphor phosphor*
South Africa

E *Callophrys mossii bayensis*
San Bruno Elfin
USA

R *Durbania amakosa albescens*
South Africa

I *Durbania amakosa flavida*
South Africa

I *Euphilotes battoides comstocki*
(*Shijimiaeoides battoides comstocki*)
Comstock's Blue
USA

E *Euphilotes bernardino allyni*
(*Shijimiaeoides battoides allyni*)
El Segundo Blue
USA

E *Euphilotes enoptes smithi*
(*Shijimiaeoides enoptes smithi*)
Smith's Blue
USA

I *Euphilotes rita mattonii*
(*Shijimiaeoides rita mattonii*)
Mattoni's Blue
USA

Ex *Everes comyntas texanus*
Texas Tailed Blue
USA

R *Iolaus diametra natalica*
(*Epamera diametra natalica*)
South Africa

Ex? *Glaucopsyche lygdamus palosverdesensis*
Palos Verdes Blue
USA

I *Hemiargus thomasi bethune-bakeri*
Miami Blue Butterfly
USA

E *Icaricia icarioides missionensis*
Mission Blue
USA

I   *Icaricia icarioides moroensis*
Moro Bay Blue
USA

I   *Icaricia icarioides pheres*
Pheres Blue
USA

R   *Lepidochrysops jamesi classensi*
South Africa

R   *Lepidochrysops jamesi jamesi*
South Africa

E   *Lepidochrysops methymna dicksoni*
South Africa

R   *Lepidochrysops oreas oreas*
South Africa

Ex? *Lycaeides argyrognomon lotis*
Lotis Blue
USA

I   *Lycaeides melissa samuelis*
Karner Blue
USA

I   *Lycaena dorcas claytoni*
Clayton's Copper
USA

E   *Maculinea teleius burdigalensis*
Scarce Large Blue
France

R   *Mitoura gryneus sweadneri*
Sweadner's Hairstreak
USA

R   *Ornipholidotos peucetia penningtoni*
White Mimic
Mozambique; South Africa

E   *Panchala ganesa loomisi*
Tailless Blue
Japan

I   *Philotiella speciosa bohartorum*
Bohart's Blue
USA

E   *Plebejus icarioides missionensis*
Mission Blue
USA

R   *Phasis thero cedarbergae*
South Africa

R   *Poecilmitis brooksi tearei*
South Africa

I   *Poecilmitis nigricans nigricans*
Blue Jewel Copper
South Africa

I   *Poecilmitis nigricans zwartbergae*
Blue Jewel Copper
South Africa

R   *Poecilmitis pyroeis hersaleki*
South Africa

I   *Pseudalmenus chlorinda chlorinda*
Australia: Tasmania

I   *Pseudalmenus chlorinda conara*
Australia: Tasmania

I   *Shijimiaeoides langstoni langstoni*
Langston's Blue
USA

R   *Strymon acis bartrami*
Bartram's Hairstreak
USA

R   *Thestor dicksoni calviniae*
Dickson's Thestor
South Africa

R   *Thestor dicksoni dicksoni*
Dickson's Thestor
South Africa

I   *Thestor montanus pictus*
South Africa

R   *Tuxentius melaena griqua*
South Africa

Family RIODINIDAE

E   *Apodemia mormo langei*
Lange's Metalmark
USA

Family SATYRIDAE

Ex *Cercyonis sthenele sthenele*
Sthenele Wood Nymph
USA

R   *Erebia annada annada*
Bhutan; India

R   *Erebia narasingha narasingha*
India

R   *Lethe dura gammiei*
Bhutan; India

R   *Lethe europa tamuna*
India: Nicobar Island

R   *Lethe gemina gafuri*
India

R   *Lethe ocellata lyncus*
Bhutan; India

E *Neonympha mitchelli mitchelli*
Mitchell's Satyr Butterfly
USA

R *Pararge menava maeroides*
India

R *Ypthima dohertyi persimilis*
India; Myanmar

Family NYMPHALIDAE

E *Antanartia borbonica mauritiana*
Mauritius

V *Charaxes druceanus entabeni*
Silver Barred Charaxes
South Africa

I *Charaxes druceanus williamsi*
Kenya

I *Charaxes durnfordi nicholi*
Chestnut Rajah
India; Myanmar

V *Charaxes karkloof capensis*
South Africa

V *Charaxes xiphares desmondi*
Kenya

V *Charaxes xiphares xiphares*
Western Forest Emperor
South Africa

V *Cymothoe alcimeda alcimeda*
Battling Glider
South Africa

R *Doleschallia bisaltide andamana*
Andaman Leafwing
India: Andaman Islands

E *Euphydryas editha bayensis*
Bay Checkerspot Butterfly
USA

I *Euphydryas editha monoensis*
Mono Checkerspot Butterfly
USA

V *Heliconius charitonius peruvianus*
Ecuador; Peru

I *Heteronympha cordacea comptena*
Australia: Tasmania

I *Hypolimnas dubius drucei*
Comoro Islands; Madagascar; Mauritius

R *Neptis sankara nar*
India: Andaman Islands

I *Salamis angustina angustina*
Salamis Retrecie
Madagascar; Réunion

Ex *Salamis angustina vinsoni*
Mauritius

I *Satyrodes eurydice fumosa*
Smokey Eyed Brown Butterfly
USA

Ex *Speyeria adiaste atossa*
Atossa
USA

I *Speyeria callippe callippe*
Callippe Silverspot
USA

I *Speyeria hydaspe conquista*
Silverspot
USA

I *Speyeria nokomis caerulescens*
Blue Silverspot
Mexico; USA

I *Speyeria nokomis nokomis*
Great Basin Silverspot
USA

I *Speyeria zerene behrensii*
Behren's Silverspot
USA

V *Speyeria zerene hippolyta*
Oregon Silverspot
USA

R *Speyeria zerene myrtleae*
Myrtle's Fritillary
USA

Family SPHINGIDAE

E *Celerio wilsoni perkinsi*
USA: Hawaiian Islands

Order HYMENOPTERA

Family SPHECIDAE

I *Ectemnius nesocrabo bidecoratus*
Bidecoratus Sphecid Wasp
USA: Hawaiian Islands

Family ANDRENIDAE

I *Perdita hirticeps luteocincta*
Yellow Banded Andrenid Bee
USA

I *Perdita scitula antiochensis*
Antioch Andrenid Bee
USA

List 5

COMMERCIALLY THREATENED SPECIES

Class MAMMALIA

Order PRIMATES

Family CERCOPITHECIDAE

CT   *Macaca nemestrina*
Pigtail Macaque
Bangladesh; Brunei; Cambodia?; China; India;
Indonesia; Laos; Malaysia; Myanmar;
Thailand; Viet Nam

Phylum CNIDARIA

Class ANTHOZOA

Order GORGONACEA

Family CORALLIIDAE

CT   *Corallium*   (20 species)
Precious Corals
Mediterranean Sea, Pacific Ocean

Order ANTIPATHARIA

Family ANTHIPATHIDAE

CT   *Anthipathidae*   (c 150 species)
Black Coral
Caribbean, Indo-Pacific

Phylum MOLLUSCA

Class GASTROPODA

Order ARCHAEOGASTROPODA

Family TURBINIIDAE

CT   *Turbo marmoratus*
Green Snail
Indo-Pacific

Family STROMBIDAE

CT   *Strombus gigas*
Queen Conch
Caribbean

Class BIVALVIA

Order PTERIOIDA

Family PTERIIDAE

CT   *Pinctada margaritifera*
Black-lipped Pearl Oyster
Indo-Pacific

CT   *Pinctada maxima*
Gold-lipped Pearl Oyster
Indo-Pacific

Phylum ARTHROPODA

Class CRUSTACEA

Order DECAPODA

Family NEPHROPIDAE

CT   *Homarus americanus*
American Lobster
North Atlantic

CT   *Homarus gammarus*
European Lobster
North-east Atlantic

CT   *Nephrops norvegicus*
Norway Lobster
North-east Atlantic

Family PALINURIDAE

CT   *Jasus edwardsii*
Rock Lobster
New Zealand

CT   *Panulirus argus*
Caribbean Spiny Lobster
Caribbean

CT   *Panulirus guttatus*
Spotted Spiny Lobster
Caribbean

CT   *Panulirus penicillatus*
Pronghorn Spiny Lobster
Indo-Pacific

Phylum ECHINODERMATA

Class ECHINOIDEA

Order ECHINOIDA

Family ECHINIDAE

CT   *Paracentrotus lividus*
Purple Urchin
North-east Atlantic, Mediterranean

INDEX

252

253

270

275